RAILWAYS RESTORED 2009

Edited by **Alan C. Butcher**

Ian Allan
PUBLISHING

Contents

Front cover: BR Standard 4-6-2 No 70013 *Oliver Cromwell* as returned to steam in 2008 as part of the 40th anniversary since the end of main line steam on British Railways. It is seen here in action on the Great Central Railway soon after its overhaul was completed. *Ian Loadsby*

Previous page: This ex-Great Western Railway 0-6-2T No 5619 would feel at home on the Pontypool & Blaenavon Railway, the class having been designed for use in the Welsh Valleys. No 5619 was on a visit from the Telford Steam Railway. *ACB*

First published 1980
Thirtieth edition 2009

ISBN 978 0 7110 3370 2

Published by Ian Allan Publishing

an imprint of Ian Allan Publishing Ltd, Hersham, Surrey KT12 4RG
Printed by Ian Allan Printing Ltd, Hersham, Surrey KT12 4RG

Code: 0903/C3

Visit the Ian Allan Publishing web site at:
www.ianallanpublishing.com

The publishers, the railway operators and the Heritage Railway Association accept no liability for any loss, damage or injury caused by error or inaccuracy in the information published in *Railways Restored 2009*. Train services may be altered or cancelled without prior notice, and at some locations diesel traction may be substituted for scheduled steam workings.

Railways
ILLUSTRATED

The best coverage of today's railway scene

Each issue of *Railways Illustrated* offers a comprehensive round-up of the latest news and topical events from the UK across the present day railway, including heritage traction in operation on the main lines.

Supported by high quality photography and editorial from experienced railway enthusiasts, *Railways Illustrated* reflects the energy and vitality of the present day railway scene.

Devoted to coverage of railway companies, train operators, infrastructure functions, main line steam operations and principal modern traction heritage sites, *Railways Illustrated* also presents a regular photographic overseas feature, some semi-technical articles, and a popular practical series on digital photography.

National Railway Heritage Awards

The Awards have been made annually since 1979 and were granted charitable status in 2004. The object remains the same: encouraging high standards of restoration of buildings, structures and signalling installations and of their environmental care, thus promoting public recognition and awareness of our historic railway and tramway heritage and its place in the environment. We aim to promote careful design and quality workmanship in restoration, modernisation, adaptation and maintenance, taking proper account of all relevant factors, particularly manpower and funding. In this way we encourage both public and heritage railways and tramways to present their operational premises as attractive 'shop-windows'. We also encourage owners and occupiers of former railway or tramway premises now used for other purposes to retain as much as possible of their original character.

The awards are organised by the National Railway Awards Committee. Our main sponsors are Ian Allan Publishing together with Westinghouse Invensys, Network Rail, London Underground and the Railway Heritage Trust. Judging is done from the beginning of May through to the end of August and those short listed are notified at the beginning of October. The Awards are presented in early December at a prestigious location by a well-known public figure, with full media coverage.

1992 saw the inclusion of Ireland in the Awards initially with the addition of a special Premier Award and up to three Certificates of Commendation in each sector.

The Ian Allan Independent Railway of the Year Award

The Ian Allan Judges pay incognito visits to each of the heritage railways around the county, buy tickets and spend the day travelling as members of the public. The judges look at the quality of service, presentation and helpfulness of the staff, the stations, the catering, the toilets and the day as a whole.

The 2008 winner was the Severn Valley Railway.

The HRA Annual Award

This, the premier award made by the HRA, is for a group or organisation making an outstanding contribution to railway heritage during the year of the Award.

The Award takes the form of a Royal Train Headboard from the London, Brighton & South Coast Railway, which is on loan to the HRA from the National Railway Museum. The Award is held for one year and the winning group also receives a commemorative plaque. The Award is announced and presented at the Association's Annual General Meeting which is held on the last weekend of January each year.

The following projects are eligible:

1 Any building, structure or signalling installation, associated with railways or tramways since their inception in the United Kingdom, the Isle of Man and the Republic of Ireland.

2 An entry may comprise a whole station or any single structure or group of structures, which form, or once formed, part of railway or tramway premises.

3 Certain types of replica are eligible. These include:

- An historic building, structure or signalling installation re-erected at a new site
- An accurate reconstruction of a specfic building, structure or signalling installation, the original of which has been removed or demolished, rebuilt on or very close to its original site
- A completely new but authentic replica of a specific historic building, structure or signalling installation on a new site
- An entry comprising a combination of restored or adapted historic building, structure or signalling installation with modern additions
- Construction of a building in the general style of an historic building, structure or signalling installation with no specific or authentic basis for its design or location, would not be eligible.

Who can enter?

Entries are invited from the following:

Train and tram operating companies.

Companies owning track, structures and stations.

Urban underground and passenger transport authorities and companies.

Operators of heritage, tourist and private railways and tramways.

Residual property owning bodies.

Owners of eligible infrastructure, whether of not still in railway or tramway use.

Architects, engineers and contractors involved in restoration, new or maintenance work.

Local Amenity groups.

Private individuals.

Any group in Great Britain and Ireland involved in the railway industry, whether as a private railway company or as a less formal organisation. Network Rail, Irish Rail, Northern Ireland Railways (NIR). Other public or commercial organisations. Private individuals.

For application forms apply to:
Robin Leleux
12 Bilsdale Way
Baildon
Shipley
West Yorkshire
BD17 5DG
Tel/Fax: 01274 593235

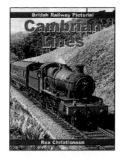

Editor's Notes

On the following pages will be found a guide to the major heritage railways, railway museums and preservation centres in the British Isles. Information for visitors has been set out in tabular form for easy reference, together with a locomotive stocklist for most centres.

Many heritage centres and operating lines provide facilities for other groups and organisations to restore locomotives and equipment on their premises. It has not been possible to include full details of these groups, but organisations which own locomotives are shown under the centres at which they operate. In addition, a full list of member societies of the HRA is given elsewhere. In the case of most operating lines their length is given, but there is no guarantee that services are operated over the entire length.

Within the heading to each entry a heading block has been incorporated for easy reference as to what each site offers in the way of passenger service to visitors. These are as follows:

Timetable Service: Railways providing a passenger service between two or more stations with public access; eg Mid-Hants Railway.

Steam Centre: A railway or heritage site offering a passenger service on a short length of line, on a regular basis, with public access at only one point; eg Lavender Line.

Museum: A museum or site that does not offer a passenger service on a regular basis, if at all; eg Science Museum, London. Some sites may however offer rides on miniature railways.

Railway Centre: A catch-all for those centres which do not fall clearly into any of the other brackets. Generally those offering rides over short distances using non-steam motive power.

Attraction: Where the railway is an addition to the main attraction of the location (eg Bicton Woodland Railway).

As well as a guide as to what to expect on each site, this year's *Railways Restored* shows what, if any, particular professional body the Companies or Societies belong to. These are:

HRA: Indicates that the organisation is a member of the Heritage Railway Association (HRA).

TT: Indicates that the organisation is a member of the Transport Trust (TT).

Membership of the HRA and TT is open to both organisations and private individuals. Private members are able to take advantage of concessions offered to them by the organisations that subscribe to these two bodies.

The concessions range from a discount on the admission price to free entry. The TT's Travel Back leaflet provides details.

Details given under **Access by public transport** should be checked beforehand to ensure services shown are operating. Unless the Heritage Railway, Steam Centre or Museum has identified the privatised train company operating the service, the phrase 'by rail', or 'main line', has been used to identify access by train.

Visitors wishing to see specific items of rolling stock or locomotives are advised to check before their visit that the exhibit is available for inspection. It should be stressed that not all items are usually available for inspection due to restoration, operating or other restrictions.

Editor's Comment

How history will tell the story of 2008 remains to be seen, but in a number of ways it was not a good year for several heritage railways. The Dartmoor Railway ceased trading when its parent company announced trading losses and, along with the Weardale Railway which has already had a chequered history, was eventually sold to Iowa Pacific Holdings, an American short line operator. A British subsidiary has been created to take over both lines, but at the time of writing the future operations at Dartmoor had still to be confirmed. The Sittingbourne & Kemsley light Railway's lease was about to expire and initially the local council refused to include the line in its regeneration plan. Again at the time of writing the line's future was still to be decided.

In Oxfordshire the Didcot Railway Centre, after years of negotiating to buy the rail-locked site was advised that the site might be required for National network use and the sale offer was withdrawn. The local council had been instumental backing in the Barry Island Railway with

financil help. This was withdrawn during 2008 and a new operator sought. At the time of writing the local preservationists are not sure if they are to be included in the new operators plans for the line.

Regular readers will see a few deletions and additions in this years edition. One site may yet live on however. The Bideford Railway Museum, closed in 2008 due to adjacent building work, may return for the 2010 edition as the developer is sympathetic to the future of the Museum.

The economic situation with fuel prices rising through most of 2008 has meant that those lines on the 'fringes' of the country have seen passenger numbers decline. Along with the availability of fewer volunteers, it has not been an easy season for several lines. The current 'credit crunch' may well see the number of families holidaying at home instead of overseas; and if the drop in fuel prices hold, should see an increase in visitors

As ever, my thanks to those who provide the updates and photographs for *Railways Restored 2009*.

Allely's Heavy Haulage Ltd. is part of the Allely Group running approximately 50 vehicles in total

The Heavy Haulage side have been specialists in the movement of railway vehicles for the last 20 years and has undertaken numerous large contracts.

We offer a full service for the movement of railway rolling stock and trackwork and will consider any rail contracts.

We have extensive knowledge of all types of rolling stock and many rail locations throughout the U.K.

Contact Robert Ford 01527 857621 or email *robert@allelys.co.uk*

Allely's Heavy Haulage Ltd
The Slough
Studley
Warwickshire B80 7EN
Telephone 01527 857621
Fax 01527 857623

Allely's Heavy Haulage Ltd. is part of the Allely Group running approximately 50 vehicles in total.

A mixed line up at the Barrow Hill Rail Power show in August 2008. In this view Nos 6430, D213, 26007, Peckett (works No 2000), 78019, and the tender of No 3440 *City of Truro* can be identified. *Phil Barnes*

Standard Abbreviations

AEC	Associated Equipment Co
AEG	Allgemeine Elektrizitaets Gesellschaft
A/Barclay	Andrew Barclay
A/Porter	Aveling & Porter Ltd
A/Whitworth	Armstrong Whitworth
B/Drewry	Baguley/Drewry
B/Peacock	Beyer Peacock & Co
B/Hawthorn	Black, Hawthorn & Co
BRCW	Birmingham Railway, Carriage & Wagon
BTH	British Thomson Houston
Buch	23 August Locomotive Works
D/Metcalfe	Davies & Metcalfe
E/Electric	English Electric Ltd
F/Jennings	Fletcher Jennings & Co
F/Walker	Fox Walker
G&S	G. & S. Light Engineering Co
G/England	George England & Co
GRCW	Gloucester Railway, Carriage & Wagon
H/Barclay	Hunslet Barclay
H/Clarke	Hudswell Clarke & Co Ltd
H/Hunslet	Hudson-Hunslet
H/Leslie	Hawthorn Leslie & Co
K/Stuart	Kerr Stuart & Co Ltd
L/Blackstone	Lister Blackstone
M/Cam	Metropolitan Cammell
M/Rail	Motor Rail Ltd
M/Vick	Metrovick (Metropolitan-Vickers)
M/Wardle	Manning Wardle & Co Ltd
N/British	North British Locomotive Co Ltd
N/Wilson	Nasmyth Wilson & Co Ltd
O&K	Orenstein & Koppel
P/Steel	Pressed Steel Co Ltd
RSH	Robert Stephenson & Hawthorn Ltd
R/Hornsby	Ruston Hornsby
R/Proctor	Ruston Proctor
S. F. Belge	Société Franco Belge
SMH	Simplex Mechanical Handling
YEC	Yorkshire Engine Co
W&M	Waggon & Maschinenbau
W/Rogers	Wingrove & Rogers

Company abbreviations

BR	British Railways
DB	German Federal Railway
DSB	Danish State Railways
GWR	Great Western Railway
JZ	Yugoslav Railways
LBSCR	London, Brighton & South Coast Railway
LMS	London, Midland & Scottish Railway
LNER	London & North Eastern Railway
LSWR	London & South Western Railway
MoS	Ministry of Supply
MR	Midland Railway
NLR	North London Railway
NS	Netherlands State Railways
NSB	Norwegian State Railways
RR	Rhodesia Railways
S&DJR	Somerset & Dorset Joint Railway

SAR	South African Railways
SECR	South Eastern & Chatham Railway
SER	South Eastern Railway
SJ	Swedish Railways
SNCF	French National Railways
SR	Southern Railway
USATC	United States Army Transportation Corps
WD	War Department

Other abbreviations

BE	Battery-electric
DE	Diesel-electric
DH	Diesel-hydraulic
DM	Diesel-mechanical
DMU	Diesel multiple-unit
E	Overhead electric
EMU	Electric multiple-unit
F	Fireless
G	Geared
GH	Gas-hydraulic
IST	Inverted saddle tank
LRO	Light Railway Order
ParM	Paraffin-mechanical
PH	Petrol-hydraulic
PM	Petrol-mechanical
PT	Pannier tank
R	Railcar
ST	Saddle tank
STT	Saddle tank and tender
T	Side tank
VB	Vertical boiler
WT	Well tank
4w	Four-wheel

Multiple-unit Type abbreviations

B	Brake
C	Composite (First/Standard class seating)
D	Driving
F	First class
K	Corridor
LV	Luggage Van
M	Motor
O	Open (seating arrangement)
P	Pullman (ex-'Brighton Belle')
R	Restaurant
S	Standard ([or Second] class)
T	Trailer

Added together these give the vehicle designation, for example: DMBS — Driving Motor Brake Second.

The addition of an L indicates that the vehicle has a lavatory (may not be operational on some vehicles).

Some lines operate a Standard class only policy and the First class facility is downgraded. This may result in some vehicles having a different designation to that originally applied.

Anyone interested in nationwide railway preservation can become a Friend of the Heritage Railway Association.

Benefits include receiving a copy of the *Heritage Railway Journal,* published three times a year, and a copy of the Annual Report, which details the work of the Association during the year. There is the opportunity of attending various business meetings, weekend meetings, which include visits to member railways, and seminars. This gives an opportunity to learn more about the preservation movement.

There is the opportunity to purchase *Railways Restored* at a reduced price and to purchase an Inter-Rail pass which allows visits to member railways at a concessionary price.

Current annual subscription is £17.63 (non UK £17.63),

For further information, please contact the Private Membership Secretary, or send this form (or a photocopy) to:
Ian Leigh, 206B Crowfield House, North Row, Milton Keynes, MK9 3LQ.
E-mail: ian.leigh4@btinternet.com

Application Form to become a Friend of the Heritage Railway Association

Name
....

Address
....

....

....

Post Code
....

Telephone
....

Subscription enclosed
....

Donation enclosed
....

England

| Timetable Service | Abbey Light Railway | West Yorkshire |

Member: HRA, TT

The Abbey Light Railway was founded in 1976. It is a family run operation supported by volunteers to restore and maintain vintage narrow gauge locomotives and stock. The railway takes visitors to the 11th century Cistercian Monastery of Kirkstall Abbey

Propriator: Mr P. N. Lowe

Location: Bridge Road, Kirkstall, Leeds LS5 3BW

Telephone: (0113) 267 5087

Internet address: *Web site:* www.freewebs.com/abbeylightrailway/index

Main station: Kirkstall Abbey

Other public station: Bridge Road (OS ref: SE 262356)

Car park: At Abbey and Bridge Road

Access by public transport: By train to Headingley station. Buses from City Square

Refreshment facilities: At nearby Morrisons supermarket

Souvenir shop: Badges on sale on the train

Depot: Workshops at Bridge Road

Length of line/gauge: Quarter mile, 2ft gauge

Period of public operation: Sundays and Bank Holiday Mondays (13.00-17.00). Also open on the Saturday of the Kirkstall Festival

Special events: Kirkstall Gala in Abbey grounds — 11 July

Facilities for disabled: In Abbey grounds

Membership details: As above

Industrial locomotives

Narrow gauge:

Name	No	Builder	Type	Built
Loweco	1	Lister (20779)	4wDM	1942
Atlas	2	Hunslet (2465)	4wDM	1943
Odin	3	Simplex (5859)	4wDM	1934
Vulcan	4	R/Hornsby (198287)	4wDM	1942
—	5	R/Hornsby (235654)	4wDM	1946
Druid	6	Simplex (8644)	4wDM	1941
—	7	O&K (5926)	4wDM	1935
Go-Go	8	Hudson (39924)	4wPM	1924
—	9	Muir Hill (110)	4wPM	1925
—	10	Baguley (736)	0-4-0PM	1917
—	11	Baguley (760)	0-4-0PM	1917
—	12	Greenbat (2848)	4wBE	1957

| Museum | Abbey Pumping Station | Leicester |

Member: TT

Narrow gauge railway (2ft gauge) formerly part of a sewage pumping station that now forms museum site. Railway relaid in concrete by MSC scheme during early 1980s to original track layout. New track layout as an extension to original laid with 35lb rail on wooden sleepers. All the railway system is now run by volunteers. Original Simplex locomotive kept on site in operational condition. Line originally used for transferring solid material from screens to tip (about

Industrial locomotives

Narrow gauge:

Name	No	Builder	Type	Built
Leonard	—	Bagnall (2087)	0-4-0ST	1919
—	—	Motor Rail (5260)	4wPM	1931
—	—	R/Hornsby (223700)	4wDM	1944
—	—	SMH (40SD515)	4wDM	1979
New Star	—	Lister (4088)	4wPM	1931

Stock

3 new passenger vehicles based on Leicester & Swannington coaches.
10 skip wagons, 2 mine tubs, 2 flats, bomb wagon, various miscellaneous.
All locomotives are restored to working order; *Leonard* returned to service in 2005 when restoration work was completed

100yd). Demonstration skip wagon trains as well as passenger trains are run when the railway is operating
Location: Abbey Pumping Station, Corporation Road, off Abbey Lane, Leicester LE4 5XP

Next to the National Space Centre
Operating group: Leicester City Council Museum, Leicester Museums Technology Association
Telephone: 0116 299 5111
Fax: 0116 299 5125
Internet address: *Web site:* www.leicester.gov.uk/museums
Car park: Free on site
Access by public transport: Main line Leicester (London Road). First Bus route 54 from city centre (alight at Beaumont Leys Lane)
Length of line/gauge: About 300yd, 2ft gauge. Passenger carrying on special event days and railway running days (small fare payable)
Period of public opening: Daily 1 February to 31 November, 11.00 to 16.30, Sundays 13.00 to 16.30. Open for special events only all year
On site facilities: Museum/shop/toilets/car park. Refreshments only on special event days
Facilities for disabled: Access to museum lower floor and grounds. Lift to Engine House and refreshments on event days. Wheelchair access to railway
Volunteer contact: Tony Kendal, c/o Abbey Pumping Station
Museum contact: Mr J. Wheat/ Mr A. Simpson, c/o Abbey Pumping Station (Tel: 0116 299 5111)
Other attractions: Museum holds various transport, steam navvy, beam engines. Some items only viewable by appointment or on special event days
Special events: Railway Running Day — 4 April; April Celebrations Steam Day (locomotives/buses) — 19 April; Railway Running Day — 2 May; Railway Running Day,Teddy Bears' Picnic — 6 June; Urban Day — 27/28 June; Railway Running Day — 4 July, 1 August, 5 September; Steam Spectacular Day — 13 September; Railway Running Day — 3 October; Christmas Toys and Steam Day — 6 December. 2010 dates include: Meccano Day — 10 January, Steam Toys in Action — 7 February

Steam Centre · Amberley Museum & Heritage Centre · West Sussex

Member: HRA, TT

Narrow Gauge & Industrial Railway Collection (incorporating the Brockham Museum of Narrow Gauge Railways)
The NG&IR Collection is part of an open air industrial museum set in 36 acres of the former Pepper & Co chalk pits. A 2ft gauge line has been constructed and this is used for carrying passengers in genuine workmen's vehicles
Location: Houghton Bridge, Amberley, West Sussex (3 miles north of Arundel) on B2139. Adjacent to Amberley main line station
OS reference: TQ 030122
Operating society/organisation: Amberley Museum Trust, Amberley Museum, Houghton Bridge, Amberley, Arundel, West Sussex BN18 9LT
Telephone: Bury (01798) 831370 (Museum office)
Internet address: *Web site:* www.amberleymuseum.co.uk
e-mail (general museum enquiries): office@amberleymuseum.co.uk
e-mail (specific railway enquiries): info@amberleynarrowgauge.co.uk
Car park: Adjacent to Amberley station
On site facilities: Shop and audio-visual show. The 'Limeburners Restaurant' opened in 2004 (event booking details from 01798 839240)
Public opening:
14 February to 1 November — Tuesday to Sunday, plus Bank Holidays. 10.00-last entry 17.00
Special events: Spring Industrial Trains Day — 26 April; Mid-Summer Steam Show — 13/14 June; Railway Gala — 11/12 July; Miniature Steam Show— 19/20 September; Autumn Industrial Trains — 18 October.

Please see press for details of further activities
Special notes: Displays include working potter, blacksmith and printer, stationary engines, historic radio collection and vintage Southdown garage and buses. A 2ft 0in gauge industrial railway system is demonstrated when possible, and a 3ft 2.25in gauge line. In addition, a 2ft 0in gauge 'main line' has been constructed. The 500yd line was officially opened by HRH Prince Michael of Kent on 5 June 1984. The railway is operated every day the museum is open (subject to mechanical availability), with steam locomotive haulage on certain days — for details contact the museum office. Wheelchairs can normally be accommodated on the train.

The 'Limeburners Restaurant' features a timber frame, cedar cladding and is floored with hand-made clay tiles
Membership details: Friends of Amberley Museum, c/o above address
Membership journal: *Wheelbarrow* — twice yearly

Locomotives
(2ft or 60cm unless otherwise indicated)

Name	No	Builder	Type	Built
Polar Bear	—	Bagnall (1781)	2-4-0T	1905
Peter	—	Bagnall (2067)	0-4-0ST	1918

Name	No	Builder	Type	Built	
Wendy	—	Bagnall (2091)	0-4-0ST	1919	
Cloister	—	Hunslet (542)	0-4-0ST	1891	
Townsend Hook	4	F/Jennings (172L)	0-4-0T	1880	(3ft 2.25in gauge)
Scaldwell	—	Peckett (1316)	0-6-0ST	1913	(3ft 0in gauge)
—	23†	Spence	0-4-0T	1921	(1ft 10in gauge)
—	—	Decauville (1126)	0-4-0WT	1947	
—**	—	Baldwin (44656)	4-6-0T	1917	
Monty	(6)	O&K (7269)	4wDM	1936	(3ft 2.25in gauge)
The Major	(7)	O&K (7741)	4wDM	1937	
—	2	Ransomes & Rapier (80)	4wDM	1937	
—	—	Hudson-Hunslet (3097)	4wDM	1944	
—	2	R/Hornsby (166024)	4wDM	1933	
—	3101	M/Rail (Simplex) (1381)	4wPM	1918	(Armoured)
Peldon	—	John Fowler (21295)	4wDM	1936	
Redland	—	O&K (6193)	4wDM	1937	
—	—	Lister (35421)	4wPM	1949	
—	—	M/Rail (Simplex) (872)	4wPM	1918	
—	27	M/Rail (Simplex) (5863)	4wDM	1934	
—	—	M/Rail (Simplex) (10161)	4wDM	1950	(2ft 11in gauge)
Ibstock	—	M/Rail (Simplex) (11001)	4wDM	1951	
Burt*	—	Simplex 9019))	4wDM	1959	
CCSW	—	Hibberd (1980)	4wDM	1936	
Thakeham Tiles	No 3	Hudson-Hunslet (2208)	4wDM	1941	
Thakeham Tiles	No 4	Hudson-Hunslet (3653)	4wDM	1948	
—	—	Hudson (45913)	4wP/ParM	1932	(2ft 6in gauge)
—	—	H/Clarke (DM686)	0-4-0DM	1948	
Star Construction	—	Hudson-Hunslet	4wDm	c1941	
—	18	R/Hornsby (187081)	4wDM	1937	
—	—	Lister (33937)	4wPM	1949	
—	—††	Hibberd 'Y-type Planet' (3627)	4wPM	1953	
—	WD 904	Wickham (3403/04)	2w-2PMR	1943	
—	2	Wingrove & Rogers (5031)	4wBE	1953	
—	—	Wingrove & Rogers (5034)	4wBE	1953	
—	—	Wingrove & Rogers (4998)	4wBE	1953	
—	—	Wingrove & Rogers (T8033)	0-4-0BE	1979	

†† not on site
** on loan to Leighton Buzzard Railway for restoration
* standard gauge
†includes hoist and 'haulage truck' for conversion to 5ft 3in gauge from Guinness Brewery

Stock
2 Penrhyn Quarry Railway 4-wheel coaches (2ft gauge, ex-1ft 10.75in gauge); RAF Fauld bogie coach (1940) (2ft gauge); Rye & Camber Tramway bogie (incomplete) (1895) (3ft gauge); Post Office Railway unit No 808 of 1930; 4 Groudle Glen Railway 4-wheel coaches (1896 and 1905) (2ft gauge); 60 other varied pieces of rolling stock of 12 different gauges ranging from 1ft 6in to 3ft 2.25in plus numerous miscellaneous exhibits including track, signals, etc

Owner
Cloister and *Wendy* the Hampshire Narrow Gauge Railway Trust

Steam Centre	**Amerton Railway**	Staffordshire

The Amerton Railway is the home of the famous 1897-built Bagnall saddletank *Isabel*, the line having been built for it in the early 1990s. The railway has developed considerably over the years and now consists of a mile-long line run through the countryside via a passing loop at Chartley Road. At Amerton station there is the locomotive shed and workshop, where items of rolling stock can be seen under restoration, the carriage shed and yard, the former GNR station building from Stowe and the Leek & Manifold Railway signalbox from Waterhouses, now under restoration

Location: Amerton Railway, Amerton Farm, Stowe-by-Chartley, Stafford ST18 0LA (situated between Stafford and Uttoxeter, signposted off A51 at Weston)

Operating company: Staffordshire Narrow Gauge Railway Ltd, c/o above address

Telephone: (Railway only) (01785) 850965; Farm (01889) 270294

OS reference: SJ 993278

On site facilities: Car park at Working Farm. Museum under construction; licensed tea room and bakery (not operated by railway). Souvenir shop in railway ticket office. The railway is one of the main attractions at the farm, admission to most other attractions is free

Access by public transport: By rail to Stafford, then Stevenson's of Uttoxeter Ltd bus to Weston, then a mile walk to Amerton (no Sunday service)

Facilities for disabled: Wheelchairs can be accommodated in our 'Highland' coach where a wide door and access ramp is available

Period of public operation: Sundays from mid-March to end of October. Saturdays from Easter until August Bank Holiday. Bank Holiday Mondays. Trains run 12.00 until 17.00. Subject to availability

Industrial locomotives (2ft gauge)

Name	No	Builder	Type	Built
Isabel	—	Bagnall (1491)	0-4-0ST	1897
No 1	—*	Bagnall (1889)	0-4-0ST	1911
Lorna Doone	—	K/Stuart (4250)	0-4-0ST	1922
—	526	Henschel (14019)	0-8-0T	1916
Paddy	—	Wilbrighton (2)	0-4-0VBTT	2007
Jennie	—	Hunsley (3905)	0-4-0ST	2005
—	746	M/Rail (40SD501)	4wDM	1975
—	—	M/Rail (7471)	4wDM	1940
Oakeley	—	Baguley (774)	0-4-0PM	1919
Golspie	—	Baguley (2085)	0-4-0DM/SO	1935
Dreadnought	—	Baguley (3024)	0-4-0DM/SO	1939
—	Yard No 70	R/Hornsby (221623)	4wDM	1943
—	—	R/Hornsby (506491)	4wDM	1964
—	—	Jung (5869)	4wDM	1934
Gordon	—	Hunslet (8561)	4wDH	1978

*3ft gauge, to be rebuilt to 2ft

Rolling stock

4 toastrack coaches, 3 by Baguley, 1 ex-WHR, SNGRS-built passenger brake van and various wagons

Owner

Lorna Doone on loan from Birmingham Museum of Science & Industry

there will be steam on Sundays and Bank Holidays. Diesel haulage generally on Saturdays

Special events: Summer Steam Gala, with visiting locomotives — 20/21 June (with at least two visiting locomotives); Santa Specials — December

Membership details: Membership Secretary, c/o above address

Membership journal: *Isabel Gazette,* quarterly

Steam Centre — Appleby Frodingham Railway Preservation Society — North Lincolnshire

The Society is pleased to be allowed to operate steam and/or diesel-hauled sightseeing rail tours within the Corus steelworks at Scunthorpe. It is one of Europe's major industrial complexes and Great Britain's premier iron and steelmaking site, covering approximately 12 square miles

Headquarters: Corus Steelworks, Scunthorpe. *Please note that due to the enclosed and secure nature of the site casual visits to the steelworks or to the Society operating base are not permitted by Corus*

Address: Appleby Frodingham RPS, PO Box 44 Brigg, North Lincolnshire DN20 8XG

Locomotives and multiple-units

Name	No	Origin	Class	Type	Built
—	2853	BR	02	0-4-0DH	1960
—	D3000	BR	08	0-6-0DE	1952
—	54207	BR	104	DTCL	1958
—	59245	BR	108	TSL	1958

Industrial locomotives

Name	No	Builder	Type	Built
Hutnik	—	Ferrum (3138)	0-6-0T	1952
—	—	Peckett (1438)	0-4-0ST	1916
—	—	Hunslet (3844)	0-6-0ST	1956
Arnold Machin	—	YEC (2661)	0-4-0DE	1958
Richard Clark	—	Bagnall (3151)	0-4-0DM	1960
—	—	H/Clarke (D1344)	0-6-0DM	1965

Stock

1 ex-BR Mk 1 coach No E4668; Director's saloon No DM395280; 3 20-ton brake vans, 11 former main line and internal wagons

England

Telephone: Enquiries (excluding booking) (01652) 656661
Internet address: *Web site:* www.afrps.co.uk
Railtour bookings and enquiries: Brigg Tourist Information Centre, 01652 657073, or *e-mail:* brigg.tic@northlinvs.gov.uk
All places on all tours MUST be pre-booked
Railtour platform: Frodingham Platform, via Corus Works Entrance/Gate 'E', Main Approach, off Brigg Road, Scunthorpe (A1029), DN16 1XA
Other platform: Appleby, for access to the refreshment coach, toilets and depot — all only accessible to railtour participants
Vehicle parking: Via Corus Works Entrance/Gate 'E', Main Approach, off Brigg Road, Scunthorpe (A1029), opposite Frodingham House, DN16 1XA. Free for the duration of railtours
Access by public transport: Rail — Scunthorpe station, 1 mile
Bus — Scunthorpe bus station 0.5 mile.
There is no public transport from either of these to or from Frodingham Platform
Souvenir shop: At the Society depot within the steelworks, only accessible to railtour participants

Other locomotives and rolling stock
There is usually the opportunity to see a variety of Corus and main line locomotives and rolling stock during railtours

Souvenir shop: Within the Corus site, only accessible to railtour participants
Length of line: There is approximately 100 miles of standard gauge track within the site. Nearly all of this is visible on tours but may not be suitable for access by coaching stock due to curvature, production processes, Corus production rail traffic, clearances etc
Passenger trains: The tours cover some 8 miles (short tour) or 15 miles (long tour) of the Corus steelworks internal system. Every effort is made to provide an informed commentary throughout the tours which utilise coaching stock. Brake van tours, both timetabled and privately chartered, tend to cover areas not accessible to hauled coaching stock. The Society cannot charge set fares but relies on donations which are collected at the end of each tour, except when private charters are operated
Period of public operation: Approximately Easter to the end of September for coaching stock, with

monthly brake van trips during October to March. Please note that brake van trips are *not* considered to be suitable for children due to the nature of the vehicles
Special events: Occasional diesel days using a variety of locomotives for haulage. These will be advertised as and when arranged. Footplate experience days on steam and/or diesel locomotives, held on dates to suit participants, usually at weekends when there is no railtour scheduled
Facilities for mobility impared visitors: Limited. Subject to notification at the time of booking wheelchair access can be provided to the departure platform and coaches. It is regretted that wheelchair access is not possible to the on-board toilet, the static refreshment coach and toilets at the depot
Membership details: Details available from Society Treasurer at the above address
Membership newsletter: Approximately 4 times/year

Steam Centre — Astley Green Colliery Museum — Lancashire

The museum occupies some 15 acres south of the Astley Green colliery site. The low-lying landscape ensures that the museum's 98ft high lattice steel headgear can be seen for many miles. Apart from the steam winding engine and headgear the museum houses many exhibits, not least of which is the collection of over 20 colliery locomotives, the largest collection of its type in the UK. The museum is now run and maintained, on behalf of the community, by the Red Rose Steam Society Ltd, a registered charity based in Lancashire. The 400m line is used for demonstration purposes
Location: Between the A580 and Bridgewater Canal in Higher Green Lane, Astley Green, Tyldesley

Industrial locomotives
(standard gauge)

Name	No	Builder	Type	Built
—	—*	R/Hornsby (244580)	4wDM	1946
(3ft gauge)				
—	17	H/Clarke (DM781)	0-6-0DMF	1953
—	—	Hunslet (4816)	0-6-0DMF	1955
—	11	H/Clarke (DM1058)	0-6-0DMF	1957
—	20	H/Clarke (DM1120)	0-6-0DMF	1957
—	18	H/Clarke (DM1270)	0-6-0DMF	1961
—	DM1439	H/Clarke (DM1439)	0-6-0DMF	1978
(2ft 6in gauge)				
—	—*	Hunslet (3411)	0-4-0DMF	1947
—	3*	E/Electric (7936)	4wBEF	1957
—	4	H/Clarke (DM1173)	0-6-0DMF	1959
—	5	H/Clarke (DM1352)	0-6-0DMF	1967
—	6	H/Clarke (DM1413)	0-6-0DMF	1970
—	7	H/Clarke (DM1414)	0-6-0DMF	1970
—	1-44-170	Hunslet (8575)	0-6-0DMF	1978
—	1-44-174	Hunslet (8577)	0-6-0DMF	1978
Newton	—	Hunslet (8975)	0-6-0DH	1979

Operating company: The Secretary, Astley Green Colliery Museum, Higher Green Lane, Astley Green, Tyldesley, Manchester M29 7JB
Internet addresses: *e-mail:* info@agcm.org.uk
For school parties *e-mail:* school.visits@agcm.org.uk
For other groups *e-mail:* group.visits@agcm.org.uk
Web site: www.acgm.org
OS reference: SJ 705998
On site facilities: Car park, toilets
Access by public transport: Train to Atherton, buses 551, 654
Facilities for disabled: Toilet
Period of public operation:
Sundays — 13.00-17.00
Tuesdays — 13.00-17.00
Thursdays — 13.00-17.00
Closed Christmas and Boxing Days
Membership details: Membership Secretary, Red Rose Steam Society, Higher Green Lane, Astley Green, Tyldesley, Manchester M29 7JB
e-mail: membership@rrss.agcm.org.uk

Name	No	Builder	Type	Built
Foggwell Flyer	—	Hunslet (8567)	0-6-0DMF	1981
Bullfrogs Bullet	—	Hunslet (8568)	0-6-0DMF	1981
(2ft 4in gauge)				
—	6	H/Clarke (DM970)	0-6-0DMF	1957
(2ft 1in gauge)				
Kestrel	2	H/Clarke (DM674)	0-6-0DMF	1954
(2ft gauge)				
Stacey	—	H/Clarke (DM804)	0-6-0DMF	1951
—	T1	H/Clarke (DM840)	0-6-0DMF	1954
George	14	H/Clarke (DM929)	0-6-0DMF	1955
—	8	M/Vickers (892)	4wBEF	1955
Warrior	14	H/Clarke (DM933)	0-6-0DMF	1956
—	—	H/Clarke (DM1164)	0-4-0DMF	1959
—	—	Hunslet (6048)	0-4-0DMF	1961
Sandy	—	M/Rail (11218)	4wDM	1962
Point of Ayr	—	R/Hornsby (497547)	4wDMF	1963
Roger Bowen	—	Hunslet (7373)	0-4-0DHF	1973
Calverton	—	Hunslet (7519)	4wDHF	1977
Mole	—	Hunslet (8834)	4wDHF	1978
Lionheart	—	Hunslet (8909)	4wDHF	1979
—	R4	H/Clarke (DM1443)	0-6-0DMF	1980

Rolling stock (standard gauge)
1 Smith & Rodley steam crane*, 1 Coles diesel crane*

*on display, remainder either sheeted over or stored in locomotive shed

Audley End Railway

Miniature Railway — **Essex**

The Audley End miniature railway is a delightful ride on Lord Braybrooke's 10.25in gauge railway through estate woodland
Location: Audley End, Saffron Walden, Essex.
Headquarters: (Postal address) Audley End Estate Office, Brunketts, Wendens Ambo, Saffron Walden, Essex CB11 4JL
Contact:
General Manager: H. T. White

Telephone: (01799) 541354 or 541956
Internet address: *e-mail:* aee@farming.co.uk
Web site: www.audley-end-railway.co.uk
Car parking: On site
Access by public transport: Rail to Audley End (1 mile)
On site facilities: Ticket office, shop and light refreshments, toilets, large picnic area

Length of line: 10.25in gauge; 1.5 miles long
Period of public operation: Please contact for details
Special events: Santa Specials — December (these can be booked by prior arrangement)
Facilities for disabled: Carriage built in 2002 to enable wheelchair access

Avon Valley Railway

Timetable Service — **South Glos**

Member: HRA
The Avon Valley Railway runs on part of the Midland Railway which connected the cities of Bristol and Bath, and currently operates over three miles of relaid track between Oldland Common to the north and Avon Riverside to the south

Avon Riverside station provides visitors with the opportunity to enjoy the riverside walks, picnic areas and links to the River Avon scenic boat trips on certain dates during the year. For 2009 the rail/river trips will be operating every steam open day from Easter

to the end of September, except for 9/10 May and 2 August
Headquarters: Avon Valley Railway Company Limited, Bitton Station, Bath Road, Bitton, Bristol BS30 6HD
Telephone: (0117) 932 5538 for general enquiries

(0117) 932 7296 for 24hr talking timetable
Internet address: *e-mail:* info@avonvalleyrailway.org
Web site: www.avonvalleyrailway.org
Main station: Bitton
Other public stations: Oldland Common, Avon Riverside
OS reference: ST 670705
Car park: Bitton station
Access by public transport: Main line train service to Keynsham. First service No 332 (Bristol-Bath), No 558 (Bristol-North Common)
Access by bike: Bitton station is on the Bristol/Bath Railway Path (route 4 of the National Cycle Network)
Catering facilities: New café/restaurant opened in July 2008 with indoor seating in Mk 1 railway carriage. Hot and cold meals and food available, with daily specials. Confectionery and ice cream also available
On site facilities: Station café/restaurant is open every daily from 1 January to 24 December. Toilets, picnic area, play area nearby
Public opening: Bitton station is open daily for viewing of its static collection of locomotives and rolling stock, except for the period between Christmas and New Year. Trains operate: 22 March; 5, 7-16, 19/26 April; 2*/3/4, 9/10, 17, 23*, 24-28, 30*/31 May; 3*, 6*, 7, 10*, 14, 17*, 20*/21, 24*, 28 June; 1, 5, 8, 12, 15, 19, 22, 25*, 26, 28-30 July; 1*/2, 4-6, 8*/9, 11-13, 15*/16, 18-20, 22*/23, 25-27, 29*, 30/31 August; 5*/6, 12*/13, 20, 27 September; 3/4, 11, 17*/18, 25, 27-29 October; 1, 29 November; 5-7, 12/13, 19/20, 23/24, 27 December; 1 January 2010
*diesel-hauled
Special events: *Advance booking is essential for some of these events. Details from Bitton station — 0117 932 5538. On-line booking is now available using the link from the railway's web site.*
Mother's Day Lunch — 22 March; Easter Steaming — 7-16 April; Day out with Thomas — 9/10 May*; Murder Mystery Evening — 16 May; 6th Bitton Beer Festival — 5-7 June; Teddy Bears' Picnic — 19 June; Father's Day Lunch — 21 June; Murder Mystery Evening — 27 June; Vintage Bus Rally — 9

Locomotives

Name	No	Origin	Class	Type	Built
Sir Frederick Pile	34058	SR	BB	4-6-2	1947
—	44123	LMS	4F	0-6-0	1925
—	D2994	BR	07	0-6-0DE	1962
The Royal Alex	73101	BR	73	Bo-Bo	1965
*—	51909	BR	108	DMBS	1958
—	52006	BR	107	DMBS	1960
—	52025	BR	107	DMCL	1960
*—	56271	BR	108	DTC	1958

*stored off-site
Locomotive notes: D2994 and 73101 in service

Industrial locomotives

Name	No	Builder	Type	Built
Edwin Hulse	—	Avonside (1798)	0-6-0ST	1918
Karel	4015	Chrzanow (4015)	0-6-0T	1954
Phoenix	70	H/Clarke (1464)	0-6-0T	1921
Littleton No 5	—	M/Wardle (2018)	0-6-0ST	1922
—	7151	RSH (7151)	0-6-0T	1944
Meteor	1	RSH (7609)	0-6-0T	1950
Grumpy	WD70031	B/Drewry (2158)	0-4-0DM	1941
—*	Army 200	Barclay (358)	0-4-0DM	1941
Kingswood	—	Barclay (446)	0-4-0DM	1959
Western Pride*	D1171	H/Clarke (D1171)	0-6-0DM	1951
—†*	—	R/Hornsby (210481)	4wDM	1941
Basil*	—	R/Hornsby (235519)	4wDM	1945
—†*	—	R/Hornsby (252823)	4wDM	1947
—	429	R/Hornsby (466618)	0-6-0DH	1961
General Lord Robertson*	610	Sentinel (10143)	0-8-0DH	1961

*stored/undergoing restoration off-site
†chassis only

Locomotive notes: *Kingswood, Karel,* 70 and 7151 are in service

Stock
22 ex-BR Mk 1 coaches (10 stored off-site); 1 ex-BR Mk 1 Restaurant coach; 1 ex-BR Mk 3 sleeper; 3 cranes; 1 Wickham trolley; numerous assorted wagons

Owners
44123 the London Midland Society
52006 and 52025 on loan from Class 107 Ltd
73101 on loan from David Hurd

August; Railway Relics Valuation Day — 6 September; Teddy Bears' Picnic — 13 September; Murder Mystery Evening — 19 September; Day out with Thomas — 3/4 October*; Murder Mystery Evening — 20 October; Wizard Specials — 23-25 October; Murder Mystery Evenings — 24, 31 October; End of Season Gala — 1 November; Santa Specials — 29 November, 5-7, 12/13, 19/20, 23/24 December; Carol Train — 1 December; Sherry and Mince Pie Specials — 27 December, 1 January 2010.
*to be confirmed.

Steam 'N Cuisine (3 course dining trains) 22 March, 26 April, 31 May, 21 June, 26 July, 16 August, 17 September, 18 October.
Bitton Bistro (2 course dining trains) 5 April, 5 July, 2 August, 6 September.
Driver experience courses — 14/15, 28/29 March; 4, 18, 28 April, 16 May, 13, 27 June, 4, 11, 18 July, 19, 26 September, 10, 24, 31 October
Special facilities: Carriage or train hire available for parties, staff outings or business functions
Facilities for disabled: Fully

accessible disabled toilet at Bitton station. Coach converted for disabled use (no toilet facilities)
Membership details: Membership

Secretary, c/o Bitton station
Membership journal: *Semaphore* — every 6 months; *Ground Signal* newsletter every 2 months

Steam Centre — Barrow Hill Roundhouse Railway Centre — Derbyshire

Member: HRA

In 1839 the North Midland Railway devised an arrangement of stabling locomotives around a turntable within a polygonal building with a conical roof, hence roundhouse. In 1864 locomotives began to be housed in buildings of a square nature (retaining the name) and in 1870 Barrow Hill was built to this design. Retained following the end of steam, Barrow Hill remained in use until 1991. Saved from demolition at the 11th hour, the Grade 2 listed building is unique in Great Britain as the last surviving working roundhouse.

The roundhouse can accommodate up to 24 main line locomotives, and includes maintenance pits and ancillary services

Location/headquarters: Barrow Hill Roundhouse Engine Shed, Campbell Drive, Barrow Hill, Nr Staveley, Chesterfield, Derbyshire S43 2PR.

Situated near junctions 29/30 on M1

OS reference: SK 4175

Project manager: Mervyn Allcock

Contact address: Barrow Hill Engine Shed Society, address as above

Telephone: 01246 472450

Fax: 01246 472450

Internet address: *Web site:* www.barrowhill.org.uk

Car park: Adjacent to site

Access by public transport: Train to Chesterfield, Stagecoach bus Nos 80/90/56

On site facilities: Refreshments, souvenir shop and museum. Toilets

Refreshment facilities: Drinks and light refreshments

Public opening: Open most weekends — 4 major open weekends a year

Locomotives and multiple-units

Name	No	Origin	Class	Type	Built
Butler Henderson	506	GCR	'Director'	4-4-0	1920
—	1217	GER	J17	0-6-0	1905
—	1708	MR	1F	0-6-0T	1880
RAF Biggin Hill	45110	LMS	5MT	4-6-0	1935
Blue Peter	60532	LNER	A2	4-6-2	1948
—	03066	BR	03	0-6-0DM	1959
—	D2302	BR	04	0-6-0DM	1960
—	08492	BR	08	0-6-0DE	1958
—	08659	BR	08	0-6-0DE	1959
Christine	D4092	BR	10	0-6-0DE	1962
—	20092*	BR	20	Bo-Bo	1959
—	20096*	BR	20	Bo-Bo	1961
—	20105	BR	20	Bo-Bo	1962
—	20106	BR	20	Bo-Bo	1962
—	20104	BR	20	Bo-Bo	1962
—	20121*	BR	20	Bo-Bo	1962
—	D8132	BR	20	Bo-Bo	1962
—	20901*	BR	20	Bo-Bo	1959
—	20904*	BR	20	Bo-Bo	1959
—	20905*	BR	20	Bo-Bo	1959
—	26007	BR	26	Bo-Bo	1958
—	26011	BR	26	Bo-Bo	1959
—	31128	BR	31	A1A-A1A	1959
—	33035	BR	33	Bo-Bo	1960
—	33103	BR	33	Bo-Bo	1960
—	33108	BR	33	Bo-Bo	1960
—	37057*	BR	37	Co-Co	1962
—	37201	BR	37	Co-Co	1962
—	37257	BR	37	Co-Co	1965
—	37372	BR	37	Co-Co	1963
—	37409*	BR	37	Co-Co	1965
—	37412*	BR	37	Co-Co	1965
—	37515	BR	37	Co-Co	1962
—	37672*	BR	37	Co-Co	1964
—	37693*	BR	37	Co-Co	1963
—	97301*	BR	97 (37)	Co-Co	
—	97302*	BR	97 (37)	Co-Co	
—	97303*	BR	97 (37)	Co-Co	
Andana	D213	BR	40	1Co-Co1	1959
Sherwood Forester	45060	BR	45	1Co-Co1	1961
—	45105	BR	45	1Co-Co1	1961
—	45112	BR	45	1Co-Co1	1961
—	47488*	BR	47	Co-Co	1964
—	47707*	BR	47	Co-Co	1966
—	47744*	BR	47	Co-Co	1966
—	47746	BR	47	Co-Co	1966
—	47801*	BR	47	Co-Co	1966

England

Special events: Easter, summer, autumn and Christmas open weekends

Membership details: Martyn Brailsford, 18 Queen Street, Brimington, Chesterfield, Derbyshire S43 1HT

Society journal: *The Roundhouse* — three times a year

Name	No	Origin	Class	Type	Built
Alycidon	D9009	BR	55	Co-Co	1961
Tulyar	55015	BR	55	Co-Co	1961
Gordon Highlander	D9016	BR	55	Co-Co	1961
Royal Highland Fusilier	55015	BR	55	Co-Co	1961
—	56006	BR	56	Co-Co	1977
—	56086	BR	56	Co-Co	1980
—	56101	BR	56	Co-Co	1981
—	57005*	BR	57	Co-Co	
—	58001*	BR	57	Co-Co	1983
—	73113	BR	73	Bo-Bo	1963
—	73134	BR	73	Bo-Bo	1966
—	81002	BR	81	Bo-Bo	1960
—	82008	BR	82	Bo-Bo	1961
—	E3035	BR	83	Bo-Bo	1961
—	84001	BR	83	Bo-Bo	1960
Doncaster Plant 150 1853-2003	85101	BR	85	Bo-Bo	1961
—	89001	BR	89	Bo-Bo	1986

Industrial locomotives

Name	No	Builder	Type	Built
Henry	—	H/Leslie (2491)	0-4-0ST	1901
The Welshman	—	M/Wardle (1207)	0-6-0ST	1890
—	—	Peckett (2000)	0-6-0ST	1941
—	9	YEC	0-6-0ST	1952
Harry	—	Drewry (2589)	0-4-0DM	1956
—	4	Hunslet (6975)	0-6-0DH	1969
—	47	Hunslet (7181)	0-6-0DH	1970
—	RFS 10	E/Electric (D1228)	0-6-0DH	1967

England

Name	No	Builder	Type	Built
Coalite 7	—	R/Royce (10279)	0-6-0DH	1970
Coalite 9	—	Vanguard	0-6-0DH	

Stock

2 ex-BR Mk 1 coaches, 3 ex-BR Mk 2 coaches, 1 ex-MR brake van, 1 ex-SR brake van, 1 ex-GWR 'Toad' brake van, 1 ex-LMS brake van, 2 ex-BR brake vans, 1 Tunny wagon, 2 ex-BR bogie vans, 1 dynamometer car, 2 ex-BR Lowmac,

Owners

*various main line companies for overhaul or storage
45110 the Severn Valley Railway (Holdings) plc
60532 on loan from North Eastern Locomotive Preservation Group
33035, 45060 and 45105 the Pioneer Diesel Group
Classes 81-9 locomotives the AC Loco Group
The Welshman and 9 the National Mining Museum

Timetable Service — The Battlefield Line Railway — Leicestershire

Member: HRA, TT

A quiet country railway operated by the Shackerstone Railway Society Ltd

Headquarters: Shackerstone station (3 miles north of Market Bosworth in Leicestershire)

Address: Shackerstone Station, Shackerstone, Nuneaton CV13 6NW

Telephone: Timetable enquiries: (01827) 880754

Internet address: *Web site*: www.battlefield-line-railway.co.uk

Operating Manager: D. Weightman

Main station: Shackerstone

Other public station: Shenton

OS reference: SK 379066

Car park: Shackerstone (free), Shenton (council car park)

Access by public transport: Bus service from Nuneaton weekends only. Ring Traveline 0870 6082608 for details

Refreshment facilities: Tea rooms on Shackerstone station. Buffet/bar on most trains

Souvenir shop: Shackerstone

Museum: Shackerstone

Depot: Shackerstone

Length of line: 4.75 miles (8km)

Passenger trains: Shackerstone-Shenton

Period of public operation: Shackerstone station is generally open weekends 11.45-17.00 and

Locomotives and multiple-units

Name	No	Origin	Class	Type	Built
Mayflower	1306	LNER	B1	4-6-0	1948
Diane	D2867	BR	02	0-4-0DH	1961
—	03170	BR	03	0-6-0DM	1960
—	03180	BR	03	0-6-0DM	1962
—	11215	BR	04	0-6-0DM	1956
—	D2310	BR	04	0-6-0DM	1960
—	08818	BR	08	0-6-0DE	1960
—	12083	BR	11	0-6-0DE	1953
—	D9529	BR	14	0-6-0DE	1965
—	20105	BR	20	Bo-Bo	1961
—	20166	BR	20	Bo-Bo	1960
—	25067*	BR	25	Bo-Bo	1963
Brush Veteran Calder Hall Power Station	D5518	BR	31	A1A-A1A	1958
	31130	BR	31	A1A-A1A	1959
—	33008	BR	33	Bo-Bo	1960
Griffon	33019	BR	33	Bo-Bo	1960
—	33053*	BR	33	Bo-Bo	1961
—	37227	BR	37	Co-Co	1964
—	37905	BR	37	Co-Co	1963
—	45015	BR	45	1Co-Co1	1960
—	47640	BR	47	Co-Co	1966
—	56098	BR	56	Co-Co	1981
—	73105	BR	73	Bo-Bo	1965
—	51131	BR	116	DMBS	1958
—	51321	BRCW	116	DMS	1959
—	55005	GRCW	122	DMBS	1958
—	59522	P/Steel	117	TC(L)	1959

*on long-term loan to Mid-Hants Railway

Industrial locomotives

Name	No	Builder	Type	Built
Waleswood	—	H/Clarke (750)	0-4-0ST	1906
Sir Gomer	—	Peckett (1859)	0-6-0ST	1932

Bank Holiday Mondays 11.00-17.00.
Trains at weekends Easter to October. Wednesday afternoons in July and August
Special events: See leaflet and press for further details.
Christmas specials weekends 25 November to 24 December
Facilities for disabled: Special car park and toilets
Special notes: Family tickets available. Scenic countryside views including Ashby Canal. Shenton station is adjacent to Bosworth Battlefield (1485) Country Park. 20 minute walk along 'Battlefield Trail' to visitor centre, return by later train
Operating company/ preservation society contact: The Secretary, Shackerstone Railway Society, Shackerstone Station, Shackerstone, Nuneaton CV13 6NW
Membership journal:
Shackerstone News — 2/3 times/year

Name	No	Builder	Type	Built
Dunlop No 7	—	Peckett (2130)	0-4-0ST	1951
Richard III	—	RSH (7537)	0-6-0T	1949
Lamport No 3	—	Bagnall (2670)	0-6-0ST	1942
—	—	Barclay (422)	0-6-0DM	1958
—	19	Barclay (594)	0-6-0DM	1974
—	—	E/Electric (8431)	0-4-0DH	1963
—	890445	GEC (5402)	0-6-0DM	1975
—	47	T/Hill (249V)	0-6-0DH	1974
—	—	R/Hornsby (263001)	4wDM	1949
—	44	Hunslet (6684)	0-6-0DM	1968
—	—	R/Royce (10254)	0-4-0DE	1966
—	—	Simplex (9921)	4wDM	1955

Stock
8 ex-BR Mk 1 coaches (including Griddle Car), 2 ex-BR Mk 2 coaches, 1 ex-BR Mk 3 sleeper; 5 passenger-rated vans; 1 rail-mounted steam crane; 2 rail-mounted diesel cranes; 35 wagons (inc 3 goods brake vans SR, MR, BR)

Owners
20105, 20166, A/Barclay (594) and GEC (5402) on loan from Harry Needle Railroad Co

---

Museum	**Beamish**	County Durham

Member: HRA
The railway station, signalbox and goods shed have been completely re-created (originally from Rowley, near Consett) along with the other exhibits to show a way of life long past. There are some very old locomotives in the collection
Location: Beamish Museum, County Durham DH9 0RG
OS reference: NZ 214548
Telephone: 0191 370 4000
Fax: 0191 370 4001
Internet address: *e-mail:* museum@beamish.org.uk
Web site: www.beamish.org.uk
Car park: At museum
Access by public transport: Bus service from Eldon Square, Newcastle upon Tyne
On site facilities: This 300-acre open air museum vividly re-creates life in the North of England in the early 1800s and 1900s. The Town has dentist's surgery, solicitor's office, Co-op shops, garage, sweet shop and bank. The Colliery Village has pit cottages, village

Locomotives

Name	No	Origin	Class	Type	Built
—	65033	NER	C	0-6-0	1889

On loan to North Norfolk Railway until 2025

Industrial locomotives

Name	No	Builder	Type	Built
*Locomotion**	1	LE (1)	0-4-0	1975
Twizell†	3	Stephenson (2730)	0-6-0T	1891
—††	14	H/Leslie (3056)	0-4-0ST	1914
South Durham Malleable Iron Co No 5	—††	Stockton Ironworks	0-4-0ST	1900
Coffee Pot§	—	Head Wrightson	0-4-0VB	1871
—††	E1	Black, Hawthorn (897)	2-4-0CT	1883
Jacob§	680	McEwan Pratt	0-4-0P	1916
—**	18	Lewin (693)	0-4-0WT	1877
Steam Elephant	—*	Wallsend Colliery	0-6-0G	2000
—	17	Head Wrightson (33)	0-4-0VB	1873
—	—	R/Hornsby (476140)	4wDM	1963
Puffing Billy	—	A/Keef (71)	0-4-0	2005

†on long-term loan to Tanfield ††on static display
§under repair **undergoing major rebuild
*replica

Locomotive notes: E1, 680 and R/Hornsby not usually on display. Others usually on display. 18 may be off site for overhaul during 2009, *Coffee Pot* in operation during second half of 2009.
Twizell on long-term loan to Tanfield Railway

school and chapel, 'drift' mine and pithead. Home Farm with farm house, livestock and exhibitions. Railway station complete with goods yard and signalbox, rolling stock on static display. Pockerley Manor illustrates the lifestyle of a yeoman farming family in the early 1800s.

Early Railways — Pockerley Waggonway — a large stone engine shed with displays illustrating the development of railways in the early 1800s. Visitors take a short ride in re-created carriages of the period pulled by the replica *Locomotion, Steam Elephant* or *Puffing Billy*

Public opening:
Summer: (4 April to 1 November) daily 10.00-17.00
Winter: (2 November to 26 March 2010) 10.00-16.00
Closed Mondays and Fridays and Christmas Day
Last admission always 15.00
NB: A winter visit to Beamish is

Trams

No	Operator	Built
10	Gateshead	1926
16	Sunderland	1900
31	Blackpool	1901
51	Gateshead	1901
114	Newcastle	1901
196	Oporto	1935
264	Sheffield	1907
513	Blackpool	1952
749	Blackpool (tower wagon)	

centred on the Town, Tramway and colliery village; other areas of the museum are closed and admission charges are, consequently, reduced
Length of line:
Pockerley Waggonway, $1/4$-mile — operational daily in summer. Rebuilt NER station, colliery sidings
Facilities for disabled: One carriage at 1825 Railway suitable for wheelchairs. Advance notice for parties to Bookings Officer preferred

Notes: Occasional visits by steam locomotives are planned to the NER station, Details of these will appear on the museum web site and in the railway press.

Demonstration trains will operate at both the NER railway station and in the Edwardian Colliery during 2009. Log onto www.beamish.org.uk for details.

See transport collection latest news at www.beamish collections.com

---

Miniature Railway	**Beer Heights Light Railway**	Devon

An extensive railway in the landscaped grounds of publisher and model railway manufacturing group
Location/Headquarters:
Pecorama, Underleys, Beer, Devon EX12 3NA
Managing Director:
C. M. Pritchard
Telephone: 01297 21542
Fax: 01297 20229
Internet address: *e-mail:* pecorama@btconnect.com
Web site: www.peco-uk.com
OS reference: SY 223891
Car parking: Ample on site, free for our visitors
Access by public transport: By rail to Axminster station, then Axe Valley Bus to Beer. By rail to Exeter station, then First Bus to Weymouth via Beer
On site facilities: Restaurant, shop, model railway exhibition and fully restored Pullman car 'Orion', extensive gardens, children's activities

Locomotives

Name	No	Builder	Type	Built
Otter	1	WNG*	2-4-2	2004
Dickie	3	D. Curwen	0-4-2	1976
Thomas II	4	R. Marsh	0-4-2ST+T	1979
Linda	5	D. Clarke	2-4-0ST+T	1983
Jimmy	6	S/Lamb	Bo-Bo	1986
Mr P	7	Macdougall	2-4-2T	1997
Gem	8	Peco	0-6-0T+T	1999
Claudine	9	Macdougall	2-4-4†	2005
Alfred	10	Macdougall / Nation	Bo-Bo Tram	2003

*built by Western Narrow Gauge, privately owned
†single Fairlie

Rolling stock — coaches
3 x 4-seat bogie open coaches built by Cromar White; 9 x 4-seat bogie open 'Pullman' coaches built by BHLR; 8 x 4-seat quad-articulated coaches built by BHLR
Rolling stock — wagons
6 x 4-wheeled wagons; 1 bogie open wagon; 2 x 4-wheel bolster wagons, 2 x 4-wheeled tipper wagons; 1 generator wagon

Note:
Some locomotives and rolling stock are not on permanent display

Length of line: 1 mile, 7.25in gauge
Period of public operation: Easter to end October — Monday to Friday 10.00-17.30; Saturdays 10.00-13.00; Sundays open at Easter and then from late spring Bank Holiday to start of September 10.00-17.30
Special events: PECO Annual Vintage/Classic Vehicle Rally —

24 May; Thomas II's Day: guest locomotives on the BHLR — 7 June; Miniature live steam traction engine rides — 14 June; Great West Classic Vehicle Rally — 28 June; Teddy Mac Days — 12-15 July; Thomas the Tank Engine Story Days — 16/17 July; PECO Gardens Open Day — 19 July; PECO Locomotive Week — 30/31 August. FREE entry to gardens

28 September to 24 October
Facilities for disabled: All toilet blocks with facilities for disabled, wheelchair access to Model Exhibition, gardens and restaurant (Note: some paths in the gardens are steep and wheelchair bound will need assistance)
Membership details: Season ticket to Pecorama available; apply to above address

---

| Attraction | ## Bicton Woodland Railway | Devon |

A passenger-carrying line of 18in gauge with stock mainly from the Woolwich Arsenal Railway and of World War 1 vintage
Location: Bicton Park, near Budleigh Salterton
OS reference: SY 074862
Operating society/organisation: Bicton Woodland Railway, Bicton Gardens, East Budleigh, Budleigh Salterton, Devon EX9 7BS
Telephone: Colaton Raleigh (01395) 568465
Fax: (01395) 568374
Internet addresses:
e-mail: info@bictongardens.co.uk
Web site: www.bictongardens.co.uk
Car park: On site
Access by public transport: Buses

Locomotives (1ft 6in gauge)

Name	No	Builder	Type	Built
Bicton	2	R/Hornsby (213839)	4wDM	1942
Clinton	4	H/Hunslet (2290)	0-4-0	1941
Sir Walter Raleigh	—	Keef	4wDM	2000

Stock
5 closed bogie coaches

pass half-hourly from Exeter, Exmouth, Sidmouth in season
On site facilities: Indoor and outdoor play areas, Glass Houses, Palm House, Grade 1 gardens, museum and restaurant
Length of line: 1.5mile (2.4km), 18in gauge
Public opening: Open all year

(except 25/26 December), winter 10.00-17.00, summer 10.00-18.00
Trains operate: Winter 12.15 and 14.30, summer 6-8 trains a day. 25min trips
Facilities for disabled: Toilets, wheelchairs available. Special carriage for wheelchairs

---

| Timetable Service | ## Blackpool & Fleetwood Tramway | Lancashire |

The Blackpool & Fleetwood Tramway is the sole surviving traditional street tramway system in the United Kingdom and attracts visitors from all over the country. During the autumn the streets are illuminated and tours are available by historic or illuminated tram.
Operating organisation: Blackpool Transport Services Ltd, Rigby Road, Blackpool, Lancashire FY1 5DD
Telephone: (01253) 473001
Managing Director: Steve Burd
Operations Director: Oliver Howarth

Trams

No	Trucks	Builder	Date (Rebuilt)
Boat Cars			
600	E/Electric	E/Electric	1934
602	E/Electric	E/Electric	1934
604	E/Electric	E/Electric	1934
605	E/Electric	E/Electric	1934
§607	E/Electric	E/Electric	1934
Toast Rack Tram			
619	E/Electric	Bolton Trams	1987
Brush Cars			
§621	EMB	Brush	1937
622	EMB	Brush	1937
623	EMB	Brush	1937
§625	EMB	Brush	1937
626	EMB	Brush	1937
§627	EMB	Brush	1937

Engineering Director:
Dave Hislop
Customer Services Co-ordinator:
Bryan Lindop
Length of line: 11.5 miles,
standard gauge
Period of public operation: Daily
throughout the year, except
Christmas Day, Boxing Day and
New Year's Day
Number of trams: 80 double and
single-deck trams

No	Trucks	Builder	Date (Rebuilt)
630	EMB	Brush	1937
631	EMB	Brush	1937
§632	EMB	Brush	1937
633	EMB	Brush	1937
§634	EMB	Brush	1937
†636	EMB	Brush	1937
§637	EMB	Brush	1937
Centenary Cars			
641	Blackpool	East Lancs	1984
642	Blackpool	East Lancs	1986
643	Blackpool	East Lancs	1986
644	Blackpool	East Lancs	1986
645	Blackpool	East Lancs	1987
646	Blackpool	East Lancs	1987
647	Blackpool	East Lancs	1988
648	Blackpool	East Lancs	1985
Towing Cars			
671	E/Electric	E/Electric / Blackpool	1960
672	E/Electric	E/Electric / Blackpool	1960
673	E/Electric	E/Electric / Blackpool	1961
674	E/Electric	E/Electric / Blackpool	1962
675	E/Electric	E/Electric / Blackpool	1958
§676	E/Electric	E/Electric / Blackpool	1958
Ex-Towing Railcoaches			
§678	E/Electric	E/Electric / Blackpool	1961
680	E/Electric	E/Electric / Blackpool	1960
Trailer Cars			
681	Maley & Taunton	MCW	1960
682	Maley & Taunton	MCW	1960
683	Maley & Taunton	MCW	1960
684	Maley & Taunton	MCW	1960
685	Maley & Taunton	MCW	1960
§686	Maley & Taunton	MCW	1960
§687	Maley & Taunton	MCW	1960
Balloon Cars			
700	E/Electric	E/Electric	1934
701	E/Electric	E/Electric	1934
702	E/Electric	E/Electric	1934
703	E/Electric	E/Electric	1934
*704	E/Electric	E/Electric	1934
706	E/Electric	E/Electric (open top)	1934
707	E/Electric	E/Electric	1934 (1998)
*708	E/Electric	E/Electric	1934
709	E/Electric	E/Electric	1934 (2000)
§710	E/Electric	E/Electric	1934
711	E/Electric	E/Electric	1934
712	E/Electric	E/Electric	1935
713	E/Electric	E/Electric	1934
715	E/Electric	E/Electric	1935
§716	E/Electric	E/Electric	1935
717	E/Electric	E/Electric	1934 (±)
718	E/Electric	E/Electric	1934
719	E/Electric	E/Electric	1935
*720	E/Electric	E/Electric	1935 (±)
721	E/Electric	E/Electric	1935
722	E/Electric	E/Electric	1935
723	E/Electric	E/Electric	1935
724	E/Electric	E/Electric	1935 (2004)
726	E/Electric	E/Electric	1935
Jubilee Cars			
761	Blackpool	E/Electric / Blackpool	1979
762	Blackpool	E/Electric / Blackpool	1982

Illuminated Trams

No	Trucks	Builder	Date (Rebuilt)
*732	EMB		1961
*733/734	E/Electric	from Pantograph 174	1962 (±)
736	E/Electric	from Pantograph 170	1965 (2004)
*737	EMB	from Brush 633	2001

Engineering Vehicles

No	Trucks	Builder	Date (Rebuilt)
260	EMB	Blackpool	1973
750	MRCW	Blackpool	1907 (2004)
754	E/Electric	Blackpool	1992

Preserved Trams

No	Trucks	Builder	Date (Rebuilt)
5	?	D/Kerr	1901
40	Preston McGuire	United Electric Co	1914
66	Brill	Electric Railway & Carriage	1901
147	Preston McGuire	Hurst Nelson	1924
304	Maley & Taunton	Hurst Nelson	1952
§513	Maley & Taunton	Charles Roberts	1950
660	Maley & Taunton	Charles Roberts	1953

*out of service
§currently mothballed
†on loan
§rebuilding work in progess

Owners

5 the Stockport 5 Trust
40 the Tramway Museum Society
66 the Bolton 66 Group
304 and 732 the Lancastrian Transport Trust
513 Beamish Open Air Museum

Timetable Service	**Bluebell Railway**	East Sussex

Member: HRA, TT

This famous steam railway was the first standard gauge passenger line to be taken over by enthusiasts. It derives its name from the bluebells which proliferate in the woodlands adjoining the line. A strong Victorian atmosphere pervades this branch line which has a large collection of Southern and pre-Grouping locomotives and coaches

Operations Manager: Mr Chris Knibbs

Headquarters: Bluebell Railway plc, Sheffield Park Station, A275, East Sussex TN22 3QL

Telephone:
For travel information (24hr talking timetable): Uckfield (01825) 720825.
General enquiries etc during office hours: (01825) 720800.
Golden Arrow Pullman, reservations and Catering Department: (01825) 720801.

Locomotives and multiple-unit

Name	No	Origin	Class	Type	Built
Stepney	55	LBSCR	A1X	0-6-0T	1875
Fenchurch	72	LBSCR	A1X	0-6-0T	1872
Birch Grove	32473	LBSCR	E4	0-6-2T	1898
—	27	SECR	P	0-6-0T	1910
—	65	SECR	O1	0-6-0	1896
—	263	SECR	H	0-4-4T	1905
—	323	SECR	P	0-6-0T	1910
—	592	SECR	C	0-6-0	1902
—	1178	SECR	P	0-6-0T	1910
—	96	LSWR	B4	0-4-0T	1893
—	488	LSWR	0415	4-4-2T	1885
—	27505	NLR	2F	0-6-0T	1880
Earl of Berkeley	9017	GWR	90	4-4-0	1938
—	541	SR	Q	0-6-0	1939
—	847	SR	S15	4-6-0	1937
Stowe	928	SR	V	4-4-0	1934
—	1618	SR	U	2-6-0	1928
—	1638	SR	U	2-6-0	1931
—	30064	SR	USA	0-6-0T	1943
Blackmoor Vale	21C123	SR	WC	4-6-2	1946
Sir Archibald Sinclair	34059	SR	BB	4-6-2	1947
Camelot	73082	BR	5MT	4-6-0	1955
—	75027	BR	4MT	4-6-0	1954

Shop: (01825) 720803
Internet address: *Web site:*
www.bluebell-railway.co.uk
Main station: Sheffield Park
Other public stations: Horsted
Keynes and Kingscote
Car parks: Sheffield Park, Horsted
Keynes
OS reference:
Sheffield Park TQ 403238,
Horsted Keynes TQ 372293
Access by public transport: Bus
service 473 between main line East
Grinstead and Kingscote (2 miles).
See timetable brochure for details
of operation
Refreshment facilities: Sheffield
Park restaurant/bar/self-service;
Horsted Keynes – 1930s bar/
buffet. The line's 'Golden Arrow'
Pullman operates a dinner service
most Saturday evenings and
luncheon service most Sundays.
  Telephone (01825) 720800 during
normal office hours for details.
Souvenir shops: Sheffield Park,
Horsted Keynes
Museum: Sheffield Park
Depots: Sheffield Park
(locomotives), Horsted Keynes
(stock)

Name	No	Origin	Class	Type	Built
—	78059†	BR	2MT	2-6-0	1956
—	80064	BR	4MT	2-6-4T	1953
—	80100	BR	4MT	2-6-4T	1954
—	80151	BR	4MT	2-6-4T	1957
—	92240	BR	9F	2-10-0	1958
—	D3023	BR	08	0-6-0DE	1953
—	11201*	BR	4COR	DMBSO	1937

†purchased without tender, for conversion to tank engine, work in hand
*on static display at Horsted Keynes

Industrial locomotives

Name	No	Builder	Type	Built
Baxter	3	F/Jennings (158)	0-4-0T	1877
†*Stamford*	24	Avonside (1972)	0-6-0ST	1927
Sharpthorn	4*	M/Wardle (641)	0-6-0ST	1877
Britannia	—	Howard (957)	4wPM	1936

*on static display
†on long-term loan to the Rutland Railway Museum

Stock
Substantial collection of pre-Nationalisation coaches including SECR, LSWR, Bulleid, Maunsell and Chesham vehicles. Also freight stock and engineers' vehicles plus 45-ton steam crane

Owners
592 the Wainwright C Class Preservation Society
541, 847, 928 and 1618 the Maunsell Locomotive Society Ltd
96 and 21C123 the Bulleid Society Ltd
263 the H Class Trust

Length of line: 9 miles
Passenger trains: Sheffield Park-
Horsted Keynes-Kingscote
Period of public operation:
Weekends all year round;
daily 16-20 February (half term),
April to October. Santa Specials
weekends in December, daily 26-31
December; 1 January 2010. Closed
25 December. Museum, locomotive
sheds, buffet and shop at Sheffield
Park open daily except Christmas
Day
Special events: Rail Ale Train —
17 April; Toy and Rail Collectors
Fair — 4 April; Spring Specials —
6-10, 13-17 April; Bluebell Specials
— 5-8 May; Southern at War
Weekend— 9/10 May; Rail Ale
Train — 29 May; Bluebell Family

73082 the Camelot Locomotive Society
80064 the 80064 Group
80151 the 80151 Group
D3023 on loan from the Heritage Shunters Trust
11201 the Southern Electric Group

Fun Weekends — 20/21, 27/28
June; An Evening with the Yetties
— 4 July; Rail Ale Train —
14 August; Vintage Transport
Weekend — 15/16 August;
Victorian Picnic — 5/6 September;
Giants of Steam — 24/25 October;
Wizard Weekend — 31 October/
1 November; Vintage Bus Running
Day — 15 November; Santa
Specials — pre-Christmas
weekends in December.
Further details of events available

on request
Facilities for disabled: All station
facilities are on the level and ramps
available for placing wheelchair
visitors into trains. Special toilets in
buffet at Sheffield Park and at
Kingscote, 'multi-purpose vehicle'
for use by groups, please telephone
to confirm availability
Membership details: Membership
Secretary, c/o above address
Membership journal: *Bluebell
News* — quarterly

Timetable Service	Bodmin & Wenford Railway	Cornwall

Member: HRA

The Bodmin & Wenford Railway
typifies the bygone branch railways
of Cornwall. The terminus at
Bodmin General, close to Bodmin
town centre, has an interesting
collection of standard gauge
locomotives and rolling stock, and
the operating line winds down to a
junction with main line rail
services at Bodmin Parkway, where
cross-platform interchange is
available. Passengers can alight at
the intermediate Colesloggett Halt
from where a footpath (not suitable
for wheelchairs or the infirm) leads
to Cardinham Woods (FC) with
waymarked trails, picnic areas and
a café. From the train there are
scenic views across the beautiful
valley of the River Fowey. A
second line circles Bodmin to
Boscarne Junction where it meets
the Camel Trail, a recreational path
for cyclists and walkers. A visit can
be made to the nearby Camel
Valley Vineyard (July and August
only). The majority of trains are
steam-hauled
Location: Bodmin General station,
on B3268
General Manager: Richard Jones
Operating society/organisation:

Locomotives and multiple-units

Name	No	Origin	Class	Type	Built
—	120	LSWR	T9	4-4-0	1898
—	30587	LSWR	0298	2-4-0WT	1874
—	4612	GWR	5700	0-6-PT	1942
—	4247	GWR	4200	2-8-0T	1916
—	5552	GWR	4575	2-6-2T	1928
—	6435	GWR	6400	0-6-0PT	1937
Triumph	50042	BR	50	Co-Co	1968
—	33110	BR	33	Bo-Bo	1960
—	37142	BR	37	Co-Co	1963
The Sapper	47306	BR	47	Co-Co	1964
—	D3452	BR	10	0-6-0DE	1957
—	08444	BR	08	0-6-0DE	1958
—	51947*	BR	108	DMBS	1960
—	52054	BR	108	DMCL	1960
—	50980	BR	108	DMBS	1960

*for spares

Industrial locomotives

Name	No	Builder	Type	Built
—	—	Bagnall (2766)	0-6-0ST	1944
—	19*	Bagnall (2962)	0-4-0ST	1950
Judy	—	Bagnall (2572)	0-4-0ST	1934
Alfred	—	Bagnall (3058)	0-4-0ST	1953
—	—	Bagnall (3121)	0-4-0F	1957
Peter	—	Fowler (22928)	0-4-0DM	1940
Lec	—	R/Hornsby (443642)	4wDM	1960

*on hire to Pontypool & Blaenavon Railway during 2009

Stock

12 BR Mk 1 coaches; 1 BR Mk 2 coach; 1 Mk 3 Sleeper; 6-wheel 10-ton
steam crane; 3 GWR coaches; 1 GWR Siphon G; various freight wagons

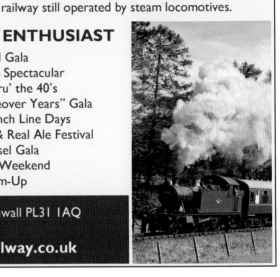
Bodmin & Wenford Railway,
Bodmin General Station, Bodmin,
Cornwall PL31 1AQ
Telephone:
Enquiries (01208) 73666
Fax: (01208) 77963
Internet address: *e-mail:*
enquiries@bodminandwenfordrailw
ay.co.uk
Web site:
www.bodminandwenfordrailway.co.
uk
Car park: Bodmin General, free
Access by public transport:
Interchange at Bodmin Parkway
arrivals by main line train; through
tickets available from most stations.
Local bus services to Bodmin
(Western Greyhound services 555,
529, 593)
Refreshment facilities: Buffet at
Bodmin General (open every day
when trains are running). Café in
the old signalbox at Bodmin
Parkway (open daily). Bar and
buffet on most trains
On site facilities: Railway gift
shop, small display of historic
artefacts, toilets (including
disabled), workshop viewing area
Length of lines: 3.5 miles General-

Owners
120, 30587 on loan from the National Railway Museum
37142, 47306 and 50042 the B&W Main Line Diesel Group

Parkway; 3 miles General-Boscarne
Passenger trains: 14/15, 18, 22,
25, 28/29 March; 1, 5-19, 22, 26,
29 April; 2-4, 6, 10, 12/13, 17,
19/20, 23-31 May; daily — 1 June-
30 September; 3/4, 7, 10/11, 14, 18,
21, 25-31 October; 1 November.
5/6, 12/13, 19/20, 23/24, 26-28
December; 26-28, 31 December
and 1-3 January 2010
Special events: Half-Price
Weekend — 14/15 March; Spring
Diesel Gala — 28/29 March; Easter
Egg-travaganza — 10-13 April;
Spring Steam Spectacular — 17-
19 April; Steaming Thru the 40s —
2-4 May; Four Days of Family Fun
— 24-27 May; The 'Changeover
Years' Gala — 30-31 May;
Paddington Bear — 31 July-3
August; Cornish Branch Line Days
— 8, 15, 22 August; Autumn Steam
Gala — 4-6 September; Autumn
Diesel Gala — 26/27 September;
Branch Line Weekend — 10/11
October; Santa by Steam — 5/6,

12/13, 19/20, 23/24 December.
Luxury Dining Trains: 22 March;
26 April; 10 May; 21 June; 4, 18
July; 8, 22 August; 20 September;
4, 25 October; 6, 12, 19/20
December.
Murder Mystery Specials: 23, 30
June; 7, 14, 21, 24, 28, 31 July; 4,
7, 11, 14, 18, 21, 25, 28 August; 1,
8, 15, 22 September; 30 October.
Steam Beer and Jazz: 18 April; 2
May; 27 June; 5, 19 September.
Disco Train: 30 June.
James Bond Evening: 29 May
Driving experience courses:
Courses held in spring and autumn.
Please apply for details
Facilities for disabled: Parking on
station forecourt at Bodmin
General. Level access to booking
hall, platform, toilets, gift shop and
buffet. Disabled toilet. Facilities for
wheelchairs available on most
trains, with purpose-built
accommodation and a ramp to ease
boarding from the platform.

Registered disabled travel at child fare, carers conveyed *free*
Membership details: Mr R. Holmes, Bodmin Railway Preservation Society, c/o above address

Special notes: Reduced fares for families. Bicycles and dogs conveyed *free*. Groups and parties welcome. Generous discounts available on many trains for pre-booked parties of 10+, with 25%

discount for groups of 25 or more. Train/carriage available for private hire — please enquire for details
Membership journal: *Bodmin & Wenford News* — 3 issues/year

Steam Centre — Bowes Railway — County Durham

Member: HRA

The railway includes the only preserved rope-hauled standard gauge inclines, whose operation requires considerable skill and dexterity. You should not miss the opportunity of inspecting the inclines and winding house and haulage engine when you can. The Engineering Workshop has just been restored

Chairman: Phillip Dawe
Location: Bowes Railway, Springwell Village, near Gateshead (on B1288)
OS reference: NZ 285589
Operating society/organisation: Bowes Railway Co Ltd
Telephone: (0191) 416 1847
Internet address: *Web site:* www.bowesrailway.co.uk
Car park: Springwell
Access by public transport: Northern Buses services Nos 184 Washington/Birtley, 187/188 Gateshead Metro/Sunderland, 189 Washington (Brady Sq)-Gateshead 638 Ryton/Sunderland
On site facilities: Exhibition of Railway's history, wagon exhibition, workshop displays. On operating days — shop, refreshments and guided tours. One of the last operational Strowger mechanical telephone exchanges still in daily use. Steam-hauled brake van rides. Rope haulage demonstration trains. Tarmac car park available for helicopter visitors (prior permission required, phone site)
Public opening: Site open Mondays to Saturdays for static viewing. Trains operate selected Sundays and special days. Santa Specials week prior to Christmas. Guided tours Saturdays, out of season can be accommodated with prior notice (not trains)

Industrial locomotives

Name	No	Builder	Type	Built
WST	—	Barclay (2361)	0-4-0ST	1954
—	22	Barclay (2274)	0-4-0ST	1949
—	20/110/709	Barclay (613)	0-6-0DH	1977
—	—	Hunslet (6263)	0-4-0DH	1964
—	503	Hunslet (6614)	0-6-0DH	1965
—	101	Planet (3922)	4wDM	1959
—	2207/456†	E/Electric (2476)	4wBE	1958
Victoria	2216/286†	H/Clarke (DM842)	0-6-0DMF	1954
BO3	20/122/514*	Hunslet (8515)	Bo-BoDMF	1981
—	—*	EIMCO (LD2163)	Rockershovel	1959
—	—§	Clayton (5921)	4wBE	1971
—	—§	Clayton (B3060)	4wBE	1983

†2ft gauge
*2ft 6in gauge
§3ft gauge

Owners
WST on loan from British Gypsum Ltd and loaned to National Railway Museum
Barclay 0-6-0DH on loan from Mr P. Dawe

Stock
20 ordinary 10-ton wooden hopper wagons (Springwell built); 16 other wooden hopper wagons (of various pedigrees); 3 steel 14-ton hopper, 2 steel 16-ton hopper wagons; 7 wagons; 7 steel 21-ton hopper wagons; 1 reel bogie (for rope replacement); 1 drift bogie (for shunting by rope); 1 loco coal wagon; 7 material wagons; 2 tool vans; 3 brake vans; 4 flat wagons; 1 18-ton wooden hopper (ex-Ashington); 1 21-ton wooden hopper (ex-Seaham); 2 steel ballast wagons; 1 tank wagon; 1 wooden side door coal wagon; 3 Londonderry Chaldron wagons, 2ft gauge 4-wheel manrider, 2ft 6in gauge R. B. Bolton-type bogie manrider, Easington Colliery weights wagon, 1 Pontop & Jarrow Railway flat bogie, 1 Dandy cart

Stationary haulage
Met-Vick/Wild, 300bhp electric (Blackham's Hill) 1950
BTH/Robey, 500bhp electric (Black Fell) 1950
Clarke Chapman, 22hp electric (Springwell Yard)
14ft diam, Gravity Dilly Wheel (Springwell)

Length of line: 1.25 miles of rope haulage incline railway.
1.5 mile line used for passenger trains as the Wreckenton extension is now open
Special notes: Preserved section of the Pontop & Jarrow Railway; designed G. Stephenson; opened 1826; largest collection of colliery wagons in country, the only preserved standard gauge rope-hauled incline railway in the world;

Railway's own historic workshops preserved, with examples of all of the Railway's wagon types
Facilities for disabled: Toilet and refreshment room

Membership details: John Young, Railway Secretary, c/o above address
Disclaimer: The Bowes Railway Co Ltd wish to point out that all

advertised facilities are subject to alteration without prior notice. The company can therefore not be held responsible for any loss or expense incurred

---

Steam Centre — Bredgar & Wormshill Light Railway — Kent

Member: HRA

A short, 2ft gauge, private railway constructed and operated to a very high standard

Location/headquarters: The Bredgar & Wormshill Light Railway, The Warren, Bredgar, Nr Sittingbourne, Kent ME9 8AT
Contact: Bill Best, David Best
Telephone: (01622) 884254
Fax: (01622) 884668
Internet address: *Web site:* www.bwlr.co.uk
Access by public transport: Main line trains to Sittingbourne (5 miles) and Hollingbourne (3.5 miles). No taxis from Hollingbourne
OS reference: TQ 868579
Car park: On site (300 places)
On site facilities: Souvenir shop, museum, light refreshments, toilets, picnic sites, traction engines, 7.25in and 15in gauge model locomotives, working beam engine, model railway. Largest UK collection of Bean motor cars. Steam-hauled train rides from Warren Wood to Stony Shaw (2km).

Industrial locomotives
(2ft gauge)

Name	No	Builder	Type	Built
Bronhilde	1	Schwartzkopf (9124)	0-4-0WT	1927
Katie	2	Arn Jung (3872)	0-6-0WT	1931
Armistice	4	Bagnall (2088)	0-4-0ST	1919
Bredgar	5	B/Drewry (3775)	0-4-0DH	1983
Eigiau	6	O&K (5668)	0-4-0WT	1912
Victory	7	Decauville (246)	0-4-2ST	1897
—	8	O&K (12722)	0-4-0WT	1936
No 1	—	Hunslet (1429)	0-4-0ST	1922
—	—	Fowler (13573)	0-4-2T	1912
Limpopo	—	Fowler (18800)	0-6-0T	1930
—	15	Huwood/Hudswell (DM1366)	0-6-0DM	1965

(2ft 6in gauge)

Name	No	Builder	Type	Built
—	105	Henschel (29582)	0-6-0WT	1956

Stock
3 bogie coaches, 1 four-wheel coach, 6 four-wheel wagons, 1 four-wheel tank wagon, 4 four-wheel works trucks, 1 open bogie coach

Public opening: First Sunday in each month May to October (11.00-17.00). Also Easter Sunday. Admission: Adults £7.50, children £3
Special events: Steam locomotive driving courses, enthusiast days
Facilities for disabled: Generally good including toilets
Note: A private site with no 'out of hours' access, but groups by arrangement

---

Steam Centre — Bressingham Steam Experience — Norfolk

Member: TT

Five miles of various gauges of railway running through extensive gardens, and a collection of well-maintained and impressive main line locomotives. All the fun of the fair, with something for everyone, a great day out for all the family
Location: Two miles west of Diss, and 14 miles east of Thetford on the A1066
OS reference: TM 080806
General Manager:
Howard Stephens

Locomotives and multiple-unit

Name	No	Origin	Class	Type	Built
Martello	662†	LBSCR	A1X	0-6-0T	1875
Thundersley	80	LTSR	3P	4-4-2T	1909
Granville	102	LSWR	B4	0-4-0T	1893
—	490	GER	E4	2-4-0	1894
Henry Oakley	990	GNR	C2	4-4-2	1898
—	251	GNR	C1	4-4-2	1902
Royal Scot	6100*	LMS	7P	4-6-0	1927
—	54347	Met/Cam	101	DTC	1958
Peer Gynt	5865	RB	52	2-10-0	1944
King Haakon VII	377†	NSB	21c	2-6-0	1919

*undergoing restoration, expected to be on site for part of 2009
†will be out on hire during 2009

32
England

Operating society/organisation:
Bressingham Steam Preservation
Co Ltd, Thetford Road, Diss,
Norfolk IP22 2AB
Charity number: 266374
Telephone:
General enquiries and bookings
(01379) 686900.
Infoline (01379) 686903
Fax: (01379) 686907
Internet addresses: *e-mail:*
info@bressingham.co.uk
Web site: www.bressingham.co.uk
(includes online bookimgs)
Car park: Plant Centre (free).
Access by public transport: Diss
main line station (3 miles)
On site facilities: 10.25/15/24in
and standard gauge lines, totalling
nearly 5 miles. Museum, steam
roundabout, souvenir shop and
restaurant, extensive gardens and
plant centre. 'Dad's Army'
permanent exhibition
Public opening: Open every day
between Easter and end of October.
Steam every day with narrow gauge
rides and the Gallopers. 10.30-
17.30. Education services for
schools are available with pre-
booking in March-October period
Special events: Please telephone
(01379) 686900 for details
Special facilities: The corporate
hospitality venue is available for
events, from parties to conferences.
Please telephone (01379) 686900
for details
Facilities for disabled: Wheelchair

Industrial locomotives

Name	No	Builder	Type	Built
Beckton	1	Neilson (4444)	0-4-0ST	1892
Beckton	25	Neilson (5087)	0-4-0ST	1896
William Francis	6841	B/Peacock (6841)	0-4-0+0-4-0T	1937
Millfield	—	RSH (7070)	0-4-0CT	1942
Bluebottle	—	Barclay (1472)	0-4-0F	1916
County School	GET 1	R/Hornsby (497753)	0-4-0DE	1963

2ft gauge locomotives

Name	No	Builder	Type	Built
Bronllwyn	—	H/Clarke (1643)	0-6-0ST	1930
Gwynedd	—	Hunslet (316)	0-4-0ST	1883
George Sholto	—	Hunslet (994)	0-4-0ST	1909
Toby	—	M/Rail (22120)	4wDM	1964
—	—	BEV	0-4-0BE	

15in gauge locomotives

Name	No	Builder	Type	Built
Rosenkavalier	—	Krupp (1662)	4-6-2	1937
Mannertreu	—	Krupp (1663)	4-6-2	1937
Flying Scotsman	4472*	W. Stewart (4472)	4-6-2	1976
Works Loco	—	Diss	0-4-0DM	1992
Replica	6353	—	Bo-Bo	—

*dismantled for overhaul

10.25in gauge locomotives

Name	No	Builder	Type	Built
Alan Bloom	1	BSM	0-4-0ST	1995

Owners
80, 251, 490 and 990 on loan from the National Railway Museum
GET 1 the Great Eastern Traction Group

access to majority of site including
toilets. Able to take wheelchairs on
Nursery Line Railway and Waveney
Line
Special notes: Reduced rates for
coach parties. Prices on application

Steam Centre	Bristol Harbour Railway	Bristol

Member: HRA
Note: The museum is closed until
spring 2011 for redevelopment and
transformation into the Museum of
Bristol. The railway will operate
occasionally (as well as the other
working exhibits). Please see local
press for details
Location: Princes Wharf, Bristol
OS reference: ST 585722
Operating society/organisation:
Bristol Museum Galleries &
Archives, Princes Wharf, Bristol
BS1 4RN
Telephone: (0117) 903 1570
Fax: (0117) 929 7318
Car parks: Available nearby

Industrial locomotives

Name	No	Builder	Type	Built
Portbury	34†	Avonside (1764)	0-6-0ST	1917
Henbury	—†	Peckett (1940)	0-6-0ST	1937
—	3*	F/Walker (242)	0-6-0ST	1874
—	—	R/Hornsby (418792)	0-4-0DM	1958

*not on public display
†only on view when in steam

Access by public transport: Buses
to centre of city, 1km from Temple
Meads station
Length of line: One mile
Facilities for disabled: Reasonable
access
Special notes: Operation of railway

on advertised weekends only,
11.30-17.00
Membership details: Officer in
charge — D. Martin, Bristol
Harbour Railway c/o above address

Brookside Miniature Railway

Member: Britain's Great Little Railways
A large extension opened in 2007
Location: Brookside Garden Centre
Headquarters: Brookside Garden Centre Ltd, Macclesfield Road, Poynton, Cheshire SK12 1BY
Contact:
Chief Executive Mr C. Halsall
Telephone: (01625) 872919
Fax: (01625) 859119
Internet address: *Web site:* www.brookside-miniature-railway.co.uk
Car parking: On site
Access by public transport: Main line stations: Hazel Grove (2.5 miles, Poynton (2 miles). Bus No 191 stops outside the Centre
On site facilities: Full restaurant/café facilities. Extensive

Locomotives

Name	No	Builder	Type	Built
Jean	—	Exmoor	0-4-2T	2000
Jane	—	Exmoor	0-4-2T	2002
Amy Louise	—	Exmoor	0-4-2T	2004
Billy May	—	Exmoor	2-4-2	1999
Mighty Max	—	Greatex	Bo-Bo	2000
Callum	—	J Horsfield	0-6-0T	2003
Annie	—	D McFarlane	Co-Co	1997
Peter the Great	—	J Horsfield/P Wilson	0-4-2PH	

museum of railwayana, large display of totems (c200) and advertising enamels
Depots: On site and visits may be made by prior arrangement
Length of line: 7.25in gauge, half mile
Period of public operation: Weekends throughout the year, plus Wednesdays April to September; every day mid-July and August. Summer — 11.00-16.30; winter — 11.00-16.00
Special events: Santa Specials — weekends in December
Facilities for disabled: Disabled toilet facilities and access to all parts
Fare: Adult/child: £1.30; under 2s free; 10 ride ticket £10

Buckinghamshire Railway Centre

Member: HRA
The Buckinghamshire Railway Centre is situated at Quainton Road on the freight-only Aylesbury-Calvert line, once part of the Metropolitan and Great Central line from London to Verney Junction. Quainton Road station is also the old junction for the Brill Tramway closed in 1935. The Centre is now home to the former LNWR Rewley Road station moved brick-by-brick from the centre of Oxford. Opened in 1851, this Grade 2* listed building is built in the same manner as the Crystal Palace Great Exhibition building of 1881 destroyed by fire in the 1930s. It is unique in its construction and provides a superb setting in which the pick of the Centre's locomotives and carriages are now displayed
Location: Adjacent to goods-only line to Aylesbury. Turn off A41 at Waddesdon 6 miles NW of Aylesbury, Bucks

Locomotives and multiple-units

Name	No	Origin	Class	Type	Built
—	1	Met Rly	E	0-4-4T	1898
—	0314	LSWR	0298	2-4-0WT	1874
Defiant	5080	GWR	'Castle'	4-6-0	1939
Wightwick Hall	6989	GWR	'Hall'	4-6-0	1948
—	7200	GWR	7200	2-8-2T	1934
—	7715†	GWR	5700	0-6-0PT	1930
—	9466	GWR	9400	0-6-0PT	1952
—	D2298	BR	04	0-6-0DM	1960
—	3405*	SAR	25NC	4-8-4	1958
—	51886	BR	115	DMBS	1960
—	51899	BR	115	DMBS	1960
—	59761	BR	115	TCL	1960

*3ft 6in gauge
†on loan to Spa Valley Railway

Industrial locomotives

Name	No	Builder	Type	Built
Scott	—	Bagnall (2469)	0-4-0ST	1932
—	—	Baguley (2161)	0-4-0DM	1941
Swanscombe	—	Barclay (699)	0-4-0ST	1891
—	—	GF3 Barclay (1477)	0-4-0F	1916
—	—	Barclay (2243)	0-4-0F	1948
Osram	—	Fowler (20067)	0-4-0DM	1933
—	3	H/Leslie (3717)	0-4-0ST	1928
Sir Thomas	—	H/Clarke (1334)	0-6-0T	1918

England

OS reference: SP 738190
Operating society/organisation:
Quainton Railway Society Ltd,
The Railway Station, Quainton,
Nr Aylesbury, Bucks HP22 4BY
Telephone: Quainton (01296)
655450
Internet address:
Web site: www.bucksrailcentre.org
Car park: Quainton Road — Free
parking
Access by public transport: Main
line Aylesbury station. Local bus
Monday-Saturday only
On site facilities: Souvenir
bookshop, light refreshments,
toilets, steam-hauled train rides.
Museum of small relics,
secondhand bookshop, miniature
railway
Catering facilities: Hot snacks and
light refreshments available
Length of line: Two half-mile
demonstration lines
Public opening: Open Wednesday
to Sunday inclusive from April to
October. Steaming days each
Sunday and Wednesdays during
school holidays, plus Bank
Holidays.
Opening times: 10.30-16.30
Special events: Day out with
Thomas — 21-24 March; Miniature
Railway Gala — 4/5 May; Bus
Rally — 26 May; Miniature
Traction Engine Rally — 31 May/1
June; Day out with Thomas —
4-6 July; Classic Car Weekend —
24/25 August; Day out with
Thomas — 6/7 September; Traction
Engine Rally — 20/21 September;
Steam Gala — 19 October
Facilities for disabled: Access to
most of site including special toilets
Special notes: One of the largest
collection of standard gauge
locomotives, together with a most
interesting collection of vintage
coaching stock, much of which was

Name	No	Builder	Type	Built
—	—	H/Clarke (1742)	0-4-0ST	1946
—	—	Hunslet (2067)	0-4-0DM	1940
Arthur	—	Hunslet (3782)	0-6-0ST	1953
Juno	—	Hunslet (3850)	0-6-0ST	1958
—	65	Hunslet (3889)	0-6-0ST	1964
—	66	Hunslet (3890)	0-6-0ST	1964
—	26	Hunslet (7016)	0-6-0DH	1971
Redland	—	K/Stuart (K4428)	0-4-0DM	1929
Coventry No 1	—	NBL (24564)	0-6-0ST	1939
—	—	Peckett (1900)	0-4-0T	1936
Gibraltar	—	Peckett (2087)	0-4-0ST	1948
—	—	Peckett (2104)	0-4-0ST	1948
—	—	Peckett (2105)	0-4-0ST	1948
—	T1	Hibberd (2102)	4wD	1937
Tarmac	—	Hibberd (3765)	0-4-0DM	1955
—	11	Sentinel (9366)	4wVBTG	1945
—	7	Sentinel (9376)	4wVBTG	1947
—	—	Sentinel (9537)	4wVBTG	1947
Chislet	9	Yorkshire (2498)	0-6-0ST	1951

Stock: *Coaches* —
1 LCDR 1st Class 4-wheeler; 1 MSLR 3rd Class 6-wheeler; 4 LNWR coach
bodies; 2 GNR 6-wheelers; 3 LNWR; 3 LMSR; 1 BR(W) Hawksworth
brake 3rd; 2 BR Mk 1; 1 BR Mk 2; 1 BR Suburban brake; 3 LNER; 1
LNWR full brake 6-wheeler; 1 LMSR passenger brake van; 1 GWR passenger brake van; 1 GCR Robinson brake third
Wagons —
A large and varied collection including 1 LNWR combination truck; 1
LSWR ventilated fruit van; 1 SR PMV; 1 BR(W) Siphon G; 1 BR horse
box; 1 BR CCT

3 ex-London Underground coaches
1 2ft gauge post office mailbag car 803
Sentinel/Cammell 3-car steam railcar unit 5208 (ex-Egyptian National)
Numerous goods vehicles/wagons/vans

Owners
9466 the 9466 Group
Defiant on loan from Tyseley Locomotive Works

built in the 19th century
General: The public area of the
centre covers some 25 acres of land
with views across the
Buckinghamshire countryside.
A picnic area is available at the
miniature railway

Member: HRA, TT

Opened in 1990, the BVR runs over the old Great Eastern Wroxham-Aylsham line. It is paralleled throughout the entire 9 miles by the Bure Valley Walk and cycle path which offers excellent photographic opportunities

Headquarters: Bure Valley Railway (1991) Ltd, Aylsham Station, Norwich Road, Aylsham, Norfolk NR11 6BW

Chairman: David Barnes

General Manager: Andrew Tunwell

Telephone: (01263) 733858

Fax: (01263) 733814

Internet address: *e-mail:* info@bvrw.co.uk

Web site: www.bvrw.co.uk

Main public station: Aylsham (Norwich Road, NR11 6BW); Wroxham (Coltishall Road, NR12 8UU)

Locomotives

Name	No	Builder	Type	Built (rebuilt)
Wroxham Broad 2nd Air Division USAAF	1	G&S/Winson	2-6-4T	1992
—	3	BVR	4w-4wDH	1989
—	4	H/Hunslet	0-4-0DH	1996
—	5	Lister	4wDM	
Blickling Hall	6	Winson*	2-6-2	1994 (2004)
Spitfire	7	Winson*	2-6-2	1994 (2006)
Thunder	8	BVR/Winson†	2-6-2T	1997 (2008)
Mark Timothy	10	Winson/Keef§	2-6-4T	2003

*based on Indian Railways 2ft 6in gauge 'ZB' class
†based on Vale of Rheidol Railway design
§based on Leek & Manifold Railway design

Stock

19 fully enclosed saloons, 2 fully enclosed compartment coaches, 6 enclosed saloons designed to carry wheelchairs, 1 fully enclosed brake saloon, 2 guard's vans, generator car, miscellaneous wagons including a rail-mounted flail and weedkilling unit and purpose-built p-way tool vehicle arrangement

Owner

1 the Wroxham Broad Preservation Group

Other public stations: Coltishall, Brampton and Buxton
Car and coach parks: Aylsham and Wroxham
OS reference:
Aylsham — TG 195264
Wroxham — TG 303186
GPS co-ordinates:
Aylsham — 52°47.29 (52.7913) North, 1°15.17 (1.2547) East X(619500) Y 326500)
Wroxham — 52°42.994 (52.7168) North, 1°24.624 (1.4076) East X(630200) Y(318700)
Access by public transport:
By rail: Wroxham station is adjacent to main line Hoveton & Wroxham station (Norwich-Cromer/Sheringham line).
By bus: First and Sanders buses run between Norwich and Aylsham or Norwich and Wroxham
Refreshment facilities:
Whistlestop Café at Aylsham with picnic area, light refreshments at Wroxham.
Aylsham's Whistlestop Café is open every day even when the railway does not operate trains
Souvenir shops:
Aylsham and Wroxham
Aylsham shop is open every day even when the railway does not operate trains
Journey time: Approximately 45min each way plus turn round time
Length of line: 9 miles; 15in gauge
Passenger trains: Frequency depends on time of year, maximum frequency one per hour
Period of public operation:
Weekends in March. Daily 28 March to 1 November. Weekends in November
Exhibit availability: The workshops at Aylsham are open to the public at most times of year for viewing
Facilities for disabled: Toilets at Aylsham and Wroxham. Main stations are all on one level, special rolling stock to carry wheelchairs; advance notice would be appreciated
Special events: Please contact for full details.
Mothers VIP Day — 22 March; Easter Eggspress — 10-13 April; Everything Goes — 2-4 May; Fathers VIP Day — 22 June; Strawberries & Steam — weekends in July; Model Railway Exhibition — 26 September; Small Engines Gala — 10/11 October; Santa Specials 28/29 November, 5/6, 8/9, 12/13, 19-24 December (advance booking essential); Mince Pie Specials 27 December 2009 to 3 January 2010
Special notes: Steam locomotive driving courses. Group discounts available. Frequent Travellers Railcards. Children's Birthday Parties. Private charters by arrangement. Special combined train and Broads boat excursions run most operating days
Membership details: Friends of the Bure Valley Railway, Membership Secretary, c/o above address

Railway Centre — Cambrian Heritage Railway — Shropshire

Member: HRA

The Cambrian Railways Trust currently operates about two-thirds of a mile of the former Cambrian Railways main line from Llynclys South to Penygarreg Lane, Pant. 2009 will see the continuation of steam haulage with the Hawthorne Leslie 0-6-0ST on Sundays and the DMU running Wednesday, Saturday and Bank Holidays. The popular driver experience days with a choice of steam or diesel operation will be extended throughout the operating season; pre-booking is essential, see the web site for details. The construction of additional sidings is under way at Llynclys South to serve the new rolling stock shed. Construction is also hoped to start soon on a new halt at Penygarreg Lane to serve as a link to the local Llanymynech Heritage area and adjacent Montgomery Canal.

The long-awaited lease for the section of line running Llynclys Junction–Gobowen is almost complete with the Trust expected to take possession in early 2009. The overall project, a joint initiative with the Cambrian Railways Society, seeks for the Trust to extend north through Oswestry to reach Gobowen Yard whilst the Society will develop connecting branch line services westwards from Llynclys Junction to Porthywaen Halt and Blodwell

Location: Llynclys is situated on the B4396 about 5 miles south of Oswestry, just off the A483 Welshpool-Oswestry road
Telephone: 01691 679007
Internet address: *e-mail:* admin@cambrianrailwaystrust.com

Locomotives and multiple-units

Name	No	Origin	Class	Type	Built
Cogan Hall	5952	GWR	Hall	4-6-0	1935
—	D2094	BR	03	0-6-0DM	1960
—	D3019	BR	08	0-6-0DE	1953
—	51187	Met-Cam	101	DMBS	1958
—	51205	Met-Cam	101	DMBS	1958
—	51512	Met-Cam	101	DMC	1959
—	54055	Met-Cam	101	DTSL	1957

Industrial locomotives

Name	No	Builder	Type	Built
Isabel	—	H/Leslie (3437)	0-6-0ST	1919

Rolling stock
9 ex-BR Mk 1 coaches, 4 ex-GWR coaches/bogie vans, 20 goods wagons
1 Plasser & Theurer maintenance vehicle No 73241

Web site:
www.cambrianrailwaystrust.com
OS reference: SJ 284239
Operating society: Cambrian Railways Trust, Llynclys South Station, Llynclys, Oswestry, Shropshire SY10 8BX
Access by public transport: Bus approx hourly from Oswestry to White Lion Inn, Llynclys crossroads (200yd from site), with connecting buses from Gobowen station and Shrewsbury. Also buses from Welshpool and Llanfyllin (Arriva Midlands / Tanat Valley Coaches)
On site facilities: Buffet, shop, station facilities including disabled
Period of public opening: Trains running 10 April to 25 October, steam most Sundays 12 April to 6 September;
DMU Wednesdays, Saturdays and Bank Holidays.
Driver experience days, themed events and Christmas steaming.

Consult the web site for full details of heritage traction and events
Disabled facilities: Level access to platforms, ramps onto trains
Membership details: c/o above address
Membership journal: Quarterly newsletter
Special note: Special trains can be arranged for parties at any time. footplate experience days available by arrangement

---

| Steam Centre | **Chasewater Railway** | Staffordshire |

Member: HRA, TT

Founded in 1959 as the Railway Preservation Society (West Midlands District), the Chasewater Railway was re-formed in 1985 as a Registered Charity. The railway operates as 'The Colliery Line' to reflect its origins and location in the heart of the Cannock Chase coalfield. A regular timetabled service operates between Brownhills West station and Chasetown (Church Street), with intermediate stations at Norton Lakeside (which adjoins Chasewater's Wildfowl Reserve) and Chasewater Heaths.
Location: Chasewater Park, Brownhills (off A5 southbound, nr jct A452 Chester Road). Brown tourism signs are provided on A5
OS reference: SK 034070
Postcodes for SatNav:
Brownhills West WS5 7NL
Chasewater Heaths WS7 3PG
Operating society/organisation: Chasewater Light Railway & Museum Co
Telephone: 01543 452623
Internet address: *e-mail:* info@chaserail.com
Web site: www.chaserail.com
Car park: Ample car parking within Chasewater Park
Access by public transport:
Nearest railway stations — Walsall and Birmingham New Street.
Bus services from Walsall Bus Station (St Paul's Street) —
Saturdays: Arriva 63 (Stand L), alight at Poole Crescent
Sundays: 362 (Stand K) and 395A (Stand L) to Brownhills West

Diesel locomotive and multiple-units

Name	No	Builder	Class	Type	Built
—	53160	BR	101	DMC	1956
—	53164	BR	101	DMBS	1957
—	W59444	BR Derby	116	TS	1958
—	W51372	Pressed Steel	117	DMBS	1960
—	W59522	Pressed Steel	117	TCL	1960
—	W59603	Pressed Steel	127	TSL	1959

Industrial locomotives

Name	No	Builder	Type	Built
Colin McAndrew	3	Barclay (1223)	0-4-0ST	1911
—	701	Barclay (1964)	0-4-0ST	1929
British Gypsum No 4	—	Barclay (2343)	0-4-0ST	1953
Linda	—	Bagnall (2648)	0-4-0ST	1941
Sheepbridge No 15	—	H/Clarke (431)	0-6-0ST	1895
Whit No 4	—	H/Clarke (1822)	0-6-0T	1949
Asbestos	4	H/Leslie (2780)	0-4-0ST	1909
Alfred Paget	11	Neilson (2937)	0-4-0ST	1882
—	6	Peckett (917)	0-4-0ST	1902
Sentinel	5	Sentinel (9632)	4wVBT	1957
Bass No 5	—	Baguley (3027)	0-4-0DM	1939
Hem Heath	—	Bagnall (3119)	0-6-0DM	1956
Dealer	—	Brush (3097)	0-4-0DE	1956
—	—	Fowler (4100013)	0-4-0DM	1948
Toad	37	Fowler (4220015)	0-4-0DH	1962
—	462	Hibberd (1891)	4wDM	1934
—	6678	Hunslet (6678)	0-4-0DH	1968
—	21	Kent Constr (1612)	4wDM	1929
—	—	NBL (27876)	0-4-0DH	1958
Ryan	—	R/Hornsby (305306)	0-4-0DM	1952
—	—	R/Hornsby (544998)	0-4-0DE	1969

Rolling stock
A variety of passenger and freight vehicles are housed on site, including a number of considerable historical importance, together with an ex-LNER steam crane

(Rising Sun Inn).
Bus services from Birmingham (Carrs Lane)
Saturdays and Sundays: 56 and 56A (Stand DJ) to Brownhills West (Rising Sun Inn).
Brownhills West station is approx 15min walk from the Rising Sun

England

Inn, 10min walk from Poole Crescent

For timetable information and details of services, contact Traveline 0870 608 2608

On site facilities: Refreshments, shop, lakeside walks and large grassed areas

Catering facilities: Hot and cold buffets at Brownhills West and Chasewater Heath stations

Length of line: Approx 2 miles

Public opening: Sundays and Bank Holiday Mondays throughout the year. Saturday, Tuesday and Wednesday services operate during summer months and school holidays. Santa Specials during December.

Trains depart from Brownhills West station at approx hourly intervals from 10.30

Check web site for running dates and timetables.

Most services are with steam traction (subject to availability). Industrial diesel locomotives are normally used at off-peak periods and on midweek trains.

All tickets give unlimited rides on day of issue. Adult, Child and Family tickets (2 adults + 4 children) available

Special events: *Asbestos* Birthday Event — 7 June; Bus Rally — 14 June; 50th Anniversary Gala — 20/21 June; Symphony Concert — 27 June; Model Railway Exhibition — 12 July; Industrial Gala — 12/13 September; Halloween Specials — 31 October; Santa Specials —throughout December

Facilities for disabled: Disabled access to stations, trains and buffet

Membership details: Membership Secretary, Brownhills West Station, Chasewater Country Park, Pool Road, Nr Brownhills, Staffs WS8 7NL

Chinnor & Princes Risborough Railway — 'The Icknield Line'

Steam Centre **Oxfordshire**

Member: HRA

The Chinnor & Princes Risborough Railway runs from Chinnor station, close to the beautiful Chiltern Hills and to the Vale of Aylesbury. Originally built in 1872 to connect the towns of Watlington in Oxfordshire to Princes Risborough in Buckinghamshire, the line was closed to all traffic by British Railways in 1989. Since then a team of volunteers has rebuilt Chinnor station to its Victorian glory. The railway operates the 3.5-mile ex-Great Western Railway branch line as a tourist attraction for both families and railway enthusiasts. A regular steam-hauled service is provided every Sunday from Mother's Day to Halloween. Special events are a feature of the programme including Teddy Bear Days and Santa Specials. Cream teas are generally served on all standard Sunday afternoon trains and on some special events

Location: M40 Junction 6 then B4009 north 4 miles towards Princes Risborough to village of Chinnor. Once in village follow brown tourist signs to station

Operating society/organisation: Chinnor & Princes Risborough Railway Co Ltd, Chinnor Station, Station Road, Chinnor, Oxon OX39 4ER

Locomotives

Name	No	Origin	Class	Type	Built
Haversham	13018	BR	08	0-6-0DE	1953
—	D8568	BR	17	Bo-Bo	1963
—	37219	BR	37	Co-Co	1964
—	55023	BR	121	DMBS	1958
—	9682	GWR	57xx	0-6-0PT	1949

Industrial locomotives

Name	No	Builder	Type	Built
Blue Circle	—	A/Porter (9449)	2-2-0TG	1926
Iris	459515	R/Hornsby (459515)	0-6-0DH	1952

Stock

1 ex-LNWR Mess coach, 1 ex-BR Mk 1 NDV, 1 ex-BR Mk 1 RMB, 1 ex-BR Mk 1 CK, 1 ex-BR Mk 1 BSK, 1 ex-BR Mk 2 FK, 16 various wagons, 1 Coles self-propelled crane

Owners

D8568 the Diesel Traction Group

9682 on loan from the Great Western Railway Preservation Group, Southall

Telephone: Talking Timetable 01844 353535. Santa Booking Line: 01844 354117 (Weekends 10.00-17.00 only)

Internet address: *e-mail:* enquiries@chinnorrailway.co.uk *Web site:* www.chinnorrailwaysco.uk

OS reference: SP 756003

Access by public transport: Nearest main line station — Princes Risborough (4 miles) Chiltern Railways

By car: M40 junction 6 then B4009 north towards Princes Risborough to village of Chinnor, then follow brown tourist signs to station

Length of line: 3.5 miles

Journey time: 45min, steam and heritage diesel trains

On site facilities: Souvenir shop, small buffet on Chinnor station. Bar/buffet on most trains (cream teas generally available on standard timetable Sunday sfternoons). Toilets, free car park, picnic area

England

Passenger trains: Chinnor-Thame Junction-Chinnor

Public opening: 22, 29 March; 5, 10-13, 19, 26 April; 2-4, 9/10, 17, 23-25, 31 May; 7, 14, 21, 27/28 June; 5, 12, 19, 26 July; 1/2, 8/9, 15/16, 22/23, 29-31 August; 6, 13, 20, 27 September; 4, 11, 17/18, 25 October; 1 November; 5/6, 12/13, 19/20, 27/28, December; 2/3 January 2010

Special events: Mother's Day — 22 March; Easter Specials — 10-13 April; Spring Diesel Gala — 26 April; Teddy Bear Days — 2-4 May; Railway Open day — 9 May; Real Ale Festival — 23-25 May; Father's Day — 21 June; Diesel Gala Weekend — 27/28 June; Senior Citizens' Day — 19 July; Steam and Autotrailer — 1, 8, 15, 22, 29 August; Annual Gala Day — 2 August; Teddy Bear Days — 30/31 August; Senior Citizens' Day — 4 October; Goodbye 9682 — 17/18 October; Halloween Spooks Express — 1 November; Santa Specials — 5/6, 12/13, 19/20 December; Mince Pie Specials — 27/28 December, 2/3 January 2010 Other dates available for party bookings

Special note: Group charter hire and film and photographic facilities available, contact: 07765 467090. Advance booking is necessary for Santa Specials

Driver Experience Courses: The railway will be offering steam and diesel driver experience days throughout the year. Gift vouchers are available for these courses. Please telephone 07784 189322 or visit the web site for details

Facilities for disabled: Ramp, toilet accessible parking area. All public areas accessible. Guide dogs welcome

Membership details: Mr Brian West, 10 Coombe Hill Crescent, Thame, Oxon OX9 2EH

Membership journal: *The Watlington Flyer* — bi-annual and newsletters

---

Cholsey & Wallingford Railway

Timetable Service   Oxfordshire

Member: HRA

Location: Hithercroft Road, Wallingford, Oxfordshire

Sales: Mrs P. Goodenough

Marketing: Mrs S. Harington, Mr C. Young

Operating Society: Cholsey & Wallingford Railway Preservation Society, 5 Hithercroft Road, Wallingford, Oxon OX10 9GQ

Telephone: (01491) 835067 (24hr information line)

Internet address: *e-mail:* cwrail@yahoo.co.uk

Web site: www.cholsey-wallingford-railway.com

Disabled access: Access direct to Wallingford station from adjoining car park, access ramp to shop, platform and traint. No disabled facilities at Cholsey station

Access by public transport: Thames Travel Buses — X39 from Oxford, X40 from Reading. First Great Western trains to Cholsey station

Public opening: Trains depart every hour from Wallingford, 11.10 to 16.10; and from Cholsey platform 11.35 to 16.35

Length of line: 2.5 miles

Journey time: Approximately 14min (one way), 40min (round trip)

On site facilities: Souvenir shop, café and museum

Special events: Ivor the Engine — 11-13 April; St George's Day Trains — 20 April; Spring Bank Holiday and two day plant sale — 3/4 May; Guinness Weekend — 16/17 May; Teddy Bears' Weekend — 24/25 May; The Bunk, 50 Years of Steam Trains — 6/7, 13/14, 20/21, 27/28 June; Local Ale and Wine Weekend — 25/26 June; Trains on a Summer Sunday — 16 August; Summer Bank Holiday Trains — 30/31 August; BunkFest Singing Trains — 5/6 September; Book Sale — 13 September; Nursery Rhyme Weekend — 26/27 September; Spooky Halloween Trains — 31 October/1 November; Santa Specials — 5/6, 12/13, 19/20 December;

Special notes: Railway crosses new bypass (A4130) at a level crossing and runs into Cholsey bay platform.

Whilst it is intended to operate as advertised all services, events and fares may be altered due to prevailing circumstances

Membership details: Alan Saunders, at above address

Membership journal: *The Bunk* — 3 issues/year

Locomotives

Name	No	Origin	Class	Type	Built
Unicorn	D3074	BR	08	0-6-0DE	1953
Lion	D3030	BR	08	0-6-0DE	1953
George Mason	D3190	BR	08	0-6-0DE	1955

Industrial locomotives

Name	No	Builder	Type	Built
Carpenter	3271	Planet (3270)	0-4-0DM	1949
—	803	Alco (77777)	Bo-Bo	1950

Rolling stock — coaches: GWR BSKe, 2 BR Mk 1 TSOs

Member: HRA

This heritage railway is situated deep in the heart of the Staffordshire moorlands. Begin your journey at Cheddleton, a Victorian country station set in picturesque countryside complete with riverside parking and picnic island. The 10.5 mile return journey takes you to the idyllic hamlet of Consall Forge and onwards to the reinstated station Kingsley & Froghall

Main station/location: Cheddleton Station, Station Road, Cheddleton, Nr Leek, Staffs ST13 7EE

OS reference: SJ 983519

Operating society/organisation: Churnet Valley Railway (1992) plc

Telephone: 01538 360522

Fax: 01538 361848

Internet address: *e-mail:* enquiries@churnetvalleyrailway.co.uk

Web site: www.churnetvalleyrailway.co.uk

Other stations: Consall, Kingsley & Froghall

Car parks: Adjacent to Cheddleton and Froghall stations

Access by public transport: Main line Stoke-on-Trent (10 miles). A regular bus service (No 16) runs from Hanley and Leek to Cheddleton village

On site facilities: Refreshment facilities at Cheddleton and Froghall

Souvenir shop: Cheddleton and Froghall

Museum: Small relics museum at Cheddleton

Length of line: 5.25 miles

Tickets: Day rover tickets available

Public opening: Steam trains Sundays — March-October. Saturdays April-end September. Bank Holidays and Wednesdays in Bank Holiday weeks, plus certain other dates (see timetable). Wednesdays in July and August.

Special events: Station at War, Steam Gala, Ghost Train and Santa Specials

Facilities for disabled: Access to station areas is possible by wheelchair, train travel by arrangement. Disabled toilet facilities at Consall and Froghall

Membership details: North Staffordshire Railway Co (1978) Ltd, Membership Secretary, c/o above address

Special facilities: Party bookings by arrangement, footplate experience courses, wine & dine dates on application. Licensed for weddings and civil partnerships at all three stations

Locomotives and multiple-units

Name	No	Origin	Class	Type	Built
—	5197	USATC	S160	2-8-0	1942
—	6046	USATC	S160	2-8-0	1945
—	48173	LMS	8F	2-8-0	1943
—	D2334	BR	04	0-6-0DM	1961
Tamworth Castle	D7672	BR	25	Bo-Bo	1967
—	33102	BR	33	Bo-Bo	1960
—	37075	BR	37	Co-Co	1962
—	37407	BR	37	Co-Co	1965
—	37424	BR	37	Co-Co	1963
—	47524	BR	47	Co-Co	1967
—	53455	BRCW	104	DMBS	1957
—	53437	BRCW	104	DMBS	1957
—	53494	BRCW	104	DMCL	1957
—	53517	BRCW	104	DMCL	1957
—	59137	BRCW	104	TSL	1957
—	62351	BR	423	MBSO	
—	71032	BR	423	MTSO	
—	76529	BR	423	DTC	
—	76712	BR	423	DTS	
—	901001	BR	101		

Industrial locomotive

Name	No	Builder	Type	Built
Brightside	—	YEC	0-4-0DH	1960

Locomotive notes: Locos expected to be in service: 5197, D8154, D3991, 33102, 47192, 73110, 4-VEP, 104 DMU, 901001 DMU

Stock

Ex-BR Mk 1 coaches: CK (1), BSK (2), SO (3), TSO (2), FK (3), RMB (2), RK (1) and BG (2); ex-BR Mk 2 coaches: BFK (1); ex-BR suburban coaches: S (1), BS (2), SLO (1); 1 ex-NSR coach saloon; 1 ex-LMS 6-wheel full brake; 2 ex-LMS goods brake vans; 1 ex-LMS 6-wheel CCT; 2 ex-LMS box vans; 3 ex-BR box vans; 2 ex-LMS five-plank wagons; 1 ex-LMS hopper wagon; 1 Esso tank wagon; 1 ex-BR standard brake van; 1 ex-BR Oyster; 5 ex-BR General Utility Vans; 2 ex-BR Medfits; 2 ex-BR Catfish; 1 ex-GWR bogie bolster; 2 Flatrols; 1 Lowmac; 7-ton diesel rail-mounted crane; 75-ton rail-mounted diesel crane; 3 ex-BR QQX tool vans; 1 ex-BR QPX staff and dormitory

Owners

33102 and D7672 the North Staffordshire Railway Co
37075 The 5C Group
47524 the Staffordshire Type 4 Ltd

Cleethorpes Coast Light Railway

Member: HRA

The East Coast's award winning seaside 15in gauge steam railway. Built in 1948 as a 10.25in line, it was converted in 1972 to 14.25in and then to 15in gauge in 1994.

The railway has a good reputation for galas and events, and facilities continue to improve year on year. In 2005 a new 'Griffon Hall' museum was officially opened.

The railway is supported by the Light Railway Association, whose members assist in running the line, undertaking a wide range of duties. This small group provides volunteers from station staff to engine drivers.

Operating society/organisation: Cleethorpes Coast Light Railway Ltd, Lakeside Station, Kings Road, Cleethorpes, Lincolnshire DN35 0AG

Telephone: (01472) 604657

Fax: (01472) 291903

Internet address: *e-mail:* office,cclr@btconnect.com *Web site:* www.cleethorpescoastlightrailway.com

Access by public transport: By rail to Cleethorpes station (First Transpennine South). Local bus service Stagecoach services 9 (all year) and 17 (summer only). Or Coopers Seafront Open Top service (summer only). Alternative seafront roadtrain from the pier to CCLR Kingsway station. By car, Kings Road is the main resort road, follow brown tourist signs for Lakeside (look for the train symbol)

Special events: Easter Egg Spress Specials — 10-13 April; Spring Steam Gala — 1-4 May; Folk and Cider Weekend — 23-25 May; The Seagull Has Landed, 1940s Weekend — 13/14 June; Father's Day Specials — 21 June; Kentucky Derby Race Night — 4 July; Teddy Bears' Picnic — 23 July; 4th Annual Rail Ale Festival — 24-

Locomotives (15in gauge)

Name	No	Built/rebuilt	Type	Date
—	7	Lister	4wDH Tram	—
The Cub/John	3	Minirail/CCLR	4w4DM	1993
—	24	Fairbourne	2-6-2	1989
—	—	A. Moss	4wDM	1995
Battison	—	Battison	2-6-4DH S/O	1958
Yvette	1	—	2-6-0	1946
Efie	—	Great Northern Steam	0-4-0	1999
—	—	Scarrott	4-4-0	1990
—	—	Massey/CCLR	0-6-4ST	2006/7

Rolling stock

10 coaches, 2 x 4-wheel wagons, 2 x 4-wheel box vans, 1 x 4-wheel goods brake van, 4 bogie flat wagons, 2 x 4-wheel ballast wagon

15in gauge Sutton Collection

Locomotives

Name	No	Built/rebuilt	Type	Date
Sutton Belle	1	BL/Cannon Ironfoundries/Hunt	4-4-2	1933
Sutton Flyer	2	Bassett Lowke/Hunt	4-4-2	1950
—	4	G&S Light Engineering	Bo-Bo	1946

Rolling stock

6 closed coaches, 4 open coaches, 4-wheel coal truck

15in gauge Bushmills Railway Collection

Locomotives

Name	No	Built/rebuilt	Type	Date
Mountaineer	—	van Heiden/Severn-Lamb	0-4-0	1985
—	DA1		4wDM	

Rolling stock

5 closed coaches

Note

During the year visiting locomotives are based on the CCLR, and locomotives and rolling stock are under repair for other operators

26 July; Little Lost Engines Weekend — 8/9 August; Sutton 60s Weekend — 29-31 August; Tanks for the Tender Memories and Model Gala — 5/6 September; Listerfest — 3/4 October; Halloween Trains — 30/31 October; Wizards Express Trains — 1 November; Santa Special Trains — 5/6, 12/13, 19-24 December

On site facilities: Large 500 space car park at Lakeside station (pay & display, local authority operated). Lakeside station — Brief

Encounters tea room; Model Box model shop; Griffon Hall museum; 4-ways café. Kingsway station — Station Masters gift shop.

Period of public opening: Please contact for details

Special events: The Works Outing (May). The new extension will be open for the gala, an extra mile of track and a new station called Humberstone North Sea Lane. Please see web site for details

Member: HRA, TT

A completely reconstructed country station and railway within sight of a 12th century castle and specialising in entertainment and education. A complementary Farm Park provides interest for all the family (May to September)

Location: Castle Hedingham Station, Yeldham Road, Castle Hedingham, Halstead, Essex CO9 3DZ

OS reference: TL 774362

Operating society/organisation: Colne Valley Railway Preservation Society Ltd

Telephone: Hedingham (01787) 461174

Internet address:
Web site: www.colnevalleyrailway.co.uk

Car park: At the site (access from A1017 road between Castle Hedingham and Great Yeldham)

Access by public transport: Eastern National bus services 88 Colchester-Halstead, 89 Halstead-Hedingham and Hedingham Omnibuses 4 Braintree-Hedingham, 5 Sudbury-Hedingham. Nearest main line station — Braintree (7 miles)

On site facilities: Depot, museum, souvenir shop, buffet, 4-acre riverside picnic area, toilets, video carriage, exhibition centre, 30 acre farm park (May to September)

Catering facilities: Buffet carriage when trains operating. Pullman on-train service on selected days for Sunday lunch, private hire and evening wine and dine (pre-booking essential for all Pullman services)

Length of line: 1 mile

Public opening: Steam trains operate every Sunday from 12 April to 25 October, also Wednesdays and Thursdays during school summer holidays, every Bank Holiday (except Christmas & New Year), Wednesdays during other school holidays (except February). Diesel railcar on many other days. Phone for free timetable or visit web site

Special events: Vintage Vehicle Rally — 18/19 April; Colne Valley

Locomotives and multiple-units

Name	No	Origin	Class	Type	Built
Blue Star	35010	SR	MN	4-6-2	1942
—	45163	LMS	5	4-6-0	1935
—	45293	LMS	5	4-6-0	1936
—	D2041	BR	03	0-6-0DM	1959
—	D2184	BR	03	0-6-0DM	1962
—	D3476	BR	10	0-6-0DE	1957
—	31255	BR	31	A1A-A1A	1961
—	47771	BR	47	Co-Co	1966
—	56287	P/Steel	121	DTS	1961
—	55033	P/Steel	121	DTC	1960
—	68009	BR	MLV / 419	DMVL	1961
—	69318	BR	4-BIG / 422	TRBS	1965
—	E79978	AC Cars	—	Railbus	1958
—	55508	BR	141	DMS	1983
—	55528	BR	141	DMS(L)	1983

plus various Class 08s between hire contracts

Industrial locomotives

Name	No	Builder	Type	Built
Victory	8	Barclay (2199)	0-4-0ST	1945
Jennifer	—	H/Clarke (1731)	0-6-0T	1942
—	WD190	Hunslet (3790)	0-6-0ST	1952
Jupiter	60	RSH (7671)	0-6-0ST	1950
Castle Donnington	—	RSH (7817)	0-4-0ST	1954
Barrington	—	Avonside (1875)	0-4-0ST	1921
—	1	H/Leslie (3715)	0-4-0ST	1928
—	—	Barclay (349)	0-4-0DM	1941
—	YD43	R/Hornsby (221639)	4wDM	1943
—	—	Hibberd (3147)	4wDM	1947
—	—	Unilok (2109)	4wDM R/R	1982
—	—	Lake & Elliot (1)	4wPM	1924
—	—	R/Hornsby (281266)	4wDM	1950

Locomotive notes: *Barrington, Castle Donnington* and *Jennifer* will be operational during 2009. Diesels 31255 and 55033 also operational

Stock

Some vehicles may be at Yeldham Transport Museum for restoration.
2 ex-Pullman cars, *Aquila* and *Hermione;* 9 ex-BR Mk 1 coaches (2xTSO, SO, 2xCK, SK, 2xBSK); 1 ex-BR Mk 3 SLEP; 9 BR NPCCS, 2 ex-LNER — 1xBTO (16551) 1xTK (42240); 1 LMS BG, 1 GER BTK; 4 goods brake vans (GWR, LNER & 2 BR), 3 oil tank wagons, BR steam crane, LT ballast wagon, BR Sturgeon, BR Conflat, GER van, BR van, BR Medfit, LNER tube wagon, BR diesel crane, BR Flatrol, BR Lowmac

Owners

35010 and 45293 the British Engineman's Steam Preservation Society
56287 and 55033 Pressed Steel Heritage Ltd
31255 and 68009 the Colne Valley Railway Diesel Group
47771 the Class 47 Preservation Project
45163 the 45163 Preservation Group
Castle Donnington on loan from Midland Railway — Butterley
Jennifer on loan from Llangollen Railway

43

England

at War — 17 May; Day out with Thomas — 13/14, 20/21 June; Model Railway Exhibition — 28 June; Freight Gala — 19 July; Travelling Post Office Operating Day — 6 September; Day out with Thomas — 26/27 September, 3/4 October; Colne Valley Gala — 25 October; Wizard's Evening — 31 October; Santa Specials — 6, 12/13, 19/20, 22/23 December

Educational events: Diesel trains available every day for school visits (steam on certain days).
Educational events: 1940s —
18/19 May; Old Smokey — 16-18, 24/25 June; Victorian Special — 6-8 October.
All educational events must be pre-booked

Family tickets: Available — 2 adults and up to 4 children, giving unlimited train rides except on special events

Facilities for disabled: Access to most areas with disabled parking available. Ramps to trains, staff will help. Special carriage and toilets available

Special notes: The railway has been completely rebuilt on part of the original Colne Valley & Halstead Railway trackbed. It offers much of educational value specialising in school party visits by appointment at any time of the year. 12 month season tickets available

Special facilities: Private or corporate hire of Pullmans is available.

Membership details: Membership Secretary, c/o Castle Hedingham Station

---

Museum	Coventry Electric Railway Centre	Warwickshire

Member: HRA

Originally commenced in 1983 as the Coventry Steam Railway Centre which was (and still is) the only standard gauge line in the county of Warwickshire, The Centre has been developed on a six acre greenfield site with no prior railway use. In 2000 the Suburban Electric Railway Association (SERA) bought controlling interest in the operating company and used the site to locate its collection of vintage electric multiple-units (EMUs); with the SERA collection and some privately owned EMU vehicles and electric locomotives on site it has become home to the largest collection of DC electric traction in preservation. This prompted a change of name and direction in 2006 for the development of the site as the UK's only Electric Railway Heritage Centre. The site has witnessed some extensive development over the last couple of years

Location: At the boundary of Coventry Airport, south of the city centre and adjacent to the East Midlands Air Museum. Reached via Rowley Road, junction with A45/A46, Coventry Eastern Bypass — M6/M69/M1 link road. Follow signs to Coventry Airport and the entrance is on Rowley Road

Internet address: *e-mail:* info@emus.co.uk
Web site: http://www.emus.co.uk

Electric multiple-units (complete)

Unit Nos	No	Origin	Class	Type	Built
4732	12795	BR	4SUB / 405	DMBSO	1951
	12354	BR	4SUB / 405	TS	1948
	10239	BR	4SUB / 405	TOS	1948
	12796	BR	4SUB / 405	DMBSO	1951
—	28690	LMS	503	DMBSO	1938
	29298	LMS	503	DTTO	1938
	29720	LMS	503	TCO	1938
5791/93	65321	BR	2EPB / 416/2	DMBSO	1954
	77112	BR	2EPB / 416/2	DTC	1954
4311	61287	BR	2HAP / 414	DMBSO	1959
	75407	BR	2HAP / 414	DTCL	1959
6307	14573	BR	2EPB / 416/3	DMBSO	1959
	16117	BR	2EPB / 416/3	DTS	1959
	61183	BR	501	DMBSO	1957
	75186	BR	501	DTBSO	1957

Electric multiple-units (from incomplete units)

From Unit No	No	Origin	Class	Type	Built
—	(7)	LOR*	—	TFO	1895
5176	15345	BR	415 / 4EPB	TSO	1954
7001	67300	BR	457	DMSO	1981

*Liverpool Overhead Railway, built by Brown Marshall & Co

Electric locomotives

Name	No	Builder	Type	Built
—	(1)	E/Electric (EE905)	4wBE/WE	1935
—	1	H/Leslie	Bo-Bo	1928

Diesel locomotives

Name	No	Builder	Type	Built
Mazda	—	R/Hornsby (268881)	0-4-0DE	1950
(Crabtree)	—	R/Hornsby (338416)	4wDM	1953

Rolling stock

Coaches — Ex-City & South London Railway trailers Nos 135, 163
Wagons — 1 bogie tool van (converted from Maunsell Ironclad coach)

44

OS reference: SP 349750
Access by public transport: National Rail services to Coventry, West Midlands bus route 1 from overbridge at north end of station to Tollbar End — 10-15min walk up Rowley Road to site. Also 737 (hourly) from station forecourt to Tollbar roundabout
Operating society/organisation: Coventry Railway Centre/Suburban Electric Railway Association
Length of line: Third of a mile (under construction)
Public opening: Due to ongoing construction work at the site there is no regular opening, but groups or parties can be accommodated by prior arrangement. Please check web site and railway press for details of other public opening/events.
Please note that many items are tarpaulined for protection
Car park: On site, at main access gate
Facilities for disabled: Site is relatively flat, assistance will be given if requested by prior notice there are no toilets on site

---

| Steam Centre | Crewe Heritage Centre | Cheshire |

Location: Crewe Heritage Centre, Vernon Way, Crewe CW1 2BD
OS reference: SJ 709552
Operating society/organisation: Crewe Heritage Trust Ltd
Telephone: (01270) 212130
Internet address: Web site: www.creweheritagecentre.co.uk
Car park: On site, town centre, Forge Street, Oak Street,
Access by public transport: Main line Crewe
Refreshment facilities: Adjacent Tesco superstore
On site facilities: Gift shop, picnic area, weekend train rides, standard gauge and miniature railway, exhibition hall, main line viewing area, 3 working signalboxes with 'hands-on' visitor operation, model railway layouts also preserved buses
Public opening: Weekends and Bank Holidays only, Easter to end of September 10.00-16.30 (last admission 15.30). Family tickets available. Please contact for details of events
Weekday visits by prior arrangement with the manager
Facilities for disabled: Toilets
Membership details: Friends of the Crewe Heritage Centre, c/o above address
Notes: Steam locomotives passed for use over main line tracks are stabled between duties from time to time

Locomotives

Name	No	Origin	Class	Type	Built
Thornbury Castle	7027	GWR	Castle	4-6-0	1950
—	D2073	BR	03	0-6-0DM	1959
—	08830	BR	08	0-6-0DE	1960
Ixion	D172	BR	46	1Co-Co1	1962
—	D1842*	BR	47	Co-Co	1965
Robert Burns	87035	BR	87	Bo-Bo	1974

*expected to be loaned to the Dartmoor Railway when reopened

Rolling stock
APT vehicle Nos 48103, 48106, 48404, 48602, 48603, 49002; various ex BR coaches and passenger brake vans from time to time for repairs

Owner
7027, D172 and 08830 the Waterman Heritage Trust

| Tram Service | Crich Tramway Village | Derbyshire |

Member: HRA, TT
An experience of living transport history with vintage horse-drawn, steam and electric trams running through a re-created townscape of authentic buildings, stone setts, iron railings and historic street furniture. The heart of the Museum is its collection of over 70 vintage trams and you can enjoy the thrill of travelling on the scenic mile-long track
Location: Crich, Nr Matlock,

Locomotives

Name	No	Builder	Type	Built
—	—	B/Peacock (2464)	0-4-0VB tram loco	1885
—	—	E/Electric (717)	4wE	1927
Rupert*	—	R/Hornsby (223741)	4wDM	1944
GMJ*	—	R/Hornsby (326058)	4wDM	1952
—*	—	R/Hornsby (373363)	4wDM	1954

*not on display

Trams

No	Operator	Built
1	Derby	1904
1	Douglas Head Marine Drive	1896

Derbyshire DE4 5DP
OS reference: SK 345549
Manager: Vacant
Operating society/organisation:
Tramway Museum Society
Telephone: 01773 854321
Internet address: *e-mail:*
enquiries@tramway.co.uk
Web site: www.tramway.co.uk
Car park: Site; coach parking also
available
Access by public transport: By
rail, nearest main line stations:
Cromford or Alfreton then by bus;
or Whatstandwell and steep uphill
walk
On site facilities: Souvenir shop,
play areas, bookshop and picnic
areas. 1-mile electric tramway.
Tramway period street, depots,
displays, exhibitions and video
theatre. Large exhibition hall with
new interpretive display depicting
the history of the tram and Turn of
the Century Trade Exhibition plus
other exhibitions/displays
Refreshment facilities: Hot and
cold snacks and meals
Public opening: Daily February
half term (10.30-16.00).
Weekends in March (10.30-16.00).
Daily end March until 1 November
(10.00-17.30).
Weekends from November to
15 December (10.30-16.00).
Special events: Easter 1940s
Weekend — 12/13 April; Models
Weekend — 9/10 May; Morris
Minor Event — 10 May; Folk
Weekend — 13/14 June; 1950s
Weekend — 27/28 June;
Enthusiasts' Tram Event —
5 June; Edwardian Weekend —
11/12 July; MiniMeet — 26 July;
Emergency Vehicles Day —
2 August; 1940s Weekend —
8/9 August; Transport
Extravaganza — 30/31 August;
Beetle Drive — 6 September;
Classic Ford Event —
20 September; Starlight Halloween
— 31 October;
Family tickets: Available
Facilities for disabled: Access to
all public facilities, Braille guide
book available, 1969 Berlin tram
specially adapted to lift and carry
people in wheelchairs. Also a
'wheelway', a smooth path
routeing around and through
cobbled areas
Special notes: Crich houses the
largest collection of preserved
trams in Europe and has a 1-mile
working tramway on which
restored electric trams are regularly
operated. Special events are

No	Operator	Built
1	Leamington & Warwick	1881
1	London Transport	1932
2	Blackpool & Fleetwood	1898
4	Blackpool Corp	1885
5	Blackpool	*1972
5	Gateshead & District	1927
7	Chesterfield	1904
8	Chesterfield	1899
9	Oporto	1873
10	Hill of Howth	1902
14	Grimsby & Immingham	1915
15	Sheffield	1874
21	Dundee & District	1894
22	Glasgow	1922
35	Edinburgh	1948
40	Blackpool & Fleetwood	†1914
40	Blackpool	1926
45	Southampton	1903
46	Sheffield	1899
(47)	New South Wales Govt	1885
49	Blackpool	1926
52	Gateshead & District	*1901
59	Blackpool	*1902
60	Johannesburg	1905
68	Paisley & District	1919
74	Sheffield	1900
76	Leicester	1904
102	Newcastle	1901
106	London County Council	1903
132	Kingston-upon-Hull	§1910
166	Blackpool	1927
167	Blackpool	1928
180	Leeds	1931
180	Prague	1908
189	Sheffield	1934
264	Sheffield	1937
273	Oporto	—
298	Blackpool	*1937
331	Metropolitan Electric	1930
345	Leeds	*—
399	Leeds	1926
510	Sheffield	1950
600	Leeds	1931/54
602	Leeds	1953
674	New York 3rd Avenue Transit	1939
812	Glasgow	1900
869	Liverpool	1936
902	Halle	
1100	Glasgow	1928
1105	Glasgow	1929
1147	Hague	1957
1282	Glasgow	1940
1297	Glasgow	1948
1622	London Transport	1912
3006	Berlin	1969
—	London Tramways	c1895

*stored off-site
†on loan to Blackpool
§on loan to Hull Museum of Transport

Note: In addition to the trams (including examples from Czechoslovakia,
Germany, The Netherlands, Portugal, USA and South Africa) — about a

England

arranged at weekends and Bank Holidays throughout the season. Part of tram line occupies route of narrow gauge mineral railway built by George Stephenson
Membership details: From above address
Membership journal: *The Journal* — quarterly

third of which have been restored to working order — there are a number of Works Cars not listed

---

<table>
<tr><td>Timetable Service</td><td>Dartmoor Railway</td><td>Devon</td></tr>
</table>

Dartmoor Railway — Devon

Member: HRA

Following its unexpected closure in 2008 the Ealing Community Transpoer (ECT) sold its interest to Iowa Pacific Holdings (IPH). IPH have created a new company British American Railways to operated both Dartmoor and Weardale. At the time of going to press, BAR was hoping to restart the heritage service in spring/summer 2009.

Dartmoor Railway is a very young railway as far as tourism is concerned although the railway has been in existence for 140 years as the Southern Railway main line from Waterloo to Plymouth. The line only survived because of ballast supplies from Meldon Quarry. Dartmoor Railway offers a unique experience which encompasses access to Dartmoor National Park for everyone including the disabled and cyclists. Views of Meldon Quarry and workings from the Cycle Route. Far reaching views at Meldon of Dartmoor, Exmoor and surrounding areas. Meldon visitor centre shows a history of the railways and tramways of Dartmoor. Okehampton station has been restored to the 1950s style
Headquarters: Dartmoor Railway, Okehampton Station, Okehampton, Devon EX20 1EJ
Telephone: 01837 55637
Fax: 01837 54588
Internet addresses: *e-mail:* info@dartmoorrailway.co.uk
Web site: www.dartmoorrailway.co.uk
General Manager: Stuart Farmer
Main station: Okehampton, access by road, rail (very restricted service), bus, or National Cycle

Locomotives and multiple-units (in use as hauled stock)

Name	No	Origin	Class	Type	Built
Bluebell Mel	08937	BR	08	0-6-0DE	1962
—	D1842*	BR	47	Co-Co	1965
unit 205028	60146	BR	205	DMBS	1957
unit 205028	60673	BR	205	DMBS	1957
unit 205028	60827	BR	205	DTC	1957
unit 205032	60150	BR	205	DMBS	1957
unit 205032	60677	BR	205	DMBS	1957
unit 205032	60831	BR	205	DTC	1957
unit 412	70826	BR	438 / 4TC	DTSO	1967
unit 412	70860	BR	438 / 4TC	DTSO	1967
unit 412	76301	BR	438 / 4TC	DTSO	1967
unit 412	76302	BR	438 / 4TC	DTSO	1967
—	69332	BR	423 / 4VEP	TRB	1969
—	69310	BR	422	TRBS	1965
—	61742	BR			
—	61743	BR			
—	76812	BR	421 / 4CIG	DTCSOL	

*expected to arrive on loan from Crewe Heritage Centre when services recommence

Industrial locomotives

Name	No	Builder	Type	Built
—	S103*	H/Clarke (1864)	0-6-0T	1952
Flying Falcon	MSC 0256*	Fowler	0-6-0DE	

*undergoing restoration, expected to enter service in 2009

Stock
ex-BR Mk 1s RBR: 1691; FO *Rosemary*
ex-BR Mk 2s TSO 5920, 6002, 6181; FO 3353, 3354, 3387, 3402, 3411, 3425; RBR 1213; BSO 9492, 9501
ex-BR Mk 3 sleeping cars 10518, 10595, 10611;
1 ex-BR sleeping car 10000; function coach, converted from 99622;
Selection of maintenance vehicles including horse box S96300 converted to Generator coach for 'Dartmoor Belle'

Owners
Class 205 units stored on behalf of Porterbrook Leasing Co
08937 and MSC 0256 Aggregate Industries
76301, 76302, 70812, 70860 and 70826 Rolltrack Trains
Groups and individuals own some of the rolling stock

Note: Some of the vehicles listed above have been advertised for sale.

Route 237 and other footpaths. Ample free parking, including coaches

Other public stations: Meldon for Meldon Viaduct and Dartmoor National park, access only by rail and National Cyclepath. Sampford Courtenay has access by road or rail, limited free parking

Access by public transport: Bus all year, check with Traveline 0870 6082608 for availability. Trains from Exeter (Sunday Rover) late May to late September

Refreshment facilities: Okehampton buffet open when summer services from Exeter run.

Model & Gift shops: Extensive model and gift shop at Okehampton, some gifts also available at Meldon buffet (tel: 01837 55637

Depot: Meldon Quarry, no public access. Viewing only from National Cyclepath

Length of line: 15.5 miles from Coleford Junction-Meldon Quarry

Passenger trains: Please see railway press/web site for resumption of service details

Special events: Please see railway press/web site for resumption of service details

Special notes: Visits for special interest groups and education tours may be arranged. Trains are available for private hire or corporate function. Trains have facilities to carry bicycles free, dogs also carried free

Facilities for disabled: Full disabled facilities and access at Okehampton, partial access to inside Meldon buffet. Toilets at Okehampton and Meldon are RADAR key operated

Membership details: Friends of Dartmoor Railway c/o Okehampton station. Various discounts available

Membership journal: Quarterly, also available to purchase

Timetable Service — Dean Forest Railway — Glos

Member: HRA, TT

Passenger services operate between Norchard and Lydney Junction (Severn & Wye Joint), and Norchard and Parkend. The line boasts five level crossings, three of which are manually operated

Location: Headquarters at Norchard station on the B4234. Signposted off the A48 Lydney bypass to town centre whence B4234 commences

SatNav postcode: Norchard GL15 4ET

OS reference: SO 629044

Operating society/organisation: Dean Forest Railway Society in conjunction with owning company, Forest of Dean Railway Ltd

Telephone: (01594) 843423 information line; (01594) 845840 (daytime)

Internet address: Web site: www.deanforestrailway.co.uk

Car park: Norchard only, adequate for cars and coaches. No parking at other stations

Access by public transport: Main line station at Lydney. Stagecoach buses (service 73 Monday-Saturday) Gloucester-Lydney-Chepstow

On site facilities: Shop at Norchard with museum, riverside walk and forest walks

Catering facilities: Hot and cold meals at Platelayer's Buffet on Norchard platform on service days.

Locomotives and multiple-units

Name	No	Origin	Class	Type	Built
—	5538±	GWR	4575	2-6-2T	1928
—	5541†	GWR	4575	2-6-2T	1928
—	9681	GWR	5700	0-6-0PT	1949
Charlie	13308	BR	08	0-6-0DE	1956
—	08734	BR	08	0-6-0DE	1960
Gladys§	D3937	BR	08	0-6-0DE	1960
—	D9521	BR	14	0-6-0DH	1964
—	D9555	BR	14	0-6-0DH	1965
—	27066	BR	27	Bo-Bo	1962
—	D7633	BR	25	Bo-Bo	1965
—	31466	BR	31	A1A-A1A	1959
—	D5634	BR	31	A1A-A1A	1960
—	37263	BR	37	Co-Co	1965
—	E6001	BR	73	Bo-Bo	1962
—*	73002	BR	73	Bo-Bo	1962
—§	E6005	BR	73	Bo-Bo	1962
—§	E6006	BR	73	Bo-Bo	1962
The Royal Alex	73101§	BR	73	Bo-Bo	1965
—	50619	BR	108	DMBS	1958
—	51566	BR	108	DMSL	1959
—	51914	BR	108	DMS	1960
—	51933§	BR	108	DMS	1960
—	56492	BR	108	DTC	1960
—	59387	BR	108	TS	1958
—	62364	BR	421	MBSO	
—	62378	BR	421	MBSO	
—	70273	BR	411	TSOL	
—	76726	BR	421	DTCSoL	
—	76740	BR	421	DTCSoL	
—	76797	BR	421	DTCSoL	
—	76811	BR	421	DTCSoL	

§on loan to Avon Valley Railway
*mobile stores vehicle
±dismantled awaiting restoration
†undergoing restoration

England

Parties catered for by appointment. Sunday lunchtime service by 'Royal Forester' first class dining car service, runs on selected Sundays in season, also evening supper trains, advance booking essential
Length of line: 4.25 miles
Public opening: Daily for static display — shop and museum, open 11.00-16.00, extended hours on running days.

Steam train rides (some days DMUs and diesels). All Sundays 22 February to 8 November; Good Friday, Easter Saturday and all Bank Holiday Sundays and Mondays (Christmas excepted). Wednesdays June to September. Thursdays in late July and August.

Heritage DMU or main line diesel service operates alone most Saturdays June, July and September, plus Thursdays in August

Special events: Day out with Thomas — 17-19 April, 29-31 May, 21-23 August (all to be confirmed); GWR Auto Train Days — 12 April, 3, 24 May, 28 June, 19 July, 2, 16, 30 August, 13 September; Steam & Diesel Gala — 13-14 June; Diesel Gala — 27 June, 26 September; Halloween Ghost Trains — 31 October

Industrial locomotives

Name	No	Builder	Type	Built
—	—	Barclay (2221)	0-4-0ST	1946
Uskmouth No 1	—	Peckett (2147)	0-4-0ST	1952
Wilbert	—	Hunslet (3806)	0-6-0ST	1953
Warrior†	—	Hunslet (3823)	0-6-0ST	1954
—	—	Hunslet (2145)	0-4-0DM	1940
—	—	Hunslet (6688)	0-4-0DH	1968
—	—	Fowler (4210127)	0-4-0DM	1957
—	—	Hibberd (3947)	4wPM	1960

†undergoing restoration

Stock
2 ex-GWR coaches; 10 ex-BR coaches; 1 DFR constructed Cafeteria coach (static at Norchard), 3 Wickham trolleys; 1 steam crane Thos Smith (Rodley) TS 5027 (10ton); Booth 15-24 tonne diesel-hydraulic crane, Cowans & Sheldon 30-ton diesel crane (ADRC 96101), Schöma p-way tram and trailer

Owners
5541 the Forest Prairie Fund
9681 the Dean Forest Locomotive Group
D9521 the D9521 Locomotive Group
13308, D3937, 08734, 27066, 31466, D5634, D7633, E6001, 73002, E6005, E6006 and 73101 the Dean Forest Diesel Association
37263 the 37263 Locomotive Group
Class 108 DMUs the Dean Forest DMU Group

(advance booking); Santa Specials — 5/6, 12/13, 19/20, 24 December (advance booking essential)
Facilities for disabled: Access to museum, shop, toilets and trains
Membership details: Mr R. Bramwell, 4 Poole Ground, Highnam, Gloucester GL2 8NA and web site
Membership journal: *DFR Magazine* — 6 per year
Marketing name: The Friendly Forest Line

Steam Centre — Derwent Valley Light Railway — North Yorkshire

Member: TT
The DVR's most notable fact about its history is that it was never nationalised. Private from its inception until the final section was closed in the early 1980s. The line was mothballed until 1989 when it was transformed into a cycleway by Sustrans. A half-mile section adjacent to the Yorkshire Museum of Farming was donated to the museum along with the most necessary Light Railway Order.
Location: Murton Park, Murton Lane, Murton, York YO19 5UF
Operating society/organisation: Derwent Valley Light Railway Society
Telephone: (01904) 489966

Locomotive

Name	No	Origin	Class	Type	Built
—	03079	BR	03	0-6-0DM	1960

Industrial locomotives

Name	No	Builder	Type	Built
—	8	A/Barclay (2369)	0-4-0ST	1955
—	65	H/Clarke (1631)	0-6-0T	1929
—	—	Fowler (4200022)	0-4-0DM	1948
Churchill	—	Fowler (410005)	0-4-0DM	1947
Jim	—	R/Hornsby (417892)	4wDM	1959
—	97088	R/Hornsby (466630)	4wDM	1962
British Sugar York	—	R/Hornsby (327964)	0-4-0DM	1953

Rolling stock
1 NER coach, 1 NER coach body, 1 Swiss-style coach (built in 2003), 12 various freight wagons, and 1 steam rail crane

Internet address: *e-mail:* dvlr@hotmail.com
Web site: www.dvlr.org.uk
OS reference: SE 651537
On site facilities: Refreshments, souvenir shop (Yorkshire Museum of Farming)
Car park: Free, on site
Length of line: Half-mile
Access by public transport: York-Stamford Bridge and York-Hull bus services from York main line station. (Tel: 0870 608 2608 or www.yorkshiretravel.net)

Souvenir shops: Within the Yorkshire Museum of Farming, and a railway souvenir shop within the station (open when trains running). Once the entrance fee to the Yorkshire Museum of Farming has been paid train rides are free
Facilities for disabled: Toilets, ramped ways, etc
Public opening: Open daily mid-February-end October, for the Yorkshire Museum of Farming, Danelaw (Viking) Village and the Derwent Valley Light Railway.

Trains operate Sundays and Bank Holidays Easter-end September and for Santa Specials
Special events: Santa Special — weekends and certain weekdays in December
Membership details: Kay Dunn, Membership Secretary, Derwent Valley Light Railway Society, Murton Park, Murton Lane, Murton, York YO19 5UF
Society journal: *DVLR News* (quarterly)

Railway Centre | Devon Railway Centre | Devon

The Devon Railway Centre features a lovingly restored Victorian Great Western Railway station together with historic locomotives, carriages and wagons as featured on TV. Unlimited passenger rides can be taken on the 2ft gauge railway and miniature railways. There is also a large model railway exhibition featuring 15 working layouts including Polchester and Chiltern Green. Edwardian Model Village and outdoor play area. All-inclusive admission price
Location: Alongside Bickleigh Bridge over the River Exe on the A396, four miles south of Tiverton and 10 miles north of Exeter
General Manager: Matthew Gicquel
Contact address: Devon Railway Centre, Bickleigh, Nr Tiverton, Devon EX16 8RG
Telephone: 01884 855671
Internet address: *Web site:* www.devonrailwaycentre.co.uk
OS reference: SS 938074
Car park: On site
Access by public transport: Regular bus service from Tiverton and Exeter, routes 55 and 55A
On site facilities: Passenger-carrying line, large model railway exhibition, restored GWR station, standard gauge static display, historic narrow gauge collection, miniature railway, refreshments and souvenirs, crazy golf, drive your own miniature railway. Model village and outdoor play area
Length of line: Half mile, 2ft

Industrial locomotives (2ft gauge)

Name	No	Builder	Type	Built
Pixie	—	K/Stuart (4260)	0-4-0ST	1922
	—	O&K (5744)	0-4-0WT	1912
Horatio	—	R/Hornsby (217967)	4wDM	1942
Pen-yr-Orsedd	—	R/Hornsby (235711)	4wDM	1945
Ruston	—	R/Hornsby (418770)	4wDM	1957
Claude W. Lane	—†	R/Hornsby (435398)	4wDM	1959
Planet	—	Planet (2201)	4wDM	1939
Lister	—	Lister (6299)	4wPM	1935
	—	Lister (34025)	4wDM	1949
	—	Planet (2025)	4wDM	1937
	—	Kent (1747)	4wPM	1931
Ivor	—	M/Rail (8877)	4wDM	1944
	—	M/Rail (20073)	4wDM	1950
Sir Tom	—	M/Rail (40s273)	4wDM	1966
	—*	M/Rail (105H006)	4wDM	1919
—	—	BEV	0-4-0BE	c1970

Pixie on hire from Leighton Buzzard Railway until September 2009
†2ft 9in gauge
*3ft gauge

Industrial locomotives (standard gauge)

Name	No	Builder	Type	Built
Boris	1	Baguley (3357)	0-4-0DM	1952

Locomotive notes: Passenger trains will be hauled by either *Pixie*, *Ivor*, *Ruston* or *Horatio*. It is expected the O&K will enter service in 2009

Rolling stock: All 2ft gauge unless indicated. Two Alan Keef bogie passenger coaches, Two Hudson bogie passenger coaches, Hudson 4-wheel coach, Dinorwic Yellow Coach, 2 slate slab wagons, 7 skip wagons, 4 mine tubs, RAF bomb wagon, Hudson 3-plank wagon, 2 bogie coach chassis. Lochaber incline wagon (3ft gauge), copper mine tub (20in gauge), Cattybrook brickworks wagon (2ft 10in gauge), assorted works wagons. Standard gauge — 3 ex-BR Mk 1 coaches, 4 ex-BR Mk 1 BGs

Miniature railway locomotives (7.25in gauge)

Name	No	Builder	Type	Built
—	D7011*	Cromar White	Bo-BoBE	1969
(Intercity)	—	—	Bo-BoBE	c1995
—	—	Pfeiferbahn	4wPH	1993

gauge; half mile 7.25in gauge, 200yd standard gauge demonstration line; 100yd 7.25in gauge drive your own train
Opening times: 10.30-17.00. 4 April until 1 November. Daily 4-19 April, 20 May to 6 September, 24 October to 1 November (closed Mondays in June).
Wednesday to Sunday 2-17 May, 9-27 September. Sataturday and Sundays in October.
Special events: Gala weekend —

Name	No	Builder	Type	Built
—	—	Chandler	4wBE	1978
—	7	Parkside	4WBER S/O	2002

*rebuilt from petrol to battery power by DRC during 2002
7 is a drive-your-own train operated by coin in the slot

Rolling stock: 3 sit-in coaches built by DRC/Roanoake, 1 bogie wagon

1/2 August; Senior Special — 19/20 September; Santa Specials — 12/13, 19/20 December
Timetable: Narrow gauge line operates every 30min, miniature

railway runs as required. Both lines operate when the Centre is open whatever the weather

---

Steam Centre Didcot Railway Centre Oxfordshire

Member: HRA, TT

The Great Western Railway was incorporated in 1835 to build the railway from Bristol to London and it was designed and engineered by Isambard Kingdom Brunel to be the finest in the land. At Didcot, half way between Bristol and London, members of the Great Western Society have created a living museum of the GWR. It is based around the original engine shed and depot, to which has been added a typical branch line with a country station, signalling demonstrations and re-creation of Brunel's broad gauge trackwork and newly built replica of the locomotive *Fire Fly* dating from 1840. There is a large collection of GWR steam locomotives, carriages and wagons. On steamdays the locomotives come to life and you can ride in the 1930s trains on one or both of the demonstration lines. The present Didcot engine shed was built in 1932 and was taken over by the Great Western Society in 1967 when it arrived with just three locomotives, the start of what was to become the Didcot Railway Centre
General Manager: —
Location: Adjacent to main line station, Didcot, Oxfordshire. Access via station subway
OS reference: SU 525907
Operating society/organisation:
Great Western Society Ltd, Didcot Railway Centre, Didcot, Oxon OX11 7NJ

Locomotives

Name	No	Origin	Class/Builder	Type	Built
Fire Fly	—†	GWR	'Fire Fly'	2-2-2	2005
—	22	GWR	Diesel Railcar	1A-A1	1940
County of Glamorgan	1014§	GWR	'County'/GWS	4-6-0	
—	1338	GWR	Kitson (3799) (Cardiff Rly)	0-4-0ST	1898
Trojan	1340	GWR	Avonside (1380)	0-4-0ST	1897
—	1363	GWR	1361	0-6-0ST	1910
—	3650	GWR	5700	0-6-0PT	1939
—	3738	GWR	5700	0-6-0PT	1937
—	3822	GWR	2884	2-8-0	1940
Pendennis Castle	4079	GWR	'Castle'	4-6-0	1924
—	4144	GWR	5101	2-6-2T	1946
—	4866	GWR	4800	0-4-2T	1936
Lady of Legend*	2999	GWR	'Saint'/GWS	4-6-0	1929
Earl Bathurst	5051	GWR	'Castle'	4-6-0	1936
—	5322	GWR	4300	2-6-0	1917
—	5572	GWR	4575	2-6-2T	1927
Hinderton Hall	5900	GWR	'Hall'	4-6-0	1931
King Edward II	6023	GWR	'King'	4-6-0	1930
—	6106	GWR	6100	2-6-2T	1931
—	6697	GWR	5600	0-6-2T	1928
Burton Agnes Hall	6998	GWR	'Hall'	4-6-0	1949
—	7202	GWR	7200	2-8-2T	1934
Cookham Manor	7808	GWR	'Manor'	4-6-0	1938
—	D3771	BR	08	0-6-0DE	1959
Shannon	5		Wantage Tramway	0-4-0WT	1857

†broad gauge reconstruction of 1840 design
*under construction using frames of No 4942 *Maindy Hall*
§under construction using frames of No 7927 *Willington Hall*

Industrial locomotives

Name	No	Builder	Type	Built
Bonnie Prince Charlie	1	RSH (7544)	0-4-0ST	1949
—	26	Hunslet (5238)	0-6-0DH	1962

Locomotive notes: Locomotives available in 2009 should be: *Fire Fly*, 22, 1338, 1340, 3650, 3738, 3822, 5322. Locomotives under restoration include: 4079, 6023, 7202. 4079 was repatriated from Australia in 2000

England

51

Telephone: Didcot (01235) 817200
Internet address: *Web site:* www.didcotrailwaycentre.org.uk
Car park: Didcot station
Access by public transport: Entry is at Didcot Parkway rail station served by First Great Western trains from London (Paddington), the Thames Valley, Oxford, Birmingham, Bristol, etc.

On the A4130 road signed from the M4 motorway (jct 13) and A34
Refreshment facilities: Refreshment room open all days centre is open (lunches, snacks). Picnic area.

Lunch is available in the GWR super-saloon carriages on Mothering Sunday and Father's Day, or Victorian Pudding Evenings (please contact the centre in advance)
On site facilities: GWR locomotive depot, replica GWR station, museum and broad gauge demonstration. Souvenir sales. Rides are available on the demonstration lines on Steamdays.

Admission prices vary according to events and included train rides on Steamdays. Party rates available for more than 15 persons, guided tours, evening visits and special menus for lunch or tea can be arranged. Private steamings when visitors can try their hand at driving locomotives can be arranged

Stock
Over 40 ex-GWR coaches are preserved along with numerous ex-GWR freight wagons

Owner
5 on loan from the National Railway Museum

Length of line: 1,000yd
Public opening: Saturdays and Sundays through out the year. Daily 14-22 February, 4-19 April, 23-31 May, 20 June-6 September, 24 October-1 November, 22/23, 27-31 December. 1-3 January 2010.

Weekends and Steamdays March to October — open 10.30-17.00 (10.30-16.00 midweek and in January, February, November and December). Closed Christmas Day and Boxing Day.
Steamdays: Sundays 15, 22 February, 5, 10-13, 19 April, 2-4, 23-25, 31 May, 6/7, 20/21, 27/28 June, all Saturdays and Sundays 5 July to 31 August, 26/27 September, 24/25 October, 2/3 January 2010.
Wednesdays 18 February, 22 July to 26 August, 28 October, plus Bank Holidays
Train rides: On Steamdays there is normally continuous operation of the passenger train, interrupted by Travelling Post Office demonstrations and turning of the locomotives on some days

Special events: All in a Day's Work — 2-4 May; Broad Gauge Steamings — 27/28 June, Wednesday 22, 25/26, Wednesday 29 July; 29-31August; Day out with Thomas — 6-8 March; 2-4 October; Day out with Thomas and Christmas Specials — weekends 5-20, 22/23 December
Facilities for disabled: Visitors are advised that there is an awkward flight of steps at the entrance, with level access within the centre (help can normally be given with prior advice)
Special facilities: Railway Experience days offer the chance to be an engine driver for a day and a Day at Didcot offers a guided tour on normal steamdays. Special steamings can be arranged for for group and party visits
Membership details: Charles Roberts, at above address
Membership journals: *Great Western Echo* — quarterly; *National Newsletter* — quarterly
Note: Children under 12 must be accompanied by an adult

Operating Museum	East Anglia Transport Museum	Suffolk

Member: TT
The East Suffolk Light Railway is the title given to the 2ft gauge railway, which winds its way 300yd or so along the northern perimeter of the museum site, between the stations of Chapel Road and Woodside. The railway commenced operation in 1973 and aims to re-create a typical passenger-carrying light railway of years gone by. Many aspects of railway interest can be found along its length. The track came from Leziate sand quarry and Canvey Island, as well as from the Southwold Railway, and signals from various local locations; all of which help to set the overall scene

Industrial locomotives

Name	No	Builder	Type	Built
Aldeburgh	2	M/Rail (5912)	4wDM	1934
Leiston	4	R/Hornsby (177604)	4wDM	1936
Orfordness	5	M/Rail (22209)	4wDM	1964
Thorpeness	6	M/Rail (22211)	4wDM	1964

Trams

No	Trucks	Body	Date	Operator
11	Maley & Taunton	E/Electric	1939	Blackpool Corp
14	Brill	Milnes	1904	Lowestoft Corp
159	Preston McGuire	Blackpool Corp	1927	Blackpool Corp
474	Beijnes	Beijnes	1929	Amsterdam
1858	EMB	E/Electric	1930	London Transport

Stock
Locally designed and built covered coach, plus combined coach and brake van, suitable for wheelchairs. Small selection of wagons. Van body ex-Southwold Railway

England

Location: Carlton Colville, three miles south-west of Lowestoft in Suffolk
OS reference: TM 505903
Operating society/organisation: East Anglia Transport Museum Society Ltd, Chapel Road, Carlton Colville, Lowestoft, Suffolk NR33 8BL
Telephone: (01502) 518459
Internet address: *Web site:* www.eatm.org.uk
Car park: Adjacent
Access by public transport: By bus: First Eastern Counties 102 and X2 from Lowestoft or Norwich. By rail: Oulton Broad South (1.5 miles) then Ambassador bus 606, 607 (Monday-Saturday)
On site facilities: Refreshments, picnic areas, souvenir and bookshop, toilets (including disabled), working transport museum, including trams, narrow gauge railway, trolleybuses, steamrollers and other commercial and public transport vehicles. Unlimited free rides
Public opening: Sundays and Bank Holidays (11.00-17.00) Easter until end of September. Also Thursdays and Saturdays (14.00-17.00) June to September. Midsummer opening, daily (except Mondays) 14 July to 28 August (14.00-17.00). Last admission 1 hour before closing
Special events: Please phone for details
Special notes: Limited facilities for the disabled. Pre-booked party rates
Membership details: From the above address

| Steam Centre | **East Anglian Railway Museum** | Essex |

Member: HRA, TT, AIM, EETB, EATL
Adjacent to Chappel Viaduct which is the most spectacular railway structure in East Anglia
Location: Chappel & Wakes Colne Station, near Colchester
OS reference: TL 898289
Operating society/organisation: East Anglian Railway Museum, Chappel & Wakes Colne Station, Station Road, Wakes Colne, Essex CO6 2DS. Registered charity No 1001579
Telephone: Colchester (01206) 242524
Fax: 01787 224473
Internet address: *e-mail:* information@earm.co.uk
Web site: www.earm.co.uk
Car park: On site
Access by public transport:
By rail: National Express East Anglia Chappel & Wakes Colne station.
By bus: First/Hedingham Omnibus service No 88 Colchester-Halstead (hourly). Sundays Network Colchester No 88 Colchester-Halstead (every 2 hours)
On site facilities: Refreshments, bookshop, museum, signalboxes, souvenir shop, picnic area, miniature railway and toilets
Public opening:
Daily 10.00-16.30 or dusk
Special events: Day out with Thomas — 10-13 April; Railway Experience — 25/26 April, 2 May; Victorian Weekend — 3/4 May; Railway Experience — 23 May;

Locomotives and multiple-units

Name	No	Origin	Class	Type	Built
A. J. Hill	69621†	GER	N7	0-6-2T	1924
—	D2279	BR	04	0-6-0DM	1960
—	50599	BR	108	DMBS	1958
—	54223	BR	108	DTCL	1959
—	51213	BR	101	DMBS	1959
—	51505	BR	101	DMC	1959
—	56358	BR	101	DTC	1959
—	54365	BR	101	DTCL	1958

† on loan to North Norfolk Railway

Industrial locomotives

Name	No	Builder	Type	Built
Jubilee	—	Bagnall (2542)	0-4-0ST	1936
—	11	Barclay (1047)	0-4-0ST	1905
Jeffery	2039	Peckett (2039)	0-4-0ST	1943
Penn Green	54	RSH (7031)	0-6-0ST	1941
—	AMW144	Barclay (333)	0-4-0DM	1938
—	23	Fowler (4220039)	0-4-0DH	1965
—	2029	Simplex (2029)	0-4-0PM	1920

Stock
4 ex-BR Mk 1 coaches (TSO, BCK, SK, BS), 1 ex-LNER TSO coach; 1 fully restored GER 6-wheel full brake; 1 GER fully restored 4-wheel coach; 1 ex-GER bogie coach; 1 SR PMV; 1 ex-BR 13-ton open wagon; 2 ex-BR 16-ton mineral wagons; 1 Lowmac wagon; 1 ex-LMS 12-ton open wagon; 1 Wickham Trolley; 1 GWR Toad brake van; 1 ex-BR brake van; Somersham 'pump' trolley, 1 Grafton steam crane, 1 LMS 5 plank wagon, 1 BR cattle van (on loan ex-NRM), 1 BR special cattle van, 1 tube wagon, 1 Pooley van, 1 LNER fish van, 1 BR box van, 2 tank wagons, 1 Molasses tank wagon

Pump trolley weekend — 24/25 May; Cider Festival — 4-7 June; Railway Experience and Minirail — 21, 28 May; Railway Experience — 11/12 July; Minirail Day — 26, 29 July, 2, 5, 9, 12, 16, 19, 23, 26 August; Day out with Thomas — 28-31 August; 23rd Chappel Beer Festival — 8-12 September; Railway Experience — 26/27 September; End of Season Steam, Diesel and Gauge 1 Display — 17/18 October; Railway Experience — 5/6 December;

Something Christmassy —
12/13, 19/20 December
Family tickets: Available on all days (unlimited rides on steam days)
Special notes: Steam days as in Special Events list. Driver experience courses available on a number of dates throughout 2009;

please phone for details or book online at http://www.earm.co.uk
  Three restored signalboxes, large goods shed and restoration shed. Original Victorian country junction station. Schools days and Santa steamings. Disabled visitors welcome — prior advice appreciated. Guided tours by prior

arrangement. Light refreshments daily
Membership details: Membership Secretary, 50 Ayr Way, Rise Park, Romford, Essex RM1 4UH
Membership journal: *Stour Valley Steam* — 3 times/year

Timetable Service	East Kent Railway	Kent

Member: HRA
The East Kent Light Railway Society was formed in 1985 with the aim of preserving the remaining 2-mile section of the Colonel Stephens light railway which originally ran from Shepherdswell to Wingham. Passenger-carrying operations between Shepherdswell and Eythorne started during 1995, and 1996 saw the first steam on the line for over 30 years. The extension to Wigmore Lane opened in August 2005 and is used on some special events
Location: Station Road, Shepherdswell, Dover, Kent CT15 7PD
Internet address: *Web site:* www.eastkentrailway.co.uk
OS reference: TR 258483
Operating organisation: East Kent Railway Trust
Car park: Shepherdswell and Eythorne stations
Access by public transport: Main line trains to Shepherdswell station (adjacent) tel: 08457 484950
On site facilities: Shepherdswell — static buffet carriage, visitor centre, 5in miniature railway, model railway carriage (3 gauges), souvenir shop, Picnic area and toilets.
Eythorne —Signalbox, shop and toilets
Length of line: 4 miles
Public opening: Most weekends throughout the year for static displays. Passenger trains — Easter to September Sundays and Bank Holidays. Also Saturdays 2 May; 13 June; 1, 8, 15, 22, 29 August; 19 September; 30 October and 5, 12, 19 December.
First trains depart Shepherdswell at 11.00 on special event days, 11.30

Locomotives and multiple-units

Name	No	Origin	Class	Type	Built
—	09025	BR	09	0-6-0DE	1961
—	50256	M/Cam	101	DMBS	1957
—	56343	M/Cam	101	DTC(L)	1958
—	65373*	BR	2EPB/416	DMBS	1956
—	77558*	BR	2EPB/416	DTS	1956
—	68001	BR	MLV/419	MLV	1959
—	68002	BR	MLV/419	MLV	1959
—	61229†	BR	412/CEP	DMSO(A)	1958
—	61230†	BR	412/CEP	DMSO(A)	1958
—	69013†	BR	412/BEP	TSRB	1958
—	70235†	BR	412/CEP	TBCK	1958
—	60154§	BR	205	DMBS	1957
—	60800§	BR	205	DTCL	1957
—	68008†	BR	MLV / 419	DMVL	1961
—	10096	SR	4COR	TTK	1938
—	11161	SR	4COR	MBT	1937
—	11825	SR	4COR	TCK	1937

§unit No 1101
*unit No 5759
†unit No 7105

Industrial locomotives

Name	No	Builder	Type	Built
Richborough Castle	—	E/Electric (D1197)	0-6-0D	1967
The Buffs	—	R/Hornsby (466616)	0-6-0DH	1961
Snowdon	—	Fowler (416002)	0-4-0DM	1952
St Dunstan	—	Avonside (2004)	0-6-0ST	1927

Rolling stock
Leyland Experimental coach, LMS brake third, LMS full brake (BG), BR Mk 1 TSO, BR Mk 2 TSO and a selection of freight vehicles including an SR GUV

Owners
St Dunstan and diesel multiple-units the East Kent Railway Trust
LMS brake third the Walmer Model Railway Group
Leyland Experimental Coach the Nene Valley Railway
EMU vehicles the EPB Preservation Group
4COR vehicles the Southern Electric Group

on other dates
Special events: Easter Bunny Specials — 10-13 April; Model Engineering Weekend — 25/26

April; Teddies' Picnic — 23-25 May; Heritage Bus Rally — 7 June; Military Weekend/Kent Coast Electrification — 13/14 June;

England

Vintage Vehicle Rally — 19 July; Summer Teddies' Picnic — 8/9 August; Beer Festival — 29-31 August; EMU Days — 19/20 September; Halloween — 31 October/1 November; ; Santa by Train — 5/6, 12/13, 19/20, 23/24

December (Santa hotline: 01634 856228)
Facilities for disabled: Disabled access to buffet at Shepherdswell, ramp to platforms at Eythorne, disabled toilets at Eythorne
Membership details: EKR

Membership Secretary, Shepherdswell Station, Dover, Kent CT15 7PD
Membership journal: *East Kent Railway News,* 3 times a year

Member: HRA, TT

A very popular railway run by the East Lancs Railway Society in close co-operation with local authorities, the line won the 1987 ARPS award. Visit the line to find out the cause of the line's popularity and success

Location: Bolton Street Station, Bury, Lancashire BL9 0EY

OS reference: SD 803109

Publicity Director: Graham Vevers

Operating society/organisation: East Lancashire Railway Preservation Society

Telephone: (0161) 764 7790

Internet address: *Web site:* www.east-lancs-rly.co.uk

Access by public transport: Main line services to Manchester, Bolton, Rochdale and Burnley. Metrolink from central Manchester to Bury Interchange. Various bus services also operate to Bury, Ramsbottom or Rawtenstall from the main line stations listed

On site facilities: Refreshments normally available when trains are running. Buffet car service on most trains. Souvenir shop, transport museum

Length of line: Approximately 12 miles

Public opening: Steam- and diesel-hauled services operate on Saturdays, Sundays and Bank Holidays throughout the year. Midweek services 8/9, 15-17 April; Wednesdays to Fridays 6 May to 11 September, Santa Specials (advance booking only) in December

Special events: Diesel Event and Night Rider — 14/15 March; Black 5 Event — 4/5 April; Classic Motor Bike Rally — 12 April; Family Event Day — 2-4 May; 1940s War Weekend —

Locomotives and multiple-units

Name	No	Origin	Class	Type	Built
—	3855	GWR	2884	2-8-0	1942
—	7229	GWR	7200	2-8-2T	1935
—	52322	L&Y	27	0-6-0	1896
—	42765	LMS	5P4F	2-6-0	1927
—	44871	LMS	5MT	4-6-0	1945
—	45231	LMS	5MT	4-6-0	1937
—	45337	LMS	5MT	4-6-0	1937
The Lancashire Fusilier	45407	LMS	5MT	4-6-0	1937
Leander	5690	LMS	'Jubilee'	4-6-0	1936
—	46428	LMS	2MT	2-6-0	1948
—	47324	LMS	3F	0-6-0T	1926
249 Squadron	34073	SR	BB	4-6-2	1948
Shaw Savill	35009	SR	MN	4-6-2	1945
Duke of Gloucester	71000	BR	8P	4-6-2	1954
—	76079	BR	4MT	2-6-0	1957
—	80097	BR	4MT	2-6-4T	1954
—	11506	BR	01	0-4-0DM	1956
—	D2062	BR	03	0-6-0DM	1959
—	D3232	BR	08	0-6-0DE	1956
—	08479	BR	08	0-6-0DE	1958
—	08944	BR	08	0-6-0DE	1962
—	D9531	BR	14	0-6-0DH	1965
—	D8233	BR	15	Bo-Bo	1959
—	20087	BR	20	Bo-Bo	1961
—	D5054	BR	24	Bo-Bo	1960
—	D5705	BR	28	Co-Bo	1958
—	31556	BR	31	A1A-A1A	1961
—	D7076	BR	35	B-B	1963
—	33109	BR	33	Bo-Bo	1960
—	33117	BR	33	Bo-Bo	1960
—	37109	BR	37	Co-Co	1963
—	37901	BR	37	Co-Co	1963
—	D335	BR	40	1Co-Co1	1961
—	D345	BR	40	1Co-Co1	1961
Onslaught	D832	BR	42	B-B	1961
3rd Carabinier	45135	BR	45	1Co-Co1	1961
Gateshead	47402	BR	47	Co-Co	1962
Valiant	50015	BR	50	Co-Co	1967
Western Prince	D1041	BR	52	C-C	1962
Royal Scots Grey	55022	BR	55	Co-Co	1961
—	51192	M/Cam	101	DMBS	1958
—	56352	M/Cam	101	DTC (L)	1959
—	51485	Cravens	105	DMBC	1958
—	56121	Cravens	105	DTC	1956
—	50627	BR	108	DMBS	1958
—	55001	BR	122	DMBS	1958

23-25 May; Morris Minor Day —
14 June; Diesel Event — 1-5 July;
Manchester Classic Ford Cars
Group — 12 July; Family Event
Day — 1/2 August; Teddy Bears'
Picnic — 31 August; Vintage
Transport Gathering —
13 September; 1940s War Weekend
— 26/27 September; Family Event
Day — 3/4 October; Diesel Event
— 17/18 October; Steam Event —
24/25 October; Halloween Night
Trains — 31 October; Diesel
Theme Day — 7 November; Santa
Specials — 28/29 November and
5/6, 12/13, 19/20, 23/4 December;
Mince Pie Specials —
26 December; Whisky Chasers —
1 January 2010.
Irwell Valley Diner, Wine & Dine
Trains (advance booking only —
please apply for details)
Special notes: The Society re-
opened the Bury-Summerseat-
Ramsbottom section in 1987 and
the Ramsbottom-Irwell-Rawtenstall
section in 1991 with the Bury-
Heywood section following in
September 2003
Membership details: D. Layland
Membership journal: *The East
Lancashire Railway News* — twice
yearly
Marketing name: East Lancs

Name	No	Origin	Class	Type	Built
—	60130†	BR	207	DMBS	1962
—	60904†	BR	207	DTS	1962
—	65451	BR	504	DMBS	1958
—	70549	BR	207	TS	1958
—	77172	BR	504	DTS	1958

†unit 207202

Industrial locomotives

Name	No	Builder	Type	Built
Gothenburg	32	H/Clarke (680)	0-6-0T	1903
—	1	Barclay (1927)	0-4-0ST	1927
MR Mercury	1	Hibberd (3438)	4wDM	1950
Winfield	—	M/Rail (9009)	4wDM	1948
—	4002	H/Clarke (D1076)	6wDM	1959

Stock
44 BR Mk 1 coaches; 11 BR Mk 2 coaches, 1 GWR coach; 1 Bogie guard's
coach; Cravens 50-ton steam crane RS1013/50 (1930), NER 5-ton hand
crane DB915390 (1880) and Smiths 5-ton diesel crane (1939) plus over 80
goods vehicles

Owners
D335 and D345 the Class 40 Preservation Society
45135 and D5705 the Pioneer Diesel Group
65451 and 77172 the Class 504 Group
35009, 45407 and 76079 Riley & Sons (Railways)
D5054 the East Lancs Type 2 Group
47402 the Waterman Heritage Trust
50015 the Manchester Class 50 Group
Class 101 on loan from the National Railway Museum
D8233 the Class 15 Preservation Society
D5705 the Co-Bo Locomotive Group
55022 Martin Walker
31556 the Harry Needle Railroad Co

Timetable Service	East Somerset Railway	Somerset

Member: HRA
The ESR was created by David
Shepherd and his friends in the
early 1970s. Cranmore is still one
of the few preserved railways
offering only steam-hauled trains.
The railway seeks to portray a
country branch line, and offers a
warm and personal welcome to all
visitors who want to experience the
sights and sounds of the steam era
Contact: Booking Office
Headquarters: East Somerset
Railway, Cranmore, Shepton
Mallet, Somerset BA4 4QP
OS reference: ST 664429
Telephone: Cranmore (01749)
880417

Locomotives

Name	No	Origin	Class	Type	Built
—	5637	GWR	5600	0-6-2T	1924
—*	B110	LBSCR	E1	0-6-0T	1877
—	30075	JZ	USA	0-6-0T	1950s

Industrial locomotives

Name	No	Builder	Type	Built
Lord Fisher	1398	Barclay (1398)	0-4-0ST	1915
—	705	Barclay (2047)	0-4-0ST	1937
Lady Nan*	1719	Barclay (1719)	0-4-0ST	1920
Cattewater	—	Sentinel (10199)	4wDH	1964
—	39	Sentinel (10204)	0-4-0DH	1965

*undergoing overhaul

Stock
Numerous ex-BR Mk 1 coaches; 25 assorted wagons, mostly LMS and SR

England

Fax: (01749) 880764
Internet address: *e-mail:*
info@eastsomersetrailway.com
Web site:
www.eastsomersetrailway.com
Main station: Cranmore
Car park: Cranmore — free
Refreshment facilities: The
Whistlestop Restaurant at
Cranmore offers lunches, snacks,
teas, etc. Group catering by
arrangement. Picnic areas at
Cranmore. Public and private Wine
& Dine trains
Souvenir shop: Cranmore
On site facilities: Station shop.
David Shepherd Gallery with
railway and wildlife prints for sale.
Children's play area. Engine shed
and workshops open for viewing.
Small railway museum
Depot: Engine shed and workshop
at Cranmore West (0.25-mile from
Cranmore)
Length of line: 2 miles

Owners
5637 the 5637 Loco Group
30075 the Project 62 Group
D3032 on loan from Foster Yeoman
Sentinel (10204) Stratford Railway Society

Passenger trains: Cranmore to
Mendip Vale via Cranmore West
and Merryfield Lane. Return trip
takes c35min. Ticket allows
unlimited travel on normal
operating days. All trains are steam-
hauled
Period of public operation:
Sundays in March; weekends and
Bank Holidays in April and May;
Wednesdays and weekends in June
and July; Wednesdays, Thursdays
and weekends in August; weekends
in September and October;
Sundays, plus 22nd, in November.
Please call for details and train
times. Last admission 30min before
closing time

Special events: Please contact for
detailsBooking required for all
Wine & Dine trains and Santa
Specials
Facilities for disabled: All public
areas and trains are accessible
Special Notes: Footplate
experience courses available, both
half day and full day. Please call for
availability, prices and brochure.
School groups, children's parties,
private parties and Wine & Dine by
arrangement — please call to
discuss your requirements
Membership details: Please call
for leaflet
Membership journal: *Cuttings* —
four per year

Miniature Railway	Eastleigh Lakeside Steam Railway	Hampshire

Location: Lakeside Country Park,
Eastleigh
Headquarters: Eastleigh Lakeside
Steam Railway, Lakeside Country
Park, Wide Lane, Eastleigh, Hants
SO50 5PE
Contact: Clive Upton
Telephone: 023 8061 2020
Internet address: *e-mail:*
elr@steamtrain.co.uk
Web site: www.steamtrain.co.uk
Car parking: On site
On site facilities: Lakeside café
open all school holidays and every
weekend
Length of line: 1.25 mile, 7.25in
and 10.25in gauges
Period of public operation:
Every weekend, daily July, August
and September and all school
holidays
Special events:
Spring Gala — 22 March; Visiting
Locomotives — 2-4 May; Day out
with Underground Ernie —
23-31 May; Double-headed
Weekends — 13/14 June; Steam
Gala — 12 July;
Day out with Underground Ernie —
5/6 September; Big Four Weekend
(GWR, LMS, LNER, SR) —

Locomotives (10.25/7.25in gauge)

Name	No	Builder	Type	Built
Sandy River	7		2-4-2	1982
			rebuilt ELR	2008
The Monarch	1001	Bullock	4-6-2	1932
The Empress	1002	Bullock	4-6-2	1933
Edward VIII	2006	Bullock	4-6-2	1936
Coronation	6200	Dove	4-6-2	1946
Rob Roy	70055	Pullen	4-6-2	1948
Sir Nigel Gresley	4498	Kirkland	4-6-2	1964
Sir Arthur Heywood	7	Williamson	2-6-2*	1990
Ernest Henry Upton	1908	G&S Engineering	4-4-2	1937
William Baker	4789	Baker	4-4-2*	1947
Royal Scot	6100	Carling	4-6-0	late 1940s
Francis Henry Lloyd	3	Guest	4-8-4*	1959
Taw	—	Horsfield	2-6-2T	1999
Florence	92	ELR	0-6-0DH	1999
Saint-Leonard	1A	Marshall	0-4-0-0-4-0*	2001
Lord Nelson	850	Moody	4-6-0	2007
Ernie	1	—	B-B	rebuilt 2008
Jubilee	—	ELR	Bo-Bo	rebuilt 2008
Sanjo	—	Battle	0-4-0*	
Sgt Murphy	—	Marshall	0-6-0T*	
David Curwen	—	Curwen	2-6-0	

*7.25in gauge, remainder 10.25in

19/20 September; Diesel Gala —
3/4 October; Day out with
Underground Ernie — 31 October/
1 November; Santa Specials —

12/13, 19/20, 23 December; Day
out with Underground Ernie —
26 December-3 January 2010
Facilities for disabled: Toilet,

wheelchair access to platform
Fare: Single: £1.50 (all ages)
Return: Adults — £2.50; Children
— £2.00.
Children under 2 travel free

Steam Centre | Ecclesbourne Valley Railway | Derbyshire

Member: HRA

Pasenger services commenced on the Ecclesbourne Valley Railway on 24 August 2004. The initial length was just half-a-mile between Wirksworth and Gorsey Bank level crossing, but the plan is to reach Duffield with a main line connection in a few years. The track is in situ but requires work to bring it up to operational standard. Meanwhile the section from Wirksworth to Ravenstor, a further half-mile, opened on 1 September 2005. This incorporates a grade of 1 in 30 and provides access to the High Peak Trail. The Wirksworth to Idridgehay section (3.5 miles) opened in March 2008 leaving a further five miles to be restored before reaching Duffield

General Manager:
Martin S. Miller

Headquarters: Wirksworth Station, Coldwell Street, Wirksworth, Derbyshire DE4 4FB

Telephone: 01629 823076

Fax: 01629 825922

Internet adresses: *e-mail:*
station@wyvernrail.co.uk
Web sites: www.wyvernrail.co.uk
www.evra.org.uk and
www.mytesttrack.com

Main station: Wirksworth

Other stations: Ravenstor, Idridgehay, Shottle (opening 2012), Duffield (opening 2010)

OS references:
Wirksworth (SK 290541),
Ravenstor (SK 287548),
Gorsey Bank (SK 288533),
Idridgehay (SK 290489),
Shottle (SK 304469),
Hazelwood (SK 319449),
Duffield (North) (SK 337439)

Car parking: Wirksworth station, there is no car parking available at Ravenstor or Idridgehay

Locomotive and multiple-units

Name	No	Origin	Class	Type	Built
—	D2084	BR	03	0-6-0DM	1959
Margaret-Ann	D2158	BR	03	0-6-0DM	1960
—	20001	BR	20	Bo-Bo	1957
—	31414	BR	31	A1A-A1A	1961
—	51073	Gloucester	119	DMBC	1958
—	51188	Met/Cam	101	DMBS	1958
—	51360	P/Steel	117	DMBS	1959
—	51505	Met/Cam	101	DMCL	1958
—	54289	P/Steel	121	DTS	1959
—	56224	BR	108	DTC(L)	1959
—	55006	Gloucester	122	DMBS	1958
—	68500*	BR	489	GLV	1959
—	68506*	BR	489	GLV	1959
—	72501*	BR	491	FO	1973
—	72617*	BR	491	TS	1973

*former Gatwick Express hauled-stock

Industrial locomotives

Name	No	Builder	Type	Built
Henry Ellison	—	Barclay (2217)	0-4-0ST	1947
Wee Yorkie	3	Barclay (2360)	0-4-0ST	1954
Cathryn	—	H/Clarke	0-6-0ST	1955
—	11520	R/Hornsby (319284)	0-4-0DM	1952
Sir Peter & Lady Hilton	—	R/Hornsby (402803)	0-4-0DE	1956
—	—	R/Hornsby (421037)	0-6-0DE	1958

Stock

1 BR Newspaper van (used as DMU support vehicle); 1 Taylor Hubbard crane and runner wagon. Around 25 wagons for use in maintaining the line, including examples of Grampus and Dogfish hopper wagons, plus 3 Road/Rail vehicles. 2 Ultra Light Rail vehicles

Owner

DMUs by Railcar Enterprises

Access by public transport:
Bus – to Wirksworth and Idridgehay, Derby/Belper/Idridgehay/Wirksworth/Matlock/Bakewell

Location of refreshment facilities:
Wirksworth station

Souvenir shops & museum:
Wirksworth station

Length of line: 4.5 miles

Opening times: Wirksworth station – daily (except Xmas day) 10.00-16.00

Public operation: Weekends March to October and Tuesdays during local school holidays. Additional services at Bank Holidays and Special Events

58

England

Facilities for the disabled:
Specially equipped toilets and fully accessible Museum Coach
Special facilities: Up to 40 covers for meals in the splendid, air-conditioned, former 'Gatwick Express' coaches. Trains can be run at anytime for the equivalent of 10 full adult fares. Day with a Driver and Diesel Driving Experiences available.
Membership details: Ecclesbourne Valley Railway Association, 530 Kedleston Road, Derby DE22 2NG
Membership Journal:
Ecclesbourne Express – quarterly

Railway Centre — Eden Valley Railway — Cumbria

Member: HRA

The Eden Valley Railway between Appleby and Warcop in Cumbria is carrying passengers again. The EVR has plans to reopen all of the 6-mile railway which still connects with the famous Settle and Carlisle line at Appleby.

Please contact or see web site for further details

Headquarters:
Eden Valley Railway Co and Eden Valley Railway Trust, 1 Victoria Road, Barnard Castle, Co Durham DL12 8HW
Internet address:
e-mail: admin@evr.org.uk
Web site: www.evr.org.uk
Secretary: —
Main station: Appleby
OS reference: NY 687208
Car park: Appleby
Access by public transport:
By bus: Stagecoach services from Penrith to Brough (stops at Warcop station (0870 6082608 for details); Carlisle to Eden Valley services (0870 6082608); K. & B. Bainbridge services from Penrith to Appleby (01768 865446).
By rail: Appleby on the Settle-Carlisle line.
By road: M6 jct 40, A66 east to Warcop (18 miles); M6 jct 38, A685, B6260 to Appleby (10 miles); A1 Scotch Corner, A66 west to Warcop (40 miles).

Locomotives and multiple-units

Name	No	Origin	Class	Type	Built
—	37250	BR	37	Co-Co	1964
—	60108†	BR	205	DMBS	1957
—	60658†	BR	205	DMBS	1957
—	60808†	BR	205	DTC	1957
—	61798	BR	412	DMSO	1956
—	61799	BR	412	DMSO	1956
—	61804	BR	412	DMSO	1956
—	61805	BR	412	DMSO	1956
—	68003	BR	419	MLV	1960
—	68005	BR	419	MLV	1960
—	70229	BR	412	TSOL	1956
—	70539	BR	412	TSOL	1956
—	70354	BR	412	TBCK	1956
—	70607	BR	412	TBCK	1956

†unit 205009

Industrial locomotives

Name	No	Builder	Type	Built
—	21	Fowler (4220045)	0-4-0DH	1967
Darlington	1	RSH	0-6-0DH	1965

Stock

3 ex-BR Mk 1 coaches; 4 passenger-rated BR Mk 1 vans; 1 rail-mounted 25-ton diesel crane (DRT81343); selection of wagons for maintenance work including a snowplough and Wickham Trolley and trailer

Refreshment facilities: Light refreshments available on open weekends, picnic area
Membership details: Membership Secretary, 41 Firshill Walk, Firshill, Sheffield S4 7BR
Membership journal: *Eden Valley Railway Magazine* — 4 times/year

Special note: Please do not confuse the Warcop site with the Appleby Training & Heritage Centre adjacent to the main line station. The EVR has no connection with the Kirkby Stephen East site

Member: HRA

The Elsecar Railway runs between Elsecar Heritage Centre and the canal basin at Hemingfield, through a scenic conservation area alongside the Elsecar branch of the Dearne & Dove Canal

Location/headquarters: Elsecar Heritage Centre, Wath Road, Elsecar, Barnsley, South Yorkshire S74 8HJ

Telephone: (01226) 746746

Internet address: *Web site:* www.elsecarrailway.cjb.net

Main station: Elsecar

Length of line: 1-mile, 20min journey

Car park location: On site, free

Access by public transport: Main rail line Elsecar from Sheffield, Huddersfield, Leeds

Refreshment facilities: On site

Souvenir shops: On site

On site facilities: Refreshments, antiques centres, crafts and souvenir shop, toilets

Museum: Attractions include Educational Workshops, 'Playmania', Living History Centre, Bottle Collection, Hot Metal Press, Newcomen Beam Engine, working crafts people, various special events. Antiques centre open 7 days a week

Facilities for disabled: There are

Locomotives

Name	No	Origin	Class	Type	Built
—	D9524	BR	14	0-6-0DH	1964

Industrial locomotives

Name	No	Builder	Type	Built
Countess Fitzwilliam	544996	R/Hornsby (382808)	4wDM	1968
Earl Fitzwilliam	1917	Avonside (1917)	0-6-0ST	1923
—	1	Avonside (1945)	0-6-0ST	1926
Gervase	—	Sentinel (6807)	0-4-0VBT	1928
William	—	Sentinel (9656)	4wVBT	1956
Earl of Strafford	2895	YEC (2895)	0-6-0DH	1963
Mardy Monster	2150	Peckett (2150)	0-6-0ST	1954
—	10432	Drewry	0-4-0DH	1955
Louise	—	Hunslet (6950)	0-6-0DH	1967
—	—	V/Foundry	0-4-0DM	1945
—	—	NBL (27097	0-4-0DM	1953

Stock

4 ex-BR Mk 1 coaches, 1 Wickham trolley

four disabled persons' toilets at different locations on the site. All buildings are fully wheelchair accessible at ground floor level

Public opening: Site open daily 10.00-17.00. The railway operates a public service on Sundays 12.00-16.00 all year, also Halloween and Christmas events, special event days and Bank Holidays

Special events: Include Thomas the Tank Engine, Vintage Weekend, Noddy Family Fun Event, 1940s Weekend (and Saturday evening wartime dance) Christmas Fair, Halloween Hauntings and Santa Specials on the railway

Special notes: Free admission to site except for some special events when a charge will be made. Charges apply to railway and special events

---

Member: HRA, TT

Yorkshire's 'Friendly Line' operates from Embsay station built in 1888. The railway is very family-orientated with many events for children. The enthusiast is not forgotten, with one of the finest collections of ex-industrial tank engines in Britain. The railway is currently constructing a new museum and workshop complex, and the line's extension to Bolton Abbey opened in 1997. Bolton Abbey station has been built to the original Midland Railway style. An

Locomotives and multiple-units

Name	No	Origin	Class	Type	Built
—	D2203	BR	04	0-6-0DM	1952
—	08054	BR	08	0-6-0DE	1953
—	08700	BR	08	0-6-0DE	1960
—	08773	BR	08	0-6-0DE	1960
—	NCB 38 (D9513)	BR	14	0-6-0DH	1964
—	D5600	BR	31	A1A-A1A	1960
—	31119	BR	31	A1A-A1A	1959
—	D5600	BR	31	A1A-A1A	1960
—	47004	BR	47	Co-Co	1963

Industrial locomotives

Name	No	Builder	Type	Built
Annie	9	Peckett (1159)	0-4-0ST	1908

England

atmosphere of the rural branch line prevails, which is operated by ex-industrial locomotives

Operating Committee: N. Hobbs

Business & Marketing Manager: Stephen Walker. Tel: 01756 710614 (ext 3). Fax: 01756 710720

Internet address: *Web site:* www.embsayboltonabbeyrailway. org.uk

Location: Bolton Abbey Station, Bolton Abbey, Skipton, Yorkshire BD23 6AF

OS reference: SE 007533

Operating society/organisation: Yorkshire Dales Railway Museum Trust

Telephone: 01756 710614, 24hr Talking Timetable 01756 795189

Car parks: Embsay and Bolton Abbey

Access by public transport: Pennine bus from Skipton, National Park bus from Ilkley

On site facilities: Souvenir shop at Bolton Abbey and Embsay — transport and industrial archaeological bookshop at Embsay

Catering facilities: Buffet and bar on most trains. Buffet at both Bolton Abbey and Embsay stations. Special charters can be arranged, meals for parties can be arranged on normal service trains, subject to advance booking, please write for further details

Length of line: 4.5 miles

Public opening: Steam trains run every Sunday throughout the year, weekends from April to October, Tuesdays in May, June, early July, daily 18 July to end of August

Special events: Easter Day out with Thomas — 10-13 April; Spring Bank Holiday Day out with Thomas — 23-25 May; Diesel Gala — July (date to be confirmed); August Bank Holiday Day out with Thomas — 29-31 August; 1940s Weekend — 12/13 September; Steam Gala — 26/27 September (date to be confirmed); Car Rally — 4 October; Bus Rally — 11 October; Santa Trains — Sundays 22 November to 19 December, Saturdays 7 to 20 December; Mince Pie Specials — 26 December; New Year's Day Specials — 1 January 2010

Special notes: Steam rides are on

Name	No	Builder	Type	Built
Gladiator	8	H/Clarke (1450)	0-6-0ST	1922
Slough Estates No 5	—	H/Clarke (1709)	0-6-0ST	1939
Ann	—	Sentinel (7232)	4wVB	1927
Beatrice	7	Hunslet (2705)	0-6-0ST	1945
Airedale	3	Hunslet (1440)	0-6-0ST	1923
York No 1	—	Yorkshire (2474)	0-4-0ST	1949
Illingworth	—	H/Clarke (1208)	0-6-0ST	1916
—	140	H/Clarke (1821)	0-6-0T	1948
Spitfire	S112	Hunslet (2414)	0-6-0ST	1942
Wheldale	S134	Hunslet (3168)	0-6-0ST	1944
Sir Robert Peel	8	Hunslet (3776)	0-6-0ST	1952
—	69	Hunslet (3785)	0-6-0ST	1953
Monkton No 1	—	Hunslet (3788)	0-6-0ST	1953
—	22	Barclay (2320)	0-4-0ST	1952
—	68005	RSH (7169)	0-6-0ST	1945
Thomas	4	RSH (7661)	0-4-0ST	1950
H. W. Robinson	—	Fowler (4100003)	0-4-0DM	1946
—	—	Fowler (4200003)	0-4-0DM	1948
—	MDE15	B/Drewry (2136)	4wDM	1938
—	887	R/Hornsby (394009)	4wDM	1955
—	—	Wickham (7610)	2w-2PMR	1957
—	—	R/Hornsby	4wDM	1957
—	—	R/Hornsby (394009)	4wDM	1955
Meaford	—	Barclay (440)	0-4-0DH	1958
—	36	H/Clarke (D1037)	0-6-0DM	1958

The following are 2ft gauge

		Builder	Type	Built
—	—	Lister (9993)	4wPM	1938
—	—	Lister (10225)	4wPM	1938
—	—	R/Hornsby (175418)	4wDM	1936
—	—	R/Hornsby	4wDM	—
—	—	M/Rail (8979)	4wDM	1946
—	—	M/Rail (5213)	4wDM	1930
—	—	Simplex (60SD754)	4wDM	1980
—	—	Simplex (60SD755)	4wDM	1980

Stock
18 ex-BR Mk 1 coaches (SK, CK, 2xBCK, 5xTSO, 2xRMB, 1xBSO(T), 1xRBR and 1xSLS), 4 ex-LNER coaches; 2 SR parcels vans; Freight stock and service vehicles, SR and GW brakes
Stephen Middleton collection of vintage coaches

Owner
08773 the Newton Heath Group

Note
Items on display may vary

the 4.5-mile line to the new station and picnic area at Bolton Abbey. Old Midland Railway buildings, fine collection of industrial locomotives

Membership details: Membership Secretary at above address

Membership journal: *Dale Steam YDR News* — 4 times/year

Epping-Ongar Railway

Member: HRA

A preserved section at the northern end of the former London Underground Central Line. The line has been closed to the public for improvement works and should reopen in 2009. Please check web site for updates

Operating society/organisation: Epping Ongar Railway, Station House, High Street, Ongar, Essex CM5 9BN

Contact: Simon Hanney

Telephone: 01277 365200

Internet address: *Web site:* http://eorailway.co.uk

Main station: Ongar

Other station: North Weald

OS references: Ongar TL 551035; North Weald TL 496036

Access by public transport: Use London Underground Central Line to Epping, then local bus service to Ongar or North Weald. Local buses also available from Harlow and Brentwood

On site facilities: The Buffet Stop (Ongar) and The Passing Loop (North Weald) sell hot and cold drinks and snacks. In the summer months you may like to picnic on the lawn at Ongar

Locomotives

Name	No	Origin	Class	Type	Built
—	(1008)	Finnish*		4-6-2	1948
—	1060	Finnish*		2-8-2	1954
—	51342	P/Steel	117	DMS	1959
—	51384	P/Steel	117	DMS	1959
—	L11	LT	—	—	1964

*1,524mm gauge, on static display

Industrial locomotives

Name	No	Builder	Type	Built
—	—*	Ruston (398616)	4wDM	1956
—	—	Ruston (512572)	4wDM	1965
Heather	D1995	Drewry (2566)	4wDM	1955

*for spares only

Stock

2 Finnish Railway wooden-bodied carriages (1,524mm gauge). Brake van, well wagon, Dogfish ballast hopper and box van

Owner

L11 Cravens Heritage Trains

Length of line: 6 miles (4.5 miles operational)

Public opening: Please see web site for details

Special events: Please see web site

Facilities for disabled: Level access to platforms. Ramp available for wheelchair access to guard's compartment

Membership details: Epping Ongar Railway Volunteer Society, c/o above address

Membership journal: *Mixed Traffic* — quarterly

Evesham Vale Light Railway

Member: BGLR

The Evesham Vale Light Railway takes you through the old apple orchards to a picnic and viewing area overlooking some of the most picturesque scenery in the Vale of Evesham. Steam locomotives are used on most days and it is possible to break your journey and walk to the river, returning on a later train. The railway is situated within Evesham Country Park, 1 mile to the north of the historic town of Evesham. Enjoy a day out and stroll around the 130 acre estate, including a mile and quarter of the River Avon. Visit the Ark

Locomotives

Name	No	Builder	Type	Built
Prince William	5751*	G&S	4-6-2	1949
St Egwin	312	Exmoor Steam Rly	0-4-0T+T	2003
Dougal	3	Severn-Lamb	0-6-2T	1970
R. H. Morse	712	Morse	0-4-0	1950
John	103	Barnes	4-4-2	1921
Sludge	—	Lister (41545)	4wDM	1955
Cromwell	13R	Keef	4wDH	1984
—	359	Morse (82)	4-4-0PM	1939
Bessie	—	Eddy/Nowell	4wDM	2002

*off-site for overhaul

Note: Engines can be viewed, by prior arrangement, on days when the railway is operating. No access when the railway is closed

Animal Sanctuary, browse in the relaxed atmosphere of the courtyard shops or try some of the freshly prepared lunches and snacks in the licensed Apple Barn restaurant
Location/headquarters: Evesham Vale Light Railway, Evesham Country Park, Twyford, Nr Evesham, Worcestershire WR11 4TP
Contact: Jim Shackell
Telephone: 01386 422282
Internet address: *e-mail:* enquiries@evlr.co.uk
Web site: www.evlr.co.uk
Main station: Twyford (adjacent to Evesham Country Park car park)
Other station: Evesham Vale (in the country park)
OS reference: SP 0446
On site facilities: Large car and coach park, licensed restaurant within park shopping complex. Small souvenir shop at Twyford station
Length of line: 1.25 miles, 15in gauge
Locomotive and carriage depots: Adjacent to Twyford station — viewing available on request
Access by public transport: By train to Evesham main line station then bus — Stagecoach No 28 — from Evesham bus station, hourly service will stop close to park entrance, then 15min walk to Twyford station
Public opening: Every weekend throughout the year plus Bank Holidays and main school holidays Phone 24 hr information line 01386 422282 or visit web site (www.evlr.co.uk) to check dates and for special events. Trains run every half-hour from 10.30 to 17.00 (16.00 November to March)
Facilities for disabled: Wheelchair facilities on all trains
Special facilities: Birthday parties can be held in railway picnic area. Group visits can be arranged on days when railway is not operating normally. Discounts available for advance bookings of groups 20+

Steam Centre — Exbury Gardens Railway — Hampshire

Member: BGLR, HRA
A comparatively new line with purpose-built locomotives and rolling stock around part of Exbury Gardens. Train fare is in addition to entrance fee
Location/headquarters: Exbury Gardens, Exbury, Southampton SO45 1AZ
Contact: Ian Wilson (railway foreman). Tel: 023 8089 2898
Telephone: 023 8089 1203
Internet address: *Web site:* www.exbury.co.uk
Access by public transport: Main line trains to Brockenhurst. New Forest Explorer bus calls into Gardens between Whitsun Bank Holiday and early September. Visit: www.newforesttour.info
Car park: On site, free
On site facilities: Souvenir shop, with railway memorabilia (including prints and videos), refreshments and toilets adjacent to main car park
Length of line: 1.25 miles, 12.25in gauge
Public opening: 7 March to 8 November. Limited winter opening for Santa Steam Specials.

Industrial locomotives

Name	No	Builder	Type	Built
Rosemary	—	Exmoor (315)	0-6-2T	2001
Naomi	—	Exmoor (316)	0-6-2T	2002
Eddy	—	Exmoor	0-4-0DH	2001
Mariloo	—	Exmoor	2-6-0	2008

Stock
8 coaches

New for 2009: engine shed extension. Visitors to the railway will be able to enter the engine shed at the end of the ride to see Exbury's engines and railway memorabilia
Special events: Engine Shed Open Weekend — 7/8 March; Easter at Exbury — 11-13 April; Narrow Gauge in the Garden — 20/21 June; Woodland Adventures — 1/2 August; Steam in the Gardens — 3/4 October; Exbury Ghost Train — 26 October to 1 November; Exbury Santa Steam Specials — 5/6, 12/13, 19-21 December
Facilities for disabled: Yes, access to 4 coaches
Tickets:
£3.50 per person, Rover Ticket (unlimited rides) £4.50 per person outside of peak season.
Garden tickets, adults £8, seniors/concessions £7.50, children (3-15) £1.50. Family ticket (2+3) £18.50
Season tickets are available for access to gardens only or gardens plus railway. Discounts are available to season ticket holders
Special facilities:
Engine shed licensed for civil weddings and partnerships and for private hire.
Railway available for private charter (£4 per person, or a minimum 'steam-up' fee of £100).
Footplate Experience days available — 1:1 course, 8 trips, covering a distance of 10 miles

Foxfield Steam Railway

Member: HRA

The railway was built in 1893 to carry coal from Foxfield Colliery to the North Staffordshire Railway at Blythe Bridge. Following closure of the colliery in 1965 the line was rescued for preservation. The Society is working towards rebuilding the railway a further 0.75 mile down the famous Foxfield Bank to the site of Foxfield Colliery as part of a half million pound lottery grant

Chairman: D. Scragg

Headquarters: Foxfield Steam Railway, Blythe Bridge, Stoke-on-Trent

Postal address: P. O. Box 1967, Stoke-on-Trent ST4 8YT

Telephone: (01782) 396210 or (01782) 259667

Fax: (01782) 396210

Internet address: *Web site:* www.foxfieldrailway.co.uk

Main station: Blythe Bridge (Caverswall Road)

OS reference: SJ 957421

Car park: Blythe Bridge

Access by public transport: Main line railway Blythe Bridge (400yd). PMT bus service to Blythe Bridge

Refreshment facilities: Buffet and real ale bar at Blythe Bridge

Souvenir shop: Blythe Bridge

Passenger trains: Steam-hauled trains operate from Blythe Bridge (Caverswall Road) to Dilhorne Park and return

Family ticket: Available (2 adults + 2 children or 1 adult + 4 children)

Length of line: 3.5 miles. Current operation over 2.5 miles of line

Period of public operation: Steam trains operate Sundays and Bank Holiday Mondays Easter-end October inclusive, also Wednesdays in July and August. Trains run between Blythe Bridge and Dilhorne Park.

Special events: Friendlt Engibes — 2-4 May; Foxfield Bank Opening Weekend — 23-25 May; Diesel Gala — 13/14 June; Morris Minor Rally — 14 June; 1940s Weekend — 4/5 July; Steam Gala — 18/19 July; Victorian Fete — 29-31 August; MG Club — 6 September; East European Car Rally — 12/13 September; Traction Engine Steam Party — 27 September; Halloween Sceem — 30/31 October; Santa Specials — December (pre-booked events)

Facilities for disabled: Access to majority of Caverswall Road station is on the level; disabled toilets. Advance notice essential for those wishing to travel on the train. Induction loop

Membership journal: *Foxfield News* — quarterly

Industrial locomotives

Name	No	Builder	Type	Built
Bellerophon*	—	Haydock Foundry (C)	0-6-0WT	1874
—	1827	B/Peacock (1827)	0-4-0ST	1879
—	6	R/Heath	0-4-0ST	1886
—	4101	Dübs (4101)	0-4-0CT	1901†
Henry Cort	—	Peckett (933)	0-4-0ST	1903††
Millom	—	Avonside (1563)	0-4-0ST	1908†
Moss Bay	—	K/Stuart (4167)	0-4-0ST	1920††
Cranford	—	Avonside (1919)	0-6-0ST	1924†
Helen	—	Simplex (2262)	4wDM	1924
Marston No 3	—	H/Leslie (3581)	0-6-0ST	1924†
—	—	K/Stuart (4388)	0-4-0ST	1926•
Lewisham	—	Bagnall (2221)	0-6-0ST	1927
Rom River	—	K/Stuart (4421)	6wDM	1929
Boots No 1	—	Barclay (1984)	0-4-0F	1930††
Ironbridge No 1	—	Peckett (1803)	0-4-0ST	1933††
Spondon No 2	—	E/Electric (1130)	4wBE	1939††
Roker	—	RSH (7006)	0-4-0CT	1940††
Hawarden	—	Bagnall (2623)	0-4-0ST	1940
—	WD820	B/Drewry (2157)	0-4-0DM	1942
(Hercules)	242915	R/Hornsby (242915)	4wDM	1946
—	11	Peckett (2081)	0-4-0ST	1947•
Whiston	—	Hunslet (3694)	0-6-0ST	1950
—	9535	Sentinel (9535)	4wVBGT	1952•
Florence No 2	—	Bagnall (3059)	0-6-0ST	1953†
Meaford No 2	—	RSH (7684)	0-6-0T	1951
—	—	Hibberd (3716)	4wDM	1955
Wimblebury	—	Hunslet (3839)	0-6-0ST	1956
(Gas-oil)	88DS	R/Hornsby (408496)	4wDM	1957†
Wolstanton No 3	—	Bagnall (3150)	0-6-0DM	1960
B. R. C. (Megan)	—	Thomas Hill (103C)	0-4-0DH	1957
Rachel	—	R/Hornsby (423637)	0-4-0DE	1958
(Roman)	165DS	R/Hornsby (424841)	0-4-0DE	1960
Ludstone	—	YEC (3207)	0-4-0DH	1961
Leys	—	Bagnall (2868)	0-6-0DE	1962
Meaford No 4	—	Barclay (486)	0-6-0DH	1964

†under overhaul
††static exhibit
•awaiting overhaul
*on loan for ten years

Stock

3 ex-BR Mk 1 CK coaches; 1 ex-BR Mk 2a TSO coach; 4 other coaches; 3 scenery vans (converted for other uses); 79 assorted wagons, 16-ton mineral wagons; 1 rail-mounted self-propelled diesel-electric crane

Owner

Bellerophon the Vintage Carriages Trust

Gartell Light Railway

Owned and operated by three generations of the Gartell family, the Gartell Light Railway offers visitors the chance to travel by train along the route of the old Somerset & Dorset Joint Railway. A half-mile section of the line from Pinesway Junction to Park Lane runs along the old S&D trackbed, while work has started on an extension northwards from Pinesway Junction along the S&D formation towards Templecombe. A flyover has been constructed to carry the extension over the existing line to the terminus at Common Lane and tracklaying has begun. On most open days a three train service is operated, with departures every 15min and trains crossing at Pinesway Junction. The GLR is fully signalled using a variety of upper and lower quadrant, colour light and shunt signals controlled by two full size signalboxes. The GLR's first steam locomotive, a locally built 0-4-2T, specially designed to cope with the steep gradients and sharp curves of the section from Common Lane up to Pinesway Junction, entered service in 1998. The line's newest locomotive, an 0-4-0 tender tank engine, again built specially for the line, will enter service at the beginning of the 2009 season

Location/headquarters: Gartell Light Railway, Common Lane, Yenston, Nr Templecombe, Somerset BA8 0NB
Telephone: 01963 370752
Internet address: *Web site:*

Industrial locomotives
2ft gauge:

Name	No	Builder	Type	Built
Amanda	1	GLR	Bo-BoDH	2003
Andrew	2	Baguley-Drewry	4wDH	1973
Alison	5	A/Keef (10)	4wDH	1983
Mr G	6	N. Dorset Loco Wks	0-4-2T	1998
Jean	9	N. Dorset Loco Wks	0-4-0T+T	2008

Rolling stock — coaches: 9 fully enclosed bogie coaches

Rolling stock — wagons: goods guard's van, tool van, beer van, milk tanker, open wagon, bogie PW gang/tool van, bogie hopper, bogie open, bogie well, bogie flat and bogie crane

http://www.glr-online.co.uk
General Manager: John Gartell
Main station: Common Lane
Other stations: Pinesway Junction, Park Lane
Car park: Large free car park at Common Lane
OS reference: ST 718218
Access by public transport: 1.5 miles south-east of Templecombe railway station
Refreshment facilities: Refreshment room at Common Lane serving a range of hot and cold snacks and drinks. Lakeside picnic area at Pinesway Junction
Visitor centre: Common Lane
Souvenir shop: Common Lane
Depot: Common Lane (not open to public)
Length of line: 0.75-mile
Facilities for disabled: Two of the three trains in service have accommodation for a disabled visitor in a wheelchair
Special facilities: Clean, well-maintained independent caravan site with running water close to the railway.
The Pines function suite available for outside hire, with entertainment licence, licensed bar and seating for 200; ideal for weddings, anniversaries, classic car and motorcycle rallies, children's parties etc. Train rides can be arranged
Period of public operation: 13 April; 4, 25 May; 28 June; 25/26 July; 2, 9, 16, 23, 30/31 August; 27 September, 25 October. 10.30-16.30
Special events: Steam & Vintage Show (vintage lorries, classic cars and motorcycles, miniatuer traction engines, live steam model railways etc) — 25/26 July; Santa Specials (must be pre-booked) — 12/13 December; Model railway exhibition with hourly train service — 13/14 February 2010

Gloucestershire Warwickshire Railway

Member: HRA
Part of an ambitious project to link Cheltenham with Stratford, much has been done to re-create the railway and buildings that made up this cross-country route. The railway is home to many owners of private locomotives and rolling stock, so from time to time the items on display may vary. The extension to Gotherington to Cheltenham Racecourse opened in April 2003.

2006 saw the centenary of the opening of the line and the 25th anniversary of the GWR Ltd

Location: Toddington station, Toddington
OS reference: SO 050322
Operating society/organisation: Gloucestershire Warwickshire Steam Railway plc, The Station, Toddington, Cheltenham, Glos GL54 5DT

Telephone: Toddington (01242) 621405

Internet address:

e-mail: enquiries@gwsr.com

Web site: www.gwsr.com

Main station: Toddington

Other public stations: Winchcombe, Cheltenham Racecourse, Gotherington (request halt, off-peak only)

Access by public transport: Hourly service from Cheltenham to Greet for Winchcombe station. Local bus service Castleways will answer timetable queries on (01242) 602949. Regular Stagecoach service to Cheltenham station. Racecourse Park & Ride (approx half mile to GWR station)

Car park: All stations

On site facilities: Sales, catering, narrow gauge rides, toilets, new children's play area

Length of line:
Standard gauge 10 miles
Narrow gauge 1 mile

Public opening: On non-operating mid weekdays the station is closed. Public services: weekends, Bank Holiday Mondays, between March and November, some summer weekdays

Special events: Spring Diesel Gala — 4/5 April; Postman Pat Weekend — 25/26 April; Steam Gala — 23-26 May; Steam and Real Ale Weekend — 6/7 June; Transport Nostalgia Day — 6 July; Summer Diesel Gala 10-12 July; Bus Rally — 12 July; Transport Nostalgia Day — 13 September; Narrow Gauge Gala — 19/20 September; Fireman Sam Weekend — 26/27 September; Steam & Vintage Rally — 10/11 October; Autumn Diesel Gala— 24/25 October; Fireworks Special — 7 November; Santa Specials — 5/6, 12/13, 19/20, 22-24 December; Mince Pie Specials — 26 December; Christmas Diesel Day — 27 December; Christmas Cracker Steam Gala —29-31 December; New Year's Day Specials — 1 January 2010

Special notes: The site is being developed as the headquarters of the railway between Cheltenham and Stratford. The GWR owns the railway land between Cheltenham and Broadway and operates over 10 miles from Toddington to

Locomotives and multiple-units

Name	No	Origin	Class	Type	Built
—	2807	GWR	2800	2-8-0	1905
—	4270	GWR	4200	2-8-0T	1919
Kinlet Hall	4936	GWR	6959	4-6-0	1929
—	5619	GWR	5600	0-6-2T	1925
Raveningham Hall	6960*	GWR	6959	4-6-0	1944
Owsden Hall	6984	GWR	6959	4-6-0	1948
Foremarke Hall	7903	GWR	6959	4-6-0	1949
—	7069	LMS	—	0-6-0DE	1939
Peninsular & Oriental SNCo	35006	SR	MN	4-6-2	1941
—	8274	LMS	8F	2-8-0	1941
—	76077	BR	4MT	2-6-0	1956
Black Prince	92203	BR	9F	2-10-0	1959
—	03069	BR	03	0-6-0DM	1959
—	D2182	BR	03	0-6-0DM	1952
—	D9553	BR	14	0-6-0DH	1965
—	D8137	BR	20	Bo-Bo	1966
—	24081	BR	24	Bo-Bo	1960
—	26043	BR	26	Bo-Bo	1959
—	37215	BR	37	Co-Co	1964
Clydebridge	37324	BR	37	Co-Co	1962
Phaeton	45149	BR	45	1Co-Co1	1961
—	47105	BR	47	Co-Co	1963
Freightliner 1995	47376	BR	47	Co-Co	1965
—	56003	BR	56	Co-Co	1977
—	73129	BR	73	Bo-Bo	1966
—	51950	BR	108	DMBS	1960
—	52062	BR	108	DMC	1960

*off-site under repair

Industrial locomotives

Name	No	Builder	Type	Built
Wemyss Private Rly	15	Barclay (2138)	0-6-0ST	1945
—	19	Fowler (4240016)	0-6-0DH	1964
—	21	Fowler (4210130)	0-4-0DM	1957
John	—	Peckett (1976)	0-4-0ST	1939
King George	—	Hunslet (2409)	0-6-0ST	1942
—	1	Drewry/RSH (2573/7859)	0-6-0DM	1956
—	2	Drewry/RSH (2574/7860)	0-6-0DM	1956
—	—	Hunslet (5511)	0-6-0DM	1957
—	372	YEC (2760)	0-6-0DE	1957

Stock

4 ex-GWR coaches; 59 ex-BR coaches; 4 ex-LMS coaches; Baguley/Drewry inspection vehicle; 2 Wickham trolleys; plus over 150 wagons (including 12 brake vans, 45-ton steam crane, 18-ton diesel crane)

Owners

2807 the Cotswold Steam Preservation Ltd (www.gwr2807.co.uk)
35006 the P&O Locomotive Society
8274 and 7069 the Churchill (8F) Locomotive Co
92203 David Shepherd
26043 and 45149 the Cotswold Mainline Diesel Group
D9553 Cotswold Diesel Preservation Group
37215 and 37324 the Growler Group
47105 and 47376 the Brush Type 4 Fund
D8137 the English Electric Type 1 Group

England

Cheltenham Racecourse with an intermediate station at Winchcombe.

No public access to restoration area or sheds except on guided tours. Please ring for details.

Guest locomotives will be operating during the year with special guest *City of Truro* expected along with GWR 2-6-2T No 5542 and others.

It is also likely that long-term restoration projects GWR No 2807 and SR No 35006 will return to steam during 2009.

Wine & Dine train 'Elegant Excursions' at www.elegantexcursions.net

Round trip tickets give unlimited travel on day of purchase.

Family tickets available

Facilities for disabled: Visitors with impaired mobility welcomed, please inform staff in advance if possible. Wheelchairs can be accommodated in specially converted carriages. The platform at Racecourse is reached via a steep

North Gloucestershire Railway
Industrial narrow gauge locomotives (2ft gauge)

Name	No	Builder	Type	Built
Isibutu	5	Bagnall (2820)	4-4-0T	1946
George B	—	Hunslet (680)	0-4-0ST	1898
Chaka	—	Hunslet (2075)	0-4-2T	1940
Justine	—	Jung (939)	0-4-0WT	1906
Brigadelok	—	Henschel (15968)	0-8-0T	1918
—	2	Lister (34523)	4wDM	1949
—	3	M/Rail (4565)	4wPM	1928
Spitfire	—	M/Rail (7053)	4wPM	1937
—	1	R/Hornsby (166010)	4wDM	1932
—	L5	R/Hornsby (181820)	4wDM	1936
—	—	R/Hornsby (354028)	4wDM	1953

Stock
3 coaches; 11 wagons

slope which may be difficult for some visitors. Disabled toilets and parking at all stations

Special facilities: Steam and diesel experience courses. Hire of train (steam or diesel). Children's parties on-train or in Flag & Whistle tea rooms.

Special trains to March and November race meetings at Cheltenham Racecourse. Contact Classic Hospitality 08456 528 888 or www.classic hospitality.co.uk (advance booking essential)

Membership details: From above address

Membership journal: *The Cornishman* — quarterly

Timetable Service	**Great Central Railway**	Leicestershire

Member: HRA, TT

The original Great Central Railway's extension to London in 1899 was the last main line to be built in this country, most of which was closed in the 1960s. Steam-hauled services operate through attractive rolling Leicestershire countryside, crossing the picturesque Swithland reservoir. The railway's aim is to re-create the experience of British main line railway operation in the days of steam. The images of a main line are backed up by a double track line with trains hauled by large locomotives

Headquarters: Great Central Railway plc, Loughborough Central Station, Great Central Road, Loughborough, Leicestershire LE11 1RW

Telephone: Loughborough (01509) 230726

Fax: 01509 239791

Internet address: *e-mail:* sales@gcrailway.co.uk

Locomotives and multiple-units

Name	No	Origin	Class	Type	Built
—	4141	GWR	41xx	2-6-2T	1946
*Witherslack Hall**	6990	GWR	'Hall'	4-6-0	1948
Sir Lamiel	30777	SR	N15	4-6-0	1925
Boscastle	34039	SR	WC	4-6-2	1946
Alderman A. E. Draper	45305	LMS	5MT	4-6-0	1936
—	46521	LMS	2MT	2-6-0	1953
—	47406	LMS	3F	0-6-0T	1926
—	48305	LMS	8F	2-8-0	1943
—	63601	GCR	8K	2-8-0	1919
—	69523	GNR	N2	0-6-2T	1921
Oliver Cromwell	70013	BR	7MT	4-6-2	1951
—	73156	BR	5MT	4-6-0	1956
—	78019	BR	2MT	2-6-0	1954
—	07005	BR	07	0-6-0DE	1962
—	D3101	BR	08	0-6-0DE	1955
§—	D4067	BR	10	0-6-0DE	1961
—	D8098	BR	20	Bo-Bo	1961
—	20142	BR	20	Bo-Bo	1966
—	D5185	BR	25	Bo-Bo	1960
Harlech Castle	25265	BR	25	Bo-Bo	1963
—	27056	BR	27	Bo-Bo	1962
—	D5830	BR	31	A1A-A1A	1962
—	33116	BR	33	Bo-Bo	1960
—	37198	BR	37	Co-Co	1954

Web site: www.gcrailway.co.uk

Main stations: Loughborough Central

Other public stations: Quorn & Woodhouse, Rothley, Leicester North

OS reference: SK 543194

Car park: Quorn, Rothley, Leicester North

Access by public transport: Loughborough Midland station (0.75-mile). Arriva, Kinch, South Notts and Trent Buses serve Loughborough Baxtergate (0.5 mile). Arriva Nos 126/7 pass end of Great Central Road (A6 Leicester Road, 300yd)

Refreshment facilities: Licensed Griddle Car with hot and cold drinks on majority of trains and at Loughborough Central station. Light refreshment facilities available weekends at all other stations. Luxurious First Class Restaurant Car, for which advance booking is obligatory, is provided on 13.15 train every Saturday and Sunday. Also provided on 19.30 train every Saturday and every Friday (June-September). Additional service may run at peak times. Private charter trains available, along with more details of all the above, on request

Souvenir shop: Loughborough

Museum: Loughborough

Depot: Loughborough

Length of line: 8 miles

Passenger trains: Loughborough-Leicester North

Period of public operation: Weekends and Bank Holidays throughout the year. Certain weekdays May to September with additional services at times of peak demand

Special events: 1960s Experience — 21/22 March; Diesel Gala — 25-26 April; 40th Anniversary of Closure — 9/10 May; Day out with Thomas — 23-25 May; Collectors' Fair Toys & Trains — 7 June; Wartime Weekend — 13/14 June; Summer Steam Gala — 25/26 July; Toy & Train Fair at Loughborough — 2 August; 'Get Some in!' National Service and Veterans— 8/9 August; Day out with Thomas — 29-31 August; September Diesel Gala — 12/13 September; Great

Name	No	Origin	Class	Type	Built
—	37255	BR	37	Co-Co	1965
†—	D123	BR	45	1Co-Co1	1961
Sparrowhawk	D1705	BR	47	Co-Co	1965
—	51427	BR	101	DMBS	1959
—	51616	BR	127	DMBS	1959
—	51622	BR	127	DMBS	1959
—	53193	BR	101	DMC	1959
—	53203	BR	101	DMBS	1957
—	53266	BR	101	DMC	1957
—	53321	BR	101	DMC	1958
—	59276	BR	120	TS	1958
—	62384	BR	421	MBSO	1970
—	69339	BR	422	TSRB	1970
—	76746	BR	421	DTCSO	1970
—	76817	BR	421	DTCSO	1971
—	70527	BR	411	TSOL	1960
—	W79976	AC Cars	—	Railbus	1958

*undergoing overhaul at Tyseley Locomotive Works
§ named *Alfred Thomas & Margaret Ethel Naylor*
† named *Leicestershire & Derbyshire Yeomanry*

Industrial locomotives

Name	No	Builder	Type	Built
(Arthur Wright)	D4279	Fowler (4210079)	0-4-0DE	1952
Duke of Edinburgh	28	A/Barclay (400)	0-4-0DM	1956
Robert	—	H/Clarke (1752)	0-6-0ST	1943

Owners
6990 the David Clarke Railway Trust
34039 the Boscastle Locomotive Syndicate
45305 the 5305 Locomotive Association
46521, 73156 and 78019 Loughborough Standard Locomotives Group
47406, D3101, D4067 private
30777, 63601, 70013 and 33116 on loan from the National Railway Museum
69523 the Gresley Society
D5830, D8098 and D1705 the Type 1 Locomotive Co
Class 101s Renaissance Railcars
D1705 the Type One Locomotive Co

Central Beer Festival — 25-27 September; Steam Railway Gala — 9-11 October; Wizards Weekend — and Halloween Night — 31 October/5 November; Bonfire Night — 5 November; Girl Guide's affinity day and Remembrance event — 8 November; Santa Specials — 28/29 November-17 December; Christmas Day Trains — 25 December; Christmas Holiday Trains — 26 December to 1 January 2010.
For additional information phone 08708 308298

Facilities for disabled: Special carriage for wheelchair/disabled persons (advance notice required).

Wheelchair access good at Quorn, Rothley and Leicester North, can be arranged at Loughborough with advance notification. Boarding ramps at all stations

Membership & share details: Share enquiries: Company Secretary, Great Central Railway plc

Special facilities: Director's saloon, beavertail observation car or complete train for hire. Drive a locomotive experience packages available.

Membership: Membership Secretary, Friends of Great Central Railway c/o above address

England

Emanating from the private Greywood Central Railway, built from 1946, the Great Cockcrow Railway opened in 1968 in the small village of Lyne near Chertsey. This is a 7.25in gauge system with a signalling system worked from three signalboxes

Headquarters: Hardwick Lane, Lyne, Chertsey, Surrey

Contact: Jill Wright

Telephone: Mon-Fri (01932) 255514; Sun (01932) 565474

Internet address: *e-mail:* jill.wright@ianallan.co.uk *Web site:* www.cockcrow.co.uk

Main station: Hardwick Central

Car parking: On site

Access by public transport: Chertsey railway station (1.25 miles); London Buslines 561, 586 Holloway Hill (half-mile)

On site facilities: Toilet, light refreshments, picnic area

Depots: Hardwick Central

Length of line: 1.75 miles, 7.25in gauge

Period of public operation: Every Sunday Easter to October inclusive, 14.00-17.30

Journey time: About 15-20min

Facilities for disabled: Limited, but staff are happy to co-operate

Special note: Sponsored by Ian Allan Group. Send second class SAE for brochure to Terminal House, Shepperton, TW17 8AS. Fare £2.50 adult, £2 child. Gladesman £4 per person

Locomotives (7.25in gauge)

Name	No	Prototype	Builder	Type	Built
—	206	LNER K5	D. Simmonds	2-6-0	1956
Grand Parade	2744	LNER A3	R. Warren	4-6-2	1990
Humorist	60097	LNER A3	N. Sleet	4-6-2	
—	30541	SR Q	J. Butt	0-6-0	2000
—	837	SR S15	D. Curwen	4-6-0	1947
Lord Nelson	850	SR LN	Scarret	4-6-0	
—	1803	SR U	Schwab	2-6-0	1970s
Winston Churchill	34051	SR BoB	N. Sleet	4-6-2	1995
General Steam Navigation	21C11	SR MN	N. Sleet & M. Lester	4-6-2	1993
—	1239	NER R1	F. Baldwin	4-4-0	1913
—	1249	NER T2	R. Sills	0-8-0	1986
—	1442	NER C1	—	4-4-2	1989
Eureka	1947	GCR	L. Shaw	4-6-2	1927
—	1401	GWR 14xx	R. Sills	0-4-2T	1980
North Foreland	2422	LBCSR H2	J. Lester	4-4-2	1981
Sister Dora	5000	LMS 5P5F	A. Glaze	4-6-0	1989
—	5145	LMS 5P5F	—	4-6-0	1989
The Glasgow Highlander	45157	LMS 5P5F	D. Grant	4-6-0	1996
—	45440	LMS 5P5F	—	4-6-0	
Royal Scot	6100	LMS 6P	Barnet & Willoughby	4-6-0	1947
Scots Guardsman	6115	LMS 6P	P. Ormand	4-6-0	1989
—	8374	LMS 8F	Glaze, Hancock & York	2-8-0	1993
Longmoor	73755	WD 2-10-0	J. Liversedge	2-10-0	1951
A. B. Macleod	7028	BR Hymek	A. Glaze	Bo-Bo	1983
Faraday	11	BR 08	Jennings & Marden	0-6-0P	1958
—	40106	BR 40	N. Sleet	1Co-Co1	1992
Sherlock Holmes	—	LT Met	Compass House	Bo-Bo	

Member: HRA

Location: Whipsnade Wild Animal Park, Dunstable, Bedfordshire LU6 2LF

Telephone: (01582) 871332 (extension 2270)

Fax: (01582) 873748

Internet address: *e-mail:* whipsnade-operations@2sl.org

Railway Engineer: Kevin Edwins

Main station: Whipsnade Central

Length: 2 miles (2ft 6in gauge)

On site facilities: Car park (100yd), souvenir shop, refreshments (30yd)

Period of public operation: January — no trains; February — weekends; March — weekends only; daily April to end of September — steam trains; October — weekends only; November — no trains; December — no trains. Subject to availability steam all year

Facilities for disabled: Carriage designed for wheelchairs

Locomotives

Name	No	Builder	Type	Built
Excelsior	2	K/Stuart (1049)	0-4-2T	1908
Superior	4	K/Stuart (4034)	0-6-2T	1920
Victor	—	Fowler (4160004)	0-6-0DM	1951
Hector	—	Fowler (4160005)	0-6-0DM	1951
Hercules	—*	23rd August Works (Bucharest)	0-6-0DH	1981
—	3	B/Drewry	4wDH	1973

*Polish State Railways Class LYD2

Rolling stock: 10 carriages, 10 wagons

Museum — Haig Colliery Mining Museum — Cumbria

Member: HRA

Haig Colliery Mining Museum, Whitehaven, is an educational and informative museum under development based on local and social mining history. The Museum is situated in Cumbria's last deep coal mine that closed in March 1986. It houses the world's only Bever Dorling & Co Ltd winding engines, one of which is restored and operated daily

Location: Kells, half-mile south of Whitehaven, take the road to St Bees and follow brown tourist signs

OS reference: NX 967176

Operating society/organisation: The Haig Colliery Mining Museum Ltd, Solway Road, Kells, Whitehaven, Cumbria CA26 9BG

Industrial locomotives

Name	No	Builder	Type	Built
Askham Hall	—	Avonside (1772)	0-4-0ST	1917
—	226	V/Foundry (5262)	0-4-0DM	
—	ND 3815	Hunslet (2389)	0-4-0DM	1941
—	244	Fowler (22971) rebuilt T/Hill (130C/1963)	0-4-0DH	1942

Charity number: 1050534
Telephone/Fax: 01946 599949 (general information)
Internet address:
e-mail: root@haigpit.com
Web site: www.haigpit.com
Car park: On site
Access by public transport:
By rail: Whitehaven is on the Barrow-Carlisle line
By bus: No 01 bus from bus station (opposite railway station) — 9min

journey
On site facilities: Small gift shop, gardened area suitable for picnics. Toilets. Meet and Greet by museum guides. Locomotives viewable on request to the guides
Public opening:
Daily (09.30-16.30). Free entry
Facilities for disabled: Parking area, toilets, wheelchair access to all areas

---

Timetable Service — Hayling Seaside Railway — Hampshire

There are three stations on the line: Beachlands, the main station/storage/workshop building located seaward of the funfair; Eastoke Corner 1-mile to the east is the other end of the line; Mengham Road with passing loop between

Headquarters: 20 Jasmond Road, Cosham, Portsmouth PO6 2SY
Managing Director:
Bob Haddock
Telephone: 023 9237 2427
Internet address:
www.haylingseasiderailway.com

Locomotives

Name	No	Builder	Type	Built
Jack	—	A/Keef (23)	0-4-0DH s/o	1988
Alister	—	Ruston (201790)	4wDH	1940
Alan B	—	M/Rail (7199)	4wDM	1937
—	—	EHLR	0-4-0T	*
Edwin	—	R/Hornsby (1002-0967-5)	4wDH	1967

*under construction

Stock

2 4-wheel enclosed coaches built 1992/1997, 2 4-wheel balcony coaches built 1996, 1 enclosed bogie coach built 2004, 3 toastrack bogie coach built 2004/5/6. All built by East Hayling Light Railway in its own works

England

Main public station: Beachlands (postcode: PO11 0AG)
Other public stations: Eastoke Corner, Mengham Road
Car parks: Pay & display at all stations. Free parking during December, January and February
Access by public transport: Regular buses from Havant railway station
Refreshment facilities: At all stations
Journey time: Departures every 45 minutes. First train 11.00 from Beachlands
Length of line: 1 mile, 2ft gauge
Period of public operation: Every weekend and Wednesday (market day) all year round, plus school holidays.
Daily 1 July to 2 September
Facilities for disabled: All platforms and coaches built to latest mobility standards
Special events: Please contact for full details; Pirates of Beachlands — May half term; Two train running, Santa Specials
Special notes: On display are the original BR station signs Hayling Island and Havant for Hayling
Special facilities: A train may be hired for birthday parties or other special occasions
Membership details: Ian Edwards 01329 519690
Membership journal: *The Hayling Billy* — quarterly

Head of Steam / Darlington Railway Museum

Museum / County Durham

Member: HRA

The site as a whole is known as the Head of Steam, and is owned by Darlington Borough Council. Within the site are four separate buildings. The former North Road Station is run as a museum by the council. Darlington Railway Preservation Society occupies the former Stockton & Darlington Railway North Road Goods and the former S&DR Hopetown Carriage Works is divided between the A1 Steam Locomotive Trust and the North Eastern Locomotive Preservation Group. Darlington Model Railway Club occupies the Museum first floor.

All organisations except the Model Railway Club are members of the HRA.

The Ken Hoole Study Centre houses a collection of reference material on the railways of north-east England including the library of the North Eastern Railway Association (access by appointment). Northern train services provide a link to Darlington's main line station and to Shildon, for 'Locomotion' and the Timothy Hackworth Museum

Museum Manager: Vacant
Location: North Road Station, Darlington, County Durham DL3 6ST. Approximately three-quarters of a mile north of town centre, off North Road (A167)
OS reference: NZ 289157
Telephone: (01325) 460532

Locomotives

Name	No	Origin	Class	Type	Built
Locomotion	1	S&DR	—	0-4-0	1825
Derwent	25	S&DR	—	0-6-0	1845
—	1463	NER	1463	2-4-0	1885
—	901	NER	Q7	0-8-0	1919

Name	No	Builder		Type	Built
—	—	Bagnall (2898)		0-4-0F	1948

Stock

1 North Eastern Railway Coach body (c1860)
1 Chaldron wagon

Owner

Locomotion, Derwent, and *1463* are all on loan from the National Railway Museum, along with the coach body

Darlington Railway Preservation Society

Member: HRA
Internet address: *Web site:* www.drps.visit.ws

Locomotives

Name	No	Origin	Class	Type	Built
—	78018	BR	2MT	2-6-0	1954

Industrial locomotives

Name	No	Builder	Type	Built
—	2	RSH (7925)	0-4-0DM	1959
—	1	Peckett (2142)	0-4-0ST	1953
David Payne	185	Fowler (4110006)	0-4-0DM	1950
Smiths Dock Co Ltd	—	Fowler (4200018)	0-4-0DM	1947
—	—	GEC	4wE	1928
—	—	R/Hornsby (279591)	0-4-0DE	1949
—	—	R/Hornsby*	4wDM	—
—	—	R/Hornsby*	4wDM	—
—	—	R/Hornsby*	4wDM	—
—	—	RSH	0-6-0T	1938

*1ft 6in gauge

Internet address: *Web site:*
www.drcm.org.uk
Car park: At museum site
Access by public transport: Rail
services to Darlington North Road
station. Local bus services along
North Road
Catering facilities: For snacks and
light refreshments
On site facilities: Souvenir and
bookshop, toilets, meeting room
Public opening:
April to September:
Closed Monday; Tuesday to Sunday
10.00-16.00.
October to March:
Closed Monday; Tuesday to Sunday
11.00-15.30.
Special events: Contact for details,
details will appear on the web site,
or write or telephone
Facilities for disabled: Access to
main museum building for wheel-
chairs. Disabled person's toilet.
Parking spaces for disabled in fore-
court
Membership details: Friends of

Stock
Various wagons, steam and diesel cranes

A1 Steam Locomotive Trust

Locomotives

Name	No	Origin	Class	Type	Built
Tornado	60163	A1SLT	8P6F	4-6-2	2008

The construction was completed in 2008 and the locomotive left for
running in and use on various heritage lines and the National Network

Darlington Railway Museum,
Darlington Railway Preservation
Society, A1 Steam Locomotive
Trust and North Eastern
Locomotive Preservation Group.
All can be contacted via the
museum. Members of these
organisations and registered
supporters of the A1 Trust,
members of the Museums
Association and holders of HRA
InterRail passes all receive free
admission except on Thomas and
Santa days
Note: The Goods Shed and part of

the Carriage Works occupied by the
North Eastern Locomotive
Preservation Group. Towards the
end of 2007 they started the heavy
overhaul of No 2392. They are
currently working on the J72. The
workshop is open only by
appointment. Visitors are welcome
at all buildings on the site, but are
strongly advised to make
arrangements in advance for all
buildings other than the main
station itself

Opened in 2000 the railway runs
through the landscaped grounds of
Hills Garden Centre
Location: Hills Garden Centre,
London Road, Allostock,
Knutsford, Cheshire WA16 9LU
Contact: Mr C. Halsall
Telephone: 01565 722567
Fax: 01565 723818
Internet address: *Web site:*
www.hills-miniature-railway.co.uk
Car parking: Space for 80 cars on
site. One coach space available
Access by public transport:
Holmes Chapel main line station is
4 miles away, as is the nearest bus
station
Access by car: Exit M6 at jct 18
and follow A54 to Holmes Chapel.

Locomotives

Name	No	Builder	Type	Built
Amy Louise	—	Exmoor	0-4-2	2005
Sir Richard	—	Greatrix	Bo-Bo	2005
—	—	N/k	4-4-0	1990
Peter the Great	—	J. Horsfield	0-4-0	2001

In Holmes Chapel turn left onto
A50 London Road, follow for
5 miles. Hills garden Centre is on
the left-hand side
On site facilities: Souvenir shop,
light refreshments
Length of line: 600yd, 7.25in
gauge
Period of public operation:
Weekends and Bank Holidays
throughout the year. Trains operate

10.45-16.30. All trains weather
permitting
Special events: Santa Specials —
December weekends up to
Christmas Eve
Facilities for disabled: Disabled
toilet, level site, wheelchair loan
and plenty of seating. Designated
disabled parking space

Steam Centre — Hollycombe Steam Collection — West Sussex

Member: HRA, TT

An extensive collection of working steam, including railways, traction engines, fairground rides, Bioscope, organs, the oldest Burrell Showman's engine *Emperor*, sawmill and engine from the paddle steamer *Caledonia*, set in woodlands and gardens

Location: Iron Hill, Hollycombe, near Liphook, Hants

OS reference: SU 852295

Operating society/organisation: Hollycombe Working Steam Museum, Iron Hill, Midhurst Road, Liphook, Hants GU30 7LP

Telephone: Liphook (01428) 724900 (24hr answerphone)

Fax: (01428) 723682

Internet address: *Web site:* www.hollycombe.co.uk

Car park: On site

Standard gauge industrial locomotives

Name	No	Builder	Type	Built
Commander B	50	H/Leslie (2450)	0-4-0ST	1899
—	3	YEC (2679)	0-4-0DH	1962

Narrow gauge locomotives (2ft gauge)

Name	No	Builder	Type	Built
Caledonia	70	Barclay (1995)	0-4-0WT	1931
Jerry M	38	Hunslet (638)	0-4-0ST	1895
—	16	R/Hornsby	4wDM	1941

Access by public transport: Liphook main line station (1 mile)

On site facilities: Shop and refreshments, toilets, car park, *dogs allowed in car park only*

Length of lines: Standard gauge – quarter mile 2ft gauge 'Quarry Railway' – 1.5 miles 7.25in gauge – quarter mile

Public opening: 12.00-17.00.

Sundays: Easter to 25 October; Daily: 23-29 May, 4-31 August; Fairground at Night: (19.00-22.00) 19, 26 September, 3, 10, 17 October

Special events: Modellers' Weekend — 16/17 May, Railway Weekend — 6/7 June; Fairground Weekend — 25/26 July.

Please phone or check web site for these and other events

Steam Centre — Irchester Narrow Gauge Railway Museum — Northants

Member: HRA

The aims of the controlling trust are to acquire and preserve narrow gauge railway locomotives, rolling stock and exhibits associated with Northamptonshire and the East Midlands, to display the collection for the benefit of the public and to restore exhibits to working order so they may be demonstrated in a proper manner

Location: Within Irchester Country Park, 2 miles south of Wellingborough

Operating society/organisation: The Irchester Narrow Gauge Railway Trust, 3 St Christopher's Close, Cranwell, Lincs NG34 8XB

On site facilities: Shop, museum, demonstration line, picnic area

Access by public transport: Main line Wellingborough (Midland Road) station, buses to Irchester and Little Irchester

Car Parks: Main park car parks

Toilets: Main park complex

Public opening: Every Sunday (summer 10.00-17.00,

Industrial locomotives

Name	No	Builder	Type	Built
—	85*	Peckett (1870	0-6-0ST	1934
—	86*	Peckett (1871	0-6-0ST	1934
—	87*	Peckett (2029)	0-6-0ST	1942
Cambrai	—*	Corpet (493)	0-6-0T	1888
—	ND3645*	R/Hornsby (211679)	4wDM	1941
—	—†	R/Hornsby (281290)	0-6-0DM	1949
—	ED10*	R/Hornsby (411322	4wDM	1958
—	—†	M/Rail (1363)	4wPM	1918
The Rock	—*	Hunslet (2419)	0-4-0DM	1941

* metre gauge
† 3ft gauge

winter 10.00-16.00), at other times by arrangement. Steam and demonstration weekends are held on last full weekend of the month — March-October

Facilities for disabled: Museum and site on level, staff available if required

Membership details: Membership Secretary, 3 St Christopher's Close, Cranwell, Lincs NG34 8XB

Ironbridge Gorge Museums

The railway items form only a small part of the displays on two of the museum's main sites: Blists Hill Victorian Town and Coalbrookdale. The Blists Hill site offers an opportunity to see a number of industrial and other activities being operated in meticulously reconstructed period buildings. A working foundry is just one of the exciting exhibits. A full size working replica of Richard Trevithick's 1802 steam locomotive built by the Coalbrookdale Company can also be seen operating at certain times at the Blists Hill site. The Ironbridge Gorge was designated a World Heritage Site in 1987

Location: Ironbridge, Shropshire
OS reference: SJ 694033
Operating society/organisation: Ironbridge Gorge Museum Trust, Coach Road, Coalbrookdale,

Industrial locomotives

Name	No	Builder	Type	Built
—	—	Sentinel/Coalbrookdale (6185)	0-4-0VBT	1925
—	—	Sentinel/M/Wardle (6155)	0-4-0VBT	1925
—	5	Coalbrookdale	0-4-0ST	1865
—	—	A/Barclay	0-6-0ST	1896

All locomotives are at the Museum of Iron site.
Phone 01952 435900 for details

Telford, Shropshire TF8 7DQ
Telephone: Telford (01952) 433522
Fax: (01952) 435999
Internet address: *Web site:* www.ironbridge.org.uk
Car park: At the sites
Access by public transport: Various operators. Please telephone Telford Travel Link 01952 200005 or 0870 6082608 for further details
Catering facilities: Licensed Victorian pub, sweet shop and tea rooms at the Blists Hill site, serving drinks and mainly cold snacks. Tea, coffee and light refreshments at the Museum of Iron, Coalbrookdale and Jackfield Tile Museum
Public opening: Main sites, including Museum of Iron and Blists Hill, daily (except Christmas Eve, Christmas Day and New Year's Day) 10.00-17.00
Special notes: Tickets for all the sites or just for single sites available. Call main phone number for special access details

---

Isle of Wight Steam Railway

Member: HRA, TT
Separated from the mainland by the Solent, the line's isolation encouraged the maintenance and retention of Victorian locomotives and coaching stock which still operate on the line today. Its rural charm enhances its attraction for the island's holidaymakers during the summer season

Commercial Manager: Jim Loe
General Manager: Peter Vail
Headquarters: Isle of Wight Steam Railway, Haven Street Station, Ryde, Isle of Wight PO33 4DS
Telephone: (01983) 882204
Internet addresses: *e-mail:* havenstreet@iwsteamrailway.co.uk
Web site: www.iwsteamrailway.co.uk
Main station: Haven Street
OS reference: SZ 556898
Other public stations: Wootton, Ashey and Smallbrook Junction

Locomotives

Name	No	Origin	Class	Type	Built
Freshwater	W8 (32646)	LBSCR	A1X	0-6-0T	1876
Newport	W11 (32640)	LBSCR	A1X	0-6-0T	1878
Calbourne	W24	LSWR	O2	0-4-4T	1891
—	41296	LMS	2MT	2-6-2T	1952
—	41313	LMS	2MT	2-6-2T	1952
—	46447	LMS	2MT	2-6-0	1952
—	D2554	BR	05	0-6-0DM	1956
—	D2059	BR	03	0-6-0DM	1959

Industrial and Army locomotives

Name	No	Builder	Type	Built
Invincible	37	H/Leslie (3135)	0-4-0ST	1915
Ajax	38	Barclay (1605)	0-6-0T	1918
Waggoner	192	Hunslet (3792)	0-6-0ST	1953
Royal Engineer	198	Hunslet (3798)	0-6-0ST	1953

Stock
1 IWR coach; 4 LBSCR coaches; 3 SECR coaches; 2 LCDR coaches; 5 IWR coaches (bodies only); 5 LCDR coaches (bodies only); 1 LBSCR coach (body only); 1 crane; 1 Wickham trolley; 30 wagons; 6 parcels vans; 2 ex-LT hoppers; 1 ex-BR Lowmac; 1 LSWR Road van; 1 cattle van (on loan from the National Railway Museum).
Non-passenger vehicles are not normally accessible for public viewing

Car park: Haven Street
Access by public transport: 'Island Line' service from Ryde or Shanklin to Smallbrook Jct
Refreshment facilities: Light refreshments available (licensed)
Souvenir shop: Haven Street
Museum: Small exhibits museum at Haven Street.
Carriage & Wagon workshop open for viewing most days

Depot: Haven Street
Length of line: 5 miles
Passenger trains: Wootton-Smallbrook Jct
Period of public operation: Daily — June to mid September. Selected days — March to May, October and November
Special events: The railway hosts a large number of special events throughout the season. Please

contact for details
Facilities for disabled: Limited facilities, but can be catered for individually, or in groups (by prior arrangement), toilets available
Membership details: Membership Secretary at above address
Membership journal: *Island Rail News* — quarterly

Timetable Service — Keighley & Worth Valley Railway — West Yorkshire

Member: HRA

1968 saw the reopening of the Worth Valley branch following the first sale of a standard gauge railway to a preservation society. Qualified volunteers have now managed and operated the KWVR every weekend, summer and winter for four decades. The KWVR is justifiably proud of having led the British independent railway movement in establishing the now ubiquitous late 1950s/early 1960s house style. Many have copied, but few succeed so well as the Worth Valley with totems, A5 handbills, period posters, red uniform ties, hanging baskets, gas lights and coal fires. One of the most community-orientated independent railways, being the first to create a 'Resident's Railcard' discount fares scheme

Chairman, Joint Management Committee: Sam MacDougal
Headquarters: Haworth Station, Keighley, West Yorkshire BD22 8NJ
Telephone: Haworth (01535) 647777 24hr recorded timetable and information service; Haworth (01535) 645214 (other calls)
Internet address: *Web site:* www.kwvr.co.uk
Main stations: Keighley, Ingrow West, Haworth, Oxenhope
Other public stations: Damems, Oakworth
OS reference: SE 034371
Car parks: Free at Keighley, Ingrow West, Oakworth and Oxenhope. Parking at Haworth (small charge, part refundable if travelling). Coaches at Ingrow

Locomotives and multiple-units

Name	No	Origin	Class	Type	Built
—	41241	LMS	2MT	2-6-2T	1949
—	43924	MR	4F	0-6-0	1920
—	45212*	LMS	5MT	4-6-0	1935
Bahamas	45596	LMS	'Jubilee'	4-6-0	1935
—	48431	LMS	8F	2-8-0	1944
—	47279	LMS	3F	0-6-0T	1925
—	1054	LNWR	—	0-6-2T	1888
City of Wells	34092	SR	WC	4-6-2	1949
—	80002	BR	4MT	2-6-4T	1952
—	75078	BR	4MT	4-6-0	1956
—	78022	BR	2MT	2-6-0	1953
—	30072	SR	USA	0-6-0T	1943
—	5775	GWR	5700	0-6-0PT	1929
—	957	L&Y	2F	0-6-0	1887
—	19*	L&Y	Pug	0-4-0ST	1910
—	51218	L&Y	Pug	0-4-0ST	1901
—	752	L&Y	—	0-6-0ST	1881
—	85	TVR	02	0-6-2T	1899
—	5820	USATC	S160	2-8-0	1945
—	90733	MoS	WD	2-8-0	1945
—	D226	BR	—	0-6-0DE	1956
—	D2511	BR	—	0-6-0DM	1961
—	D3336	BR	08	0-6-0DE	1954
—	D5209	BR	25/1	Bo-Bo	1963
—	D8031	BR	20	Bo-Bo	1960
—	50928	BR	108	DMBS	1959
—	51189	BR	101	DMBS	1958
—	51565	BR	108	DMC	1959
—	51803	BR	101	DMCL	1959
—	79962	W&M	—	Railbus	1958
—	79964	W&M	—	Railbus	1958

Industrial locomotives

Name	No	Builder	Type	Built
Hamburg	31	H/Clarke (679)	0-6-0T	1903
Nunlow	—	H/Clarke (1704)	0-6-0T	1938
Brussels	118	H/Clarke (1782)	0-6-0ST	1945
Tiny	—	Barclay (2258)	0-4-0ST	1949
Merlin	231	H/Clarke (D761)	0-6-0DM	1951
—	MDHB No 32	Hunslet (2699)	0-6-0DM	1944

*away on loan

75

England

West and Oxenhope only

Access by public transport: Fast and frequent electric Metro trains from Leeds, Bradford and Skipton to Keighley (joint station with KWVR). National Express East Coast direct services to Leeds and Keighley. Northern Trains through services from Carlisle, Morecambe, Heysham Port, Lancaster to Keighley station. Northern Train services from Blackpool, Preston, Blackburn, Accrington, Burnley, Manchester to Hebden Bridge for connection via bus service 500 to Oxenhope (tel 01535 603284 for days of operation and timings)

Refreshment facilities: Buffet facilities at Oxenhope and Keighley (open when train service in operation). The only CAMRA-approved 'Real Ale' bar operates on most steam trains. Wine and Dine services by prior booking only — the 'White Rose Pullman' and 'West Riding Ltd'

Picnic areas: Keighley Station, Haworth Locomotive Depot, Oxenhope Station

Viewing areas: Keighley (ex-Garsdale) turntable, Haworth Locomotive Depot

Souvenir shops: Keighley, Haworth and Oxenhope stations; Ingrow Vintage Carriages Museum

Museums: Vintage Carriages Trust's carriage and locomotive museum at Ingrow Railway Centre. Open daily 11.00-16.30

Depots: Carriage and wagon — Oxenhope; Motive power/loco works — Haworth, 'Bahamas Locomotive Society' workshops and museum at Ingrow Railway Centre

Stock

30 coaches including examples of pre-Grouping types; BR Mk 1 stock including the oldest vehicle in existence, part of the prototype batch; 2 Pullman cars, NER and L&Y observation cars

Owners

19, 752 and 51218 the L&YRPS Trust
75078 and 78022 the Standard 4 Preservation Society
Bahamas, Nunlow, Tiny the Bahamas Locomotive Society
1054 the National Trust
52044 the Bowers 957 Trust
34092 the *City of Wells* Syndicate

Length of line: 4.75 miles

Passenger trains: Early morning local shoppers' services worked by diesel railbus/diesel multiple-unit, otherwise all steam-hauled

Frequent bus service between Haworth station and Haworth village top on Sundays (May-September) and Bank Holidays

Period of public operation: Steam-hauled passenger services every weekend and Bank Holiday throughout the year (in December diesel-hauled). Daily during July and August

Special events:
Diesel Traction Weekend 5-7 June; Steam Gala — 26-28 June; Family Fun Weekend (provisional) — 26/27 September; Beer & Music Festival — 23-25 October; Midweek Steam Trains — 26-30 October; Santa Specials — 28/29 November, 5/6, 12/13, 19/20 December; Carol YTrain Service — 19 December

Vintage Trains and Dining Trains — ring for details

Behind the Scenes guided tours — 19 April, 31 May, 14 June, 19 July, 16 August, 13 September,

11 October, please ring for details

Facilities for disabled: Level access to all stations. Wheelchair ramps available at all stations (except Damems). Full disabled toilet facilities at Haworth station. Non-folding wheelchairs can be accommodated in guard's compartments. Staff available to offer assistance and advice at all stations. Museum of Rail Travel at Ingrow offers easy access to wheelchair users (inc toilet facilities). Audio loop and Braille facilities available and attention given to those with special needs

Special notes: Accompanied children under 5 years of age free. Children 5-15 and senior citizens at discount rate. Family ticket available (2 adults + 3 children/senior citizen). Free entry to VCT Museum with rover tickets

Membership details: Membership Secretary c/o above address

Membership journal: *Push & Pull* — quarterly

Marketing name: Worth Valley

Kent & East Sussex Railway

Timetable Service

Kent

Member: HRA, TT

The Kent & East Sussex Railway owes much of its charm to its origin as the world's first light railway. The tightly curved line with steep gradients is typical of those country railways that were developed on shoestring budgets to bring the 'iron horse' to sparsely populated areas. Services operate over 10.5 miles of line from the picturesque town of Tenterden to Bodiam.

Pride of the line's coach fleet is the magnificently restored train of vintage carriages built between 1860 and 1901

Company Secretary: Nick Pallant

Headquarters: Kent & East Sussex Railway Co Ltd, Tenterden Town Station, Tenterden, Kent TN30 6HE

Telephone: Tenterden (01580) 762943 (24 hour talking timetable);

Tenterden 01580 765155 (office)

Internet address: *Web site:* www.kesr.org.uk

Main station: Tenterden Town

Other public stations: Rolvenden, Wittersham Road, Northiam, Bodiam

Car parks: Tenterden, Northiam

OS reference:
Tenterden TQ 882336,
Northiam TQ 834266

Access by public transport:
Stagecoach No 400 from Ashford (Kent) main line station. Arriva No 12 Maidstone-Headcorn station-Tenterden & Rye.
Private hire: Wealden Cars
Refreshment facilities: Tenterden Town. Also on many trains. Lunch and afternoon teas on many trains (advance booking essential). Picnic areas at Tenterden, Wittersham Road; seasonally at Northiam and Bodiam
Souvenir shop: Tenterden Town Station; seasonally at Northiam and Bodiam
Museum: Colonel Stephens Railway Museum at Tenterden Town
Depot: Rolvenden
Length of line: 10.5 miles
Passenger trains: Tenterden-Bodiam. All Bank Holidays and school holidays. Daily end July to early September. Most days ring for details, full service in August
Special events: Branch Line Weekend — 21/21 March; Bug Kent Day Out — 28 March; Grandparents Weekend — 18/19 April; Gala — 2-4 May; 1940s Weekend — 16/17 May; Half Term Fun Week — 26-31 May; Ashford Weekend — 6/7 June; Strawberry Express — 20/21 June; Beer Festival (CAMRA) — 27 June; Eastbourne Mini Club Pilgrimage — 28 June; Antiques Railshow — 4 July; All Aboard with Ivor — 26/27 July; Pensioners' Treat — 8-10 September; Hoppers' Weekend — 12/13 September; Day out with Thomas — 19/20, 26/27 September; Tenterden Folk Festival — 3/4 October; Austin Counties Car Rally — 10/11 October; Halloween, Half Term Fun — 26-31 October; Santa Specials — 5/6, 12/13, 19/20, 22-24 December; Post Christmas Blues 28-31 December, 1 January 2010
Facilities for disabled: A special coach for disabled people, 'Petros', is conveyed in many trains

Locomotives and multiple-units

Name	No	Origin	Class	Type	Built
Bodiam	3	LBSCR	A1X	0-6-0T	1872*
Knowle	2678	LBSCR	A1X	0-6-0T	1880
—	753	SECR	P	0-6-0T	1909*
Wainwright	DS238	SR	USA	0-6-0T	1943
Maunsell	65	SR	USA	0-6-0T	1943*
—	1638	GWR	1600	0-6-0PT	1951*
—	20	GWR	AEC	diesel railcar	1940
Norwegian	376	NSB	21c	2-6-0	1919
—	D2023	BR	03	0-6-0DM	1958◊
—	D2024	BR	03	0-6-0DM	1958*
—	D9529	BR	14	0-6-0DH	1964
—	08108	BR	08	0-6-0DE	1955*
Ashford	D6570	BR	33	Bo-Bo	1961*
—	51571	BR	108	DMC	1959*
—	53971	BR	108	DMBS	1959*

Industrial locomotives

Name	No	Builder	Type	Built
Marcia	12	Peckett (1631)	0-4-0T	1923
Charwelton	14	M/Wardle (1955)	0-6-0ST	1917
Holman F. Stephens	23	Hunslet (3791)	0-6-0ST	1952*
Rolvenden	24	Hunslet (3800)	0-6-0ST	1953*
Northiam	25	Hunslet (3797)	0-6-0ST	1953*
—	40	BTH	Bo-Bo	1932*

*in passenger traffic
Charwelton and *Knowle* will enter service during 2009

Passenger stock in service
SECR family saloon; LNWR 6-wheel director's saloon; SECR 4-wheel full third; SR Maunsell CK; GER 6-wheel composite; District Railway 4-wheel full first; 2 SR Maunsell brake open 1st Class; SR Maunsell non-descript brake-open; BR Mk 1 RU and 5 other BR Mk 1 coaches; 1926 Pullman Parlour Cars *Barbara* and *Theodora*

Stock
2 ex-SECR 'Birdcage' coaches; 2 ex-LSWR coaches; 1 GER observation car; 2 Pullman cars; 3 ex-SR Maunsell coaches; 3 steam cranes; large interesting collection of freight vehicles, totalling 51 vehicles

(telephone for confirmation of availability), reserved parking at Tenterden and Northiam.
Toilets with disabled access at Tenterden, Northiam and Bodiam, also in 'Petros'.
Plus induction loop at Tenterden
Special notes: The Wealden Pullman luxury dining car service operates on most Saturday evenings April to October. Roast lunch served most Sundays. Advance booking is essential for these trains. Santa Special services operate on each Saturday and Sunday in December. Advance booking recommended
Membership details: Membership Secretary, c/o above address
Membership journal: *The Tenterden Terrier* — 3 times/year

Kew Bridge Steam Museum

The museum is housed in a magnificent 19th century Pumping Station and centres around the station's five world famous Cornish Beam Engines, three of which can be seen in steam on selected 'Giants of Steam' weekends. Originally used to pump West London's water supply for more than a century, one of them, the 'Grand Junction 90', is the world's largest working beam engine. In surrounding buildings other large engines work at weekends, demonstrating more modern steam and diesel pumping machinery.

The Water For Life Gallery reveals the fascinating history of London's water supply from Roman toilet spoons to the massive 'high-tec' London ring main.

Many Victorian waterworks had their own railway. At Kew Bridge this is demonstrated by a short line, operated by the Museum

Location: 100yd from the north side of Kew Bridge, next to the tall Victorian tower

Operating group: Kew Bridge Engines Trust, Green Dragon Lane, Brentford, Middx TW8 0EN

Telephone: 020 8568 4757 (information line)

Internet address: *Web site:* www.kbsm.org

Car park: Free on site

Access by public transport: *Rail*: SouthWest Trains, Kew Bridge (from Waterloo via Clapham Junction) and North London Line to Gunnersbury; *Bus:* Nos 65, 237, 267, 391; *Tube:* Gunnersbury (District Line, then 237 or 267 bus),

Industrial locomotives
2ft gauge:

Name	No	Builder	Type	Built
—	—*	Hunslet	0-4-0ST	2009
Alister	2	Lister (44052)	4wDM	1958

*new build based on Kerr Stuart 'Wren' class, expected to arrive during spring 2009

Stock
1 manrider

Kew Gardens (District Line, then 391 bus)

Length of line/gauge: About 140yd, 2ft gauge

Public opening:
Museum: Tuesdays to Sundays 11.00-16.00, . Closed Mondays (except Bank Holidays), Good Friday and 22-29 December 2009. Railway: see below

Special events: Stirling & Hot Air Engine Rally — 5 April; Magic of Meccano — 18/19 April; Historic Fire Engine Rally — 17 May; World War 2 and You — 1940s Event — 29-31 August; Festival of Models — 3/4 October; Live Steam Model Railway Show — 14/15 November. Grand New Year Steam up — 1-3 January 2010.

The railway is scheduled to operate on 18/19 April; 3/4, 10, 17, 24, 31 May; 7, 14, 28 June; 5, 12, 18/19, 26 July; 2, 9, 16, 23, 30/31 August; 6, 13, 20, 27 September; 3/4, 11, 18, 25 October; 14/15 November

On site facilities:
Bookshop/toilets/car park. Refreshments available at weekends only 11.00-15.30 (with hot meals available 12.30-14.30)

Facilities for disabled: Wheelchair access to 90% of ground floor areas via ramp and lift. Large print guide available and guide dogs welcome. Wheelchair loan service and wheelchair accessible toilet. Railway carriage can accommodate wheelchairs

Special note: Groups of 20 or more can be given guided tours and a 5% discount on admission charges. Special steaming can be arranged and touch tours are available for partially sighted groups. All groups must be pre-booked.

Children under 16 must be accompanied by an adult

Special facilities: The museum can be hired for corporate or private events. Special steamings can be arranged. Please contact for brochure

Museum contact: Kew Bridge Engines Trust, c/o above address

Other attractions: Museum displays a selection of stationary steam engines and associated water supply displays

---

Kidderminster Railway Museum

Established in an 1878 GWR warehouse, the museum houses an enormous collection of railway relics, photographs and documents, with a number of 'hands-on' exhibits.

Contact address: Station

Approach, Comberton Hill, Kidderminster, Worcestershire DY10 1QX

General Manager: David Postle

Telephone: Kidderminster (01562) 825316

Internet address:

e-mail: krm@krm.org.uk

Web site: www.krm.org.uk

OS reference: SO 837763

Location: Adjacent to SVR station

Car park: SVR car park

Access by public transport: Kidderminster main line station,

Midland Red bus service X92 to Kidderminster
Facilities for disabled: Ramp access for wheelchairs to ground level

Special events: Practical signalling courses using Museum and SVR resources. Film shows, model railway exhibitions, railway art exhibitions, postcard/photograph

fairs,
On site facilities: Souvenirs, refreshments
Public opening: Open on SVR operating days

| Timetable Service | Kirklees Light Railway | West Yorkshire |

Member: HRA
Location/headquarters: Clayton West, A636 Wakefield-Denby Dale road
General Manager: Graham Hurd
Operating society/organisation: Kirklees Light Railway, Park Mill Way, Clayton West, Nr Huddersfield HD8 9XJ
Telephone: (01484) 865727
Internet address: *Web sites:* www.kirkleeslightrailway.com www.friendsofklr.co.uk
Location: Clayton West, the terminus of the railway, is situated midway between Wakefield, Barnsley, Holmfirth and Huddersfield, on the A636 Wakefield-Denby Dale Road
Main station: Clayton West
Other station: Cuckoos Nest, Skelmanthorpe, Shelley
Length of line: 4 miles, 15in gauge
Car park: Clayton West — free
Access by public transport:
By bus: from Holmfirth No 484, from Leeds No 435, from Wakefield No 435, from Huddersfield Nos 80 and 81. Ask driver for Park Mill Way, Clayton West
By rail: to Huddersfield, Wakefield or Denby Dale stations

Locomotives

Name	No	Builder	Type	Built
Fox	—	Taylor	2-6-2T	1987
Badger	—	Taylor	0-6-4T	1991
Tram	7	Taylor	0-4-0	1995
Jay	—	Taylor	4wDH	1992
Hawk	—	Taylor	0-4-4-0*	1998
Owl	—	Taylor	4w-4wTG*	2000

*articulated

Rolling stock
2 x 16-seat guard's vans (heated in winter), 10 x 20-seat closed coaches (heated in winter), 2 x 20-seat semi-open coaches, 1 x 4-wheel flat wagon, 2 x heavy bogie wagons

Refreshment facilities: Clayton West and Shelley station, visitor centre and café
Souvenir shop: Clayton West
On site facilities: Toilets, lake, new picnic area and new play area at both Clayton West and Shelley stations. HQ of Barnsley Society of Model Engineers
Facilities for disabled: None at present
Period of public operation:
Winter— weekends and most school holidays.
Summer — daily from 23 May to end August
Special events: Day out with

Thomas — 28/29 March; Easter Eggspress —10-14 April; Day out with Thomas —29-31 May; Teddy Bears' Picnic — 27/28 June; Day out with Thomas — 19-23, 25-28 August; Friends of Kirklees Light Railway 4th Gala Weekend — 12/13 September; Halloween Ghost Train — 30 October to 1 November; Day out with Thomas — 14/15 November; Santa Specials — weekends 28 November to 24 December
Special facilities: Footplate experience courses

| Timetable Service | Lakeside & Haverthwaite Railway | Cumbria |

Member: HRA, TT
Originally this Furness Railway branch line carried passengers and freight from Ulverston to Lakeside but now the only part remaining is the 3.5-mile section from Haverthwaite to the terminus at Lakeside where connections are made with the steamers which ply

the 10-mile length of Windermere
General Manager: M. A. Maher
Headquarters: Lakeside & Haverthwaite Railway Co Ltd, Haverthwaite Station, Nr Ulverston, Cumbria LA12 8AL
Telephone: Newby Bridge (015395) 31594
Internet address: *Web site:*

www.lakesiderailway.co.uk
Main station: Haverthwaite
Other public stations:
Intermediate station at Newby Bridge. Terminus at Lakeside
OS reference: SD 349843
Car parks: Haverthwaite, Lakeside, charges payable at both
Access by public transport:

Lakeside steamers on Windermere call at Lakeside. CMS bus to Haverthwaite

Refreshment facilities: Haverthwaite

Souvenir shop: Haverthwaite

On site facilities: Picnic area at Haverthwaite. Disabled toilets

Depot: All rolling stock at Haverthwaite

Length of line: 3.5 miles

Passenger trains: Steam-hauled Haverthwaite-Lakeside

Period of public operation: 4 April to 1 November 2009 (inclusive)

Special events: Santa Specials, Day out with Thomas, Halloween (advance booking essential) please contact for details

Facilities for disabled: Access to trains and restaurant

Special notes: Combined railway/lake steamer tickets available, from the station at Haverthwaite and lake steamer piers at Bowness and Ambleside. Lake steamers are operated by Windermere Lake Cruises Ltd

Membership journal: *The Iron Horse* — quarterly

Locomotives and multiple-units

Name	No	Origin	Class	Type	Built
—	20	FR	A5	0-4-0	1863
—	42073	LMS	4MT	2-6-4T	1950
—	42085	LMS	4MT	2-6-4T	1951
—	17(AD601)	LMS	—	0-6-0DE	1945
—	5643	GWR	5600	0-6-2T	1925
—	8(D2117)	BR	03	0-6-0DM	1959
—	D2072	BR	03	0-6-0DM	1959
—	20214	BR	20	Bo-Bo	1967
—	D5301	BR	26	Bo-Bo	1958
—	52071	BRCW	110	DMBC	1961
—	52077	BRCW	110	DMBC	1961

Industrial locomotives

Name	No	Builder	Type	Built
*Caliban**	1	Peckett (1925)	0-4-0ST	1937
Rachel	9	M/Rail (2098)	4wDM	1924
Repulse	11	Hunslet (3698)	0-6-0ST	1950
Princess	14	Bagnall (2682)	0-6-0ST	1942
—	—	Bagnall (2996)	0-6-0ST	1951
—	10	Barclay (1245)	0-6-0T	1911
David	13	Barclay (2333)	0-4-0ST	1953
Cumbria	10	Hunslet (3794)	0-6-0ST	1953
Fluff	16	Hunslet/Fowler	0-4-0DM	1937
—	20	Jones crane	0-4-0DM	1952
Sir James	21	Barclay (1550)	0-6-0F	1917

*under restoration at Steamtown, Carnforth

Stock

10 ex-BR Mk 1 coaches; 1 ex-LNER BG; 1 ex-BR Mk 1 miniature buffet coach, Royal saloon No 5 (built GER, Stratford 1898), North London coach (c1890); selection of freight vehicles

---

Miniature Railway	**Lakeside Miniature Railway**	Lancashire

The longest continuously running 15in gauge railway in Great Britain, running during both world wars. The first train ran at 3pm on 25 May 1911. The line was extended in 1948, now running between two stations, Pleasureland and Marine Parade-Ocean Plaza.

Location: Marine Lake, Southport

Headquarters: 1 Wingates, Penwortham, Preston, Lancs PR1 9YN

Contact: Mr D. Clark

Telephone: 01772 745511

Internet address: *e-mail:* jenc47@hotmail.co.uk

Web site: www.lakesideminiaturerailway.co.uk

Car parking: In Ocean Plaza car parks, opposite

SatNav postcodes: Pleasureland station PR8 1RX Marine Parade station PR8 1RA

On site facilities: Shop (selling ice cream, soft drinks, and Thomas the Tank Engine)

Length of line: 800yd, 15in gauge

Period of public operation: Easter to end of October, and during school holidays (weather permitting). 12.00-16.30. Journey time 5min (single) 14min (return)

Facilities for disabled: Wheelchair access

Membership details: See web site

Fare: £1.50 (single), £2.00 (return)

Locomotives

Name	No	Builder	Type	Built
Duke of Edinburgh	—	Barlow	4-6-2+4-4DE	1947
Prince Charles	—	Barlow	4-6-2+4-4DE	1954
Golden Jubilee	—	Barlow	4-6w+4-4DE	1963
Princess Anne	—	S/Lamb	6w-6DH	1971
Jenny	—	A. Moss	2-6-2DH	2006

Rolling stock

3 sets of carriages each seating 72 passengers

England

Lappa Valley Railway

Member: TT
Location/headquarters:
Benny Halt, St Newlyn East,
Nr Newquay, Cornwall TR8 5LX
Telephone: 01872 510317
Internet address: *Web site:*
www.lappavalley.co.uk
General Manager: Miss Amanda
Booth
Main station: Benny Halt
Other station: East Wheal Rose,
Newlyn Downs Halt
Car park: Benny Halt
Access by public transport: Bus
service, Newquay to Truro and
return. Western Greyhound coaches
to St Newlyn East. Signposted,
half-mile walk from bus stop to
railway. No direct bus service
Refreshment facilities: Café at
East Wheal Rose serving hot and
cold food, snacks, hot and cold
drinks; licensed
Souvenir shop: East Wheal Rose
and Benny Halt
On site facilities: 15in, 10.25in and
7.25in gauge railways. Canoes,
paddle boats, crazy golf, pedal cars,
electric motorbikes, children's play
area, brick path maze, listed engine
house, walks and a video
Depot: Benny Halt
Facilities for disabled: Limited

Locomotives
(15in gauge)

Name	No	Builder	Type	Built
Muffin	2	Berwyn	0-6-0	1967
		rebuilt Tambling		1991
Zebedee	1	S/Lamb	0-6-4T	1974
		rebuilt Tambling		1990
Gladiator	3	Minirail	4w-4wDH	c1960
Pooh	4	Lister (20698)	4wDM	1942

(10.25in gauge)

Name	No	Builder	Type	Built
Duke of Cornwall	—	S/Lamb	4w-4wDH	c1980
Eric	—	Keef	0-6-0DH	2008

Rolling stock
15in gauge — 10 passenger coaches
10.25in gauge — 4 passenger coaches
7.25in gauge — 1 Mardyke APT set

number of reserved parking bays.
Toilets at East Wheal Rose and
Benny Halt. All buildings are single
storey with no steps. Level or
gently sloping paths with even
surfaces. Main steam train has
compartments with doors that will
accommodate wheelchairs (only the
largest motorised wheelchairs are
excluded), ramps and staff available
to assist. The smaller train at East
Wheal Rose cannot take
wheelchairs. Some other attractions
are not suitable for wheelchair users
(eg canoes, mine building, maze
and country walks)
Public opening: Easter to end of
October, usually daily but ring for
early and late season opening days
Special notes: Entry by one all-in
price, except for electric bikes.
   Family tickets and reduced
afternoon saver fares are available
all days. Under 3s free

Launceston Steam Railway

Member: HRA, TT
The railway runs through the
beautiful Kensey Valley on a track
gauge of 1ft 11.5in, following the
trackbed of the old North Cornwall
line. The locomotives formerly
worked on the Dinorwic and
Penrhyn railways in North Wales.
Launceston station contains a
museum of vintage cars and
motorcycles and a collection of
stationary steam engines which are
demonstrated at work. There are
catering, gift shop and bookshop
facilities. At the far end of the line
there are pleasant riverside walks

Industrial locomotives

Name	No	Builder	Type	Built
Lilian	—	Hunslet (317)	0-4-0ST	1883
Velinheli	—	Hunslet (409)	0-4-0ST	1886
Covertcoat	—	Hunslet (679)	0-4-0ST	1898
Sybil	—	Bagnall (1760)	0-4-0ST	1906
Dorothea	—	Hunslet (763)	0-4-0ST	1901
—	—	M/Rail (5646)	4wDM	1933
—	—	M/Rail (9546)	4wDM	1950

Locomotive notes: All passenger trains are steam-hauled

Stock
1 electric inspection trolley; 4 bogie carriages (2 open, 2 closed), 1 diesel-
electric railcar for maintenance staff
2 Post Office Railway 'Mail Train' units

England

and a shaded picnic area, adjacent to Newmills Farm Park (a popular separate attraction). The covered rolling stock ensures an enjoyable visit whatever the weather. The station area was once the site of an Augustinian Priory some of which can be seen by visitors to the railway

Location: Newport Industrial Estate, Launceston, Cornwall

OS reference: SX 328850

Operating society/organisation: The Spice Settlement Trust Co Ltd, trading as the Launceston Steam Railway, Newport, Launceston PL15 8DA

Telephone: (01566) 775665

Stations: Launceston-Hunts Crossing-New Mills

Car park: Newport Industrial Estate, Launceston

Length of line: 2.5 miles

Gauge: 1ft 11.5in

Access by public transport: Main line Gunnislake 13 miles, Plymouth or Bodmin 25 miles then bus

On site facilities: Buffet, transport museum, workshop tours, gift and bookshop, all situated at Launceston

Period of public operation: Easter (10-17 April). Whitsun (24-29 May). Peak season, daily 5 July until 25 September EXCEPT Saturdays. Half term in October

Public opening: Trains run from 10.30-16.30. Departures about every 50min — 11.00, 11.50, 12.45, 14.00, 14.45, 15.35, 16.30. Day Rover Tickets, unlimited riding on date of issue of ticket. Fares held for 2009

Family ticket: Available, 2 adults and up to 4 children, £25. Adults £8.25, children £5.50

Free travel: Children under three years old

Senior citizens: Discounted tickets £6.50

Groups: Discounted tickets

Journey time: Return 35min

Facilities for disabled: Easy access to all areas except bookshop and motorcycle museum. No toilet facilities for disabled. However, public toilets are reasonably accessible

Special events: Double-headed trains on Wednesdays in August (whenever possible). Demonstration freight trains (contact for details)

Steam Centre — Lavender Line — East Sussex

Member: HRA

The Lavender Line is centred around a typical country station, which, somewhat untypically, is in the village it was built to serve. The image portrayed is of the transition steam-diesel era of the 1950s/1960s on the Southern Region of British Railways

Location: Isfield Station, Isfield, Nr Uckfield, East Sussex TN22 5XB. Isfield village is off the A26 between Lewes and Uckfield

OS reference: TQ 452171

Operating society/organisation: The Lavender Line Preservation Society

Telephone/Fax:
Information line: 0891 800645
Business/fax: 01825 750515 (24hr answerphone when not manned)

Internet address: Web site: www.lavender-line.co.uk

Car park: On site, free to patrons

Access by car: The village of Isfield lies just off the A26 between Lewes and Uckfield and is clearly signposted. From the Little Horstead roundabout on the A22 just outside Uckfield, take the A26 south towards Lewes and after about 1 mile take the small right-hand turn marked Isfield. Follow the road until you see the railway on your right. From the A272 running between Uckfield and Haywards Heath, take the turn at Piltdown and follow the signs to the Lavender Line and Isfield. From Lewes take the A26 northwards towards Uckfield. After about 5 miles look for a turning on the left to Isfield, follow the road until you see the railway on your right

Access by public transport:

Multiple-unit

Name	No	Origin	Class	Type	Built
—	69333	BR	422 / 4BIG	TRBS	1965
—*	60151	BR	205	DTC	1962
—*	60678	BR	205	DMBS	1962
—	60822	BR	205	DTC	1957
—*	60832	BR	205	DTC	1962

*unit 205033

Industrial locomotives

Name	No	Builder	Type	Built
Blackie	68012	Hunslet (3193)	0-6-0ST	1944
—	—	Sentinel (6515)	0-4-0VBT	1945
—	—	Barclay	0-4-0DM	1945
—	—	Vulcan	0-4-0DM	1945
—	15	Planet (3865)	4wDM	1965

*2ft gauge

Stock

A selection of BR Mk 1 vehicles including BCK, TSO and BG, as well as a selection of wagons

By bus: Service 29 run by Brighton & Hove Buses calls at Isfield and runs between Brighton and Tunbridge Wells. Tel: 01273 886200 or visit http://www.buses.co.uk

By rail: Main line stations at Lewes and Uckfield. On Sundays trains to Uckfield only operate on a much reduced frequency. Tel: 08457 484950

On site facilities: 'Cinders' buffet/restaurant, gift shop, goods shed museum, picnic area, access to signalbox. Children's parties arranged on operating days. Family area. Private functions, weddings and parties etc catered for
Length of line: 1 mile each out and back trip, takes 15min
Public opening: Open Sundays all year, Bank Holidays, weekends in June, July and August. Wednesdays and Thursdays in August. Closed 26/27 December.
Please note that the Isfield site is normally open for viewing outside of operating dates
Facilities for disabled: Access to most facilities on site. Toilets with wheelchair access and baby changing facilities. Wheelchair access to most of site except signalbox and trains. A ramp is available for partially disabled access to the trains
Special events: Ivor the Engine — 16/17, 24/25 May. Please ring or see web site for details of this and other special events.
Ticket price is valid for unlimited rides on day of issue; however, on special event days entry prices, and conditions, may vary
Special facilities: Footplate courses, occasional wine and dine services. Please contact for details

| Museum | Leeds Industrial Museum | Leeds |

Location: The Leeds Industrial Museum, Armley Mills, Canal Road, Leeds LS12 2QF
OS reference: SE 275342
Operating society/organisation: Leeds City Council, Department of Learning & Leisure, The Town Hall, Headrow, Leeds LS1 2QF
Curator of Engineering: N. Dowlan
Telephone: (0113) 263 7861
Internet address: www.leeds.goc.uk/armleymills
Car park: Cark park adjacent to the Museum
Access by public transport: Nos 5, 14 and 67 from City Square, Leeds (outside the railway station). Services 15, 33, 33A, 670 and 760 go to the VUE Cinema complex on Kirkstall Road from Leeds city bus station
Public opening: Tuesdays to Saturdays 10.00-17.00, Sundays 13.00-17.00. Closed Sundays and Mondays (except Bank Holidays). Last admission 16.00 on all days
On site facilities: Museum shop, refreshments (vending machines), picnic area
Special notes: Facilities for the disabled (toilets etc), lifts. Museum can be viewed by visitors in wheelchairs (most areas are accessible)
Details of locomotive and rolling stock: Locomotive collection includes steam, diesel, mines locomotives and a narrow gauge railway and engines

Industrial locomotives

Name	No	Builder	Type	Built
1ft 6in gauge				
Jack	—	Hunslet 684)	0-4-0WT	1898
Coffin	—*	G/Bat (1326)	0-4-0BE	1933
2ft gauge				
Barber	—	T/Green (441)	0-6-2ST	1908
Cheetal	—	Fowler (15991)	0-6-0WT	1923
Simplex	—	M/Rail (1369	4wPM	1918
Hudson Fordson	—	Hudson (36863)	4wDM	1928
Layer	—*	Fowler (21294)	4wDM	1936
Hudson Hunslet	—	Hunslet (2959)	4wDM	1944
Resin	—	Hunslet (2008)	0-4-0DM	1939
Nacob	—*	Hunslet (5340)	0-4-0DM	1957
Sharlston	—†	H/Clarke (1164)	0-4-0DM	1959
Demtox	—†*	Hunslet (6048)	0-4-0DM	1961
2ft 1in gauge				
Fricl	—*	Hunslet (4019)	0-4-0DM	1948
Pitpo	—*	Hunslet	0-4-0	1955
Calverton	—*	H/Clarke (1368)	0-4-0DM	1965
2ft 6in gauge				
Junin	—	H/Clarke (D557)	2-6-2DM	1930
Fimyn	—†	Hunslet (3411)	0-4-0DM	1947
2ft 8in gauge				
Ficol	—*	Hunslet (3200)	0-4-0DM	1945
2ft 11in gauge				
Lurch	—	H/Clarke (D571)	4wDM	1932
3ft gauge				
Lord Granby	—*	H/Clarke (633)	0-4-0ST	1902
Cement	—*	Fowler (20685)	2-4-0DM	1935
Lofti	—*	Hunslet (4057)	0-6-0DM	1953
3ft 6in gauge				
Pioneer	—	H/Clarke (D634)	0-6-0DM	1946
Festival of Britain	—*	H/Clarke (D733)	0-6-0DM	1951
Standard gauge				
Hodbarrow	—*	Hunslet (299)	0-4-0ST	1882

England

Name	No	Builder	Type	Built
Aldwyth	—	M/Wardle (865)	0-6-0ST	1882
Capper	—	Fowler (22060)	0-4-0DM	1938
Fort William	—*	Fowler (22893)	0-4-0DM	1940
Trecwn	—	Hunslet (2390)	0-4-0DM	1941
Elizabeth	—	H/Clarke (1888)	0-4-0ST	1958
Southam No 2	—*	H/Clarke (D625)	0-4-0DM	1942
Luton	—	G/Bat (1210)	0-4-0BE	1930
Smithy Wood	—*	G/Bat (2543)	0-4-0WE	1955

Notes

*not currently on public display
†on loan to Red Rose Steam Society/Astley Green Colliery Museum
Simplex is on loan to Moseley Industrial Railway Museum
Barber is on loan to the South Tynedale Railway Trust from February 2004

Timetable Service — Leighton Buzzard Railway — Bedfordshire

Member: HRA, TT

The LBR enables visitors to take a 70min journey into the vanished world of the English light railway. Sharp curves and steep gradients make the locomotives work hard and it is unique with its roadside running. The LBR possesses one of the largest collection of narrow gauge locomotives in Britain together with a varied selection of coaches and wagons — an important part of the national railway heritage. Many items are on permanent display, and some can be seen in action at special events

General Manager: J. Horsley

Headquarters: Leighton Buzzard Railway, Page's Park Station, Billington Road, Leighton Buzzard, Bedfordshire LU7 4TN

OS reference: Page's Park SP 928242

Telephone: (01525) 373888, 24hr answerphone with service and event details

Fax: (01525) 377814

Internet address: *e-mail:* station@lbngrs.org.uk
Web site: www.buzzrail.co.uk

Main station: Page's Park. The station is on the south side of Leighton Buzzard, near the A505/A4146 roundabout

Other public stations: Stonehenge Works

Car park: Page's Park, free

Access by public transport:
Leighton Buzzard main line station, London Midland services from London (Euston), Watford, Hemel

Locomotives

Name	No	Builder	Type	Built
—	—	O&K (2544)	0-4-0WT	1907
Pedemoura	—	O&K (10808)	0-6-0WT	1924
—	778	Baldwin (44656)	4-6-0T	1917
—	—	Freudenstein (73)	0-4-0WT	1901
Sezela No 4	—	Avonside (1738)	0-4-0T	1915
Elidir	—	Avonside (2071)	0-4-0T	1933
Peter Pan	114	K/Stuart (4256)	0-4-0ST	1922
Chaloner	1	de Winton	0-4-0VBT	1877
Bluebell	1	Hibberd (2631)	4wDM	1938
Pixie	2	K/Stuart (4260)	0-4-0ST	1922
Rishra	3	Baguley (2007)	0-4-0T	1921
Doll	4	Barclay (1641)	0-6-0T	1919
Elf	5	O&K (12740)	0-6-0WT	1936
Falcon	7	O&K (8986)	4wDM	1938
—	8	Ruston (217999)	4wDM	1943
Madge	9	O&K (7600)	4wDM	1934
Haydn Taylor	10	M/Rail (7956)	4wDM	1945
P. C. Allen	11	O&K (5834)	0-4-0WT	1912
—	12	M/Rail (6012)	4wPM	1930
Arkle	13	M/Rail (7108)	4wDM	1937
—	14	Hunslet (3646)	4wDM	1946
—	15	Hibberd (2514)	4wDM	1941
—	16	Lister (11221)	4wDM	1939
Damredub	17	M/Rail (7036)	4wDM	1936
Feanor	18	M/Rail (11003)	4wDM	1956
—	19	M/Rail (11298)	4wDM	1965
—	20	M/Rail (60s317)	4wDM	1966
Festoon	21	M/Rail (4570)	4wPM	1929
—	22	under construction	4wDM	—
—	23	Ruston (164346)	4wDM	1932
—	25	M/Rail (7214)	4wDM	1938
—	24	M/Rail (11297)	4wDM	1965
Yimkin	26	Ruston (203026)	4wDM	1941
—	27	Ruston (408430)	4wDM	1957
RAF Stanbridge	28	Ruston (200516)	4wDM	1940
Creepy	29	Hunslet (6008)	4wDM	1963
—	30	M/Rail (8695)	4wDM	1941
—	31	Lister (4228)	4wPM	1931
—	32	Ruston (172892)	4wDM	1934
—	33	Hibberd (3582)	4wDM	1954

England

Hempstead, Milton Keynes and Northampton (Tel: 08457 484950). Nearest bus stops at Morrisons supermarket (5min walk) and Leighton Buzzard town centre (20 min walk). (Tel: 01234 228337 for details)

Refreshment facilities: Buffet at Page's Park for hot & cold snacks, drinks and ice creams. Refreshments also at Stonehenge Works

Souvenir shop: Page's Park and Stonehenge Works

Depots: Page's Park and Stonehenge Works

Length of line: 2.85 miles, 2ft gauge

Journey time: Single 25min, return 70min

Passenger trains: Page's Park-Stonehenge Works

Group discounts for pre-booked parties of 10 or more people. Packages such as Birthday Breaks, Schools trains and Sunset Specials available, plus train hire

Period of public operation:
Sundays 15 March-8 November;
Mondays 13 April, 4, 25 May, 31 August;
Tuesdays 26 May, 4-25 August;
Wednesdays 15 April, 27 May-2 September, 28 October;
Thursdays 28 May, 6-20 August
Friday s10 April, 29 May
Saturdays 11 April, 2, 23, 30 May, 1 August to 5 September, 7 November.

Special events: Mothering Sunday — 22 March; Teddy Bears' Bank Holiday — 4 May; Narrow Gauge at War — 23-31 May; Father's Day — 21 June; Vintage Vehicles Rally — 28 June; *Doll's* Birthday Party — 23-31 August; Steam Up Weekend — 6/7 September;

Name	No	Builder	Type	Built
Red Rum	34	M/Rail (7105)	4wDM	1936
Binky	35	Hunslet (6619)	0-4-0DM	1966
Caravan	36	M/Rail (7129)	4wDM	1938
—	37	Ruston (172901)	4wDM	1934
Harry Barnet	38	Lister (37170)	4wDM	1951
T. W. Lewis	39	Ruston (375316)	4wDM	1954
Trent	40	Ruston (283507)	4wDM	1949
Somme	41	Hunslet (2536)	4wDM	1941
Sarah	42	Ruston (223692)	4wDM	1944
—	43	M/Rail (10409)	4wDM	1954
—	44	M/Rail (7933)	4wDM	1941
—	45	M/Rail (21615)	4wDM	1957
—	46	Ruston (209430)	4wDM	1942
—	47	Hudson (38384)	4wDM	1930
MacNamara	48	Hunslet (4351)	4wDM	1952
—	49	Hibberd (2586)	4wDM	1941
—	50	Hibberd (1568)	4wPM	1927
Beaudesert	80	A/Keef (59R)	4wDH	1999
Peter Wood	81	Hunslet (9347)	4wDH	1994
—	3098	M/Rail (1369)	4wPM	1918
—	2182	M/Rail (461)	4wPM	1917
LOD 758009	—	M/Rail (8641)	4wDM	1941
LOD 758220	—	M/Rail (8745)	4wDM	1942
RTT/767182	—	Wickham (2522)	4wPMR	1938
WD 767139	—	Wickham (3282)	4wPMR	1943

Stock
10 coaches and a wide selection of wagons

A selection of locomotives and rolling stock is on public display at any one time. Viewing of other stock is by prior arrangement. Some items stored off site

Halloween Haunting — 1 November; 90th Birthday Party — 7/8 November

Facilities for disabled: Priority parking at Page's Park. Ramp access to all facilities including dedicated toilet at Page's Park. Wheelchairs are conveyed in specially adapted coaches. Advance notice appreciated. Web site pages and leaflets available in large print on request

Membership details: The line is operated by unpaid volunteers. Membership secretary, c/o above address

Membership journal: *Chaloner* — quarterly

Marketing name: The Leighton Buzzard Slow Train, England's Friendly Little Line

Miniature Railway	Lightwater Valley Theme Park	North Yorkshire

Location: Lightwater Valley Theme Park

Headquarters: North Stainley, Ripon, North Yorkshire HG4 3HT

Contact: Paul Walker (Operations Manager), Tony Bolsover (Maintenance Manager)

Telephone: 0871 720 0011

Fax: 0871 720 0011

Internet addresses: *e-mail:* leisure@lightwatervalley.co.uk
Web site: www.lightwatervalley.co.uk

Car parking: On site, free

Access by public transport: By rail: Harrogate (12 miles) and Thirsk (9 miles)

On site facilities: Home to three great attractions, all set in 175 acres of gorgeous North Yorkshire parkland (theme park, shopping village and birds of prey centre)

Length of line: 15in gauge; 1 mile long loop circuit including four stations

Period of public operation: Easter-October. Telephone for details

Lincolnshire Wolds Railway

Members: HRA
The only standard gauge steam railway in Lincolnshire open to the public. The location is part of the original Great Northern Railway, which opened in 1848
Headquarters: The Railway Station, Ludborough, Grimsby, NE Lincs DN36 5SQ
Telephone: 01507 363881
Internet address: *Web site:* www.lincolnshirewoldsrailway. co.uk
Contacts: David Ambler / Frank Street / Neil Brown
Main station: Ludborough
OS reference: TF 302986
Car park: Opposite station site
Access by public transport: No access by rail, very limited Grimsby-Louth bus service
Refreshment facilities: Light refreshments available in buffet car in bay platform on diesel and steam days
Souvenir shop: On site
Museum: On site
Depot: On site
Length of line: 1.5 miles
Period of public operation: Site open for static viewing all weekends except Christmas. April to September 09.00-16.00, October to March 09.00-15.00. First train leaves at 11.00 on following dates: 29 March; 12/13, 26 April; 3/4, 24/25 May; 7, 21 June; 5, 19, 26 July; 2, 5, 9, 12, 16, 19, 23, 26, 30/31 August; 12/13, 27 September; 11, 25, 28, 31 October; 22

Locomotives and multiple-units

Name	No	Origin	Class	Type	Built
—	D3167	BR	08	0-6-0DE	1955
—	97650	BR	—	0-6-0DE	1953
—	62887*	BR	4CIG/ 421	MBS	1970

*non-runner in use as disabled buffet coach

Industrial locomotives

Name	No	Builder	Type	Built
Lion	—	Peckett (1657)	0-4-0ST	1914
Fulstow	2	Peckett (1749)	0-4-0ST	1928
Moorbarrow	—	RSH (7849)	0-6-0ST	1955
M. F. P. No 1	—	Fowler (4210131)	0-4-0DM	1957
M. O. P. No 8	—	Fowler (4210145)	0-4-0DM	1958
Tioxide No 4	—	R/Hornsby (375713)	0-4-0DM	1954
Tioxide No 6	—	R/Hornsby (414303)	0-4-0DM	1957
Tioxide No 7	7	R/Hornsby (421418)	0-4-0DM	1958
—	—	Sentinel (10166)	0-6-0DH	1963
Colonel B	—	Hunslet (5308)	4wDH	1963

Stock
6 ex-BR Mk 2 coaches, various wagons

Owner
D3167 and 97650 on loan from Lincoln City Council

November; 13, 20, 28 December
Special events: Steam dates for 2009 are: Lincolnshire Louth Motor Club — 21 June; Strawberry Cream Scones — 5 July; Fund raising day for Lincolnshire & Nottinghamshire Air Ambulance — 19 July; 1940s Weekend — 12/13 September; Halloween Themed Month — 11, 25, 28, 31 October; Santa arrives to receive children's letters — 22 November; Santa Specials —13, 20 December (booking only)

Facilities for disabled: Disabled persons can ride on the train, have access to the buffet car and disabled toilets
Membership journal: *On the Line* — is the society magazine produced by the supporting association, 3 times/year
Special note: Unlimited travel on the day

Locomotion — The NRM at Shildon

Member: HRA
Locomotion is an £11 million project, a joint venture between the local authority and the National Railway Museum at York, the first branch of a national museum in the region. The development includes interactive displays within buildings which are of historical

Locomotives and multiple-units

Name	No	Origin	Class	Type	Built
Sans Pareil		L&MR		0-4-0	1829
Cornwall	3020	LNWR	—	2-2-2	1847
—	158A	MR	—	2-4-0	1866
—	563	LSWR	T3	4-4-0	1893
—	1247	GNR	J52	0-6-0ST	1899
—	1	NER	BTH	Bo electric	1904
—	2	NSR	New L	0-6-2T	1923

England

importance in terms of the town's railway heritage and a brand new high quality 6,000 sq ft centre, which houses up to 60 vehicles from the national collection

Museum Manager: Dr George Muirhead

Location/address: Locomotion, Shildon, Co Durham DL4 1PQ

Telephone: (01388) 777999 / 772000

Telephone/Fax: (01388) 771448

Internet addresses: *e-mail:* info@locomotion.uk.com
Web site: www.locomotion.uk.com

Car parking: Available on site, also disabled and coach parking

Access by public transport: Rail – 3min walk from Shildon station. Bus – local bus services (call Traveline on 0870 608 2608).

Access by car: From the south, junction 60 A1M, take A689 and A6072 to Coundon roundabout then turn left by a minor road to Shildon

On site facilities: Café, children's playground, picnic area, public art sculpture, shop

Length of line: 1 kilometre

Public opening: 10.00-17.00 every day from Easter to early October. 10.00-16.00 Wednesday to Sunday from early October to Easter. Closed over Christmas and New Year. Limited opening on Mondays and Tuesdays — please call for information

Special events: A full and exciting events programme, contact Locomotion for full details

Access for disabled: All buildings fully accessible. Call Locomotion in advance to book a wheelchair. Bio-bus accommodates disabled visitors to transport from one end of the site to the other

Special facilities: There are three conference rooms, each holding from 10 to 65 people, catering and presentation equipment available. Space for 200 people for a sit down meal in the Collection building.

Special note: Steam train rides on some school holidays and event days

Name	No	Origin	Class	Type	Built
—	2700	LMS	5P4F	2-6-0	1934
—	10656	SR	2BIL	DMBSK	1937
—	12123	SR	2BIL	DTCK	1937
Green Arrow	4771	LNER	V2	2-6-2	????
Deltic	—	E/Electric	-	Co-Co	1955
—	E5001	BR	71	Bo-Bo	1959
—	03090	BR	03	0-6-0DM	1960
Sans Pareil	—*	L&MR		0-4-0	1980

Industrial and Army locomotives

Name	No	Builder	Type	Built
Hetton Loco	—	G. Stephenson	0-4-0	1851
—	755	Siemens	4wRE	1898
—	—	Simplex (4217)	4wPM	1925
Merlin	—	Peckett	0-4-0ST	1939
Eustace Forth	15	RSH (7063)	0-4-0ST	1942
Eustace Forth	—	R/Hornsby (7063)	0-6-0ST	1942
King Fisal of Iraq	—	Hunslet (3183)	0-6-0ST	1944
—	1	Barclay (2373)	0-4-0F	1956
Rowntrees No 3	—	R/Hornsby (441934)	4wDM	1960
—	14†	H/Clarke (D1274)	0-6-0DM	1961
MTR	9†	Hunslet (9227)	B-BDH	1986
—	H001	Sentinel (100003)	4wDH	1959

*replica of original Liverpool & Manchester Railway built for the 150th anniversary
†3ft gauge

Rolling stock powered units – gas turbine
1972   BR Advanced Passenger Train

Rolling stock powered units – electric
1983   BR APT prototype train

Rolling stock powered units — Diesel
1937   SR Driving Motor Brake Third No S10656S
1937   SR Driving Trailer Composite No S12123S

Rolling stock – departmental
1850   GNR 4-wheel hand crane No 112
1891   NER snowplough No DE900566
1904   MR Officers' Saloon No 2234
1949   BR Matisa tamping machine No 74007
1957   BR Track recording trolley No DX 50002 Neptune

Rolling stock — passenger
1845   S&DR 1st/3rd Composite No 59
1850   SDR 3rd No 179
1872   NLR Directors' Saloon No 1032
1887   GWR 6-wheel tricomposite No 820
1905   LNWR Corridor 1st Brake 5154 (Royal Train)
1905   LNWR Corridor 1st Brake 5154 (support vehicle)
1908   ECJS Passenger Brake Van No 109
1928   LMS 3rd Sleeping Car No 14241
1962   BR Mk I 1st corridor No 21274

Rolling stock – freight and non passenger carrying
1826   Cramlington Colliery Chaldron Wagon
1870   S&DR Chaldron Wagon (replica)
1870   Seaham Harbour Colliery Chaldron Wagon
1889   Shell-Mex oil tank wagon No 512

England

1901	Shell/BP Tank Wagon No 3171
1907	NER 16-ton bogie stores van No 041273
1912	NER Sand wagon No DE14974
1920	GCR single bolster wagon
1920	GNR double bolster wagon
1926	GWR Fitted open wagon No 108246
1935	GWR Motor car van No 126438
1936	LMS Tube wagon No 499254
1940	WD Warflat No 161042
1940	LNER Tunnel Van No DE471818
1946	SNCF 16-ton mineral wagon No ADB192437
1946	LNER 20-ton hopper wagon No E270919
1950	BR 24-ton iron ore hopper wagon No B436275
1951	BR(SR) Show cattle wagon No S3733S
1952	BR 30-ton bogie bolster wagon No B943139
1953	Buxton Lime Quarries 23-ton bogie hopper wagon No 19154
1954	National Benzole oil tank wagon No 2022
1955	BR china clay tip wagon No B743141
1957	BR Horse box No S96369
1959	BR Conflat No B737725
1960	BR Banana Van No B882593
1961	BR Presflo cement wagon No B873368
1964	Prototype HAA coal hopper wagon, No 350000
1965	BR Boiler Wagon Nos DB902805, DB902806, DB902807, DB902808
1970	Phillips Petroleum 100-ton GLW tank wagon No PP85209
1970	S&D Chaldron Wagon (replica), Shildon

Locomotive tender
SDR 'collier' class *Etherley*

Powered units
SR   2BIL unit, No 2090

Passenger stock
| 1850 | SDR 3rd No 179 |
| 1908 | ECJS Passenger brake van LNER No 396 S&D Chaldron wagon |

Owner
R/Hornsby (441934) on loan from North Yorkshire Moors Railway

London Transport Museum

Museum — London

Member: HRA, TT
Lively new galleries tell the story of London's transport system and how it shaped the lives of people living and working in London, including current and future transport developments.The Design for Travel gallery showcases original artworks and advertising posters
Location: Covent Garden Piazza, London WC2E 7BB
OS reference: TQ 303809
Operating society/organisation: Transport for London
Telephone:
020 7567 7299 (24hr recorded information)
020 7565 7298 (Administration, education service, group bookings, events and activities, corporate hospitality, mail order enquiries)
Fax: 020 7565 7250
Internet address:
e-mail: enquiry@ltmuseum.co.uk
Web site: www.ltmuseum.co.uk
Access by public transport: Tube stations: Covent Garden, Holborn, Leicester Square
Main line station: Charing Cross, Buses to Strand or Aldwych
On site facilities: Photo and research library (by appointment

Locomotives

Name	No	Origin	Class	Type	Built
—	23	Met Rly	A	4-4-0T	1866
John Hampden	5	Met Rly		Bo-Bo	1922

Electric stock
4248 District Rly Q23 stock driving motor coach 1923
11182 LPTB 1938 stock driving motor coach
400 Met Rly bogie stock coach 1899
30 City & South London Rly 'Padded Cell' coach 1890

Stock
1 electric tram; 2 horse buses; 4 motorbuses; 1 trolleybus; 1 horse tram

only), Resource Centre, Lecture Theatre. Shop, café, lift, toilets (inc disabled) and baby changing facilities
Public opening (museum):
Saturday to Thursday: 10.00-18.00.
Fridays: 11.00-21.00 (last admission 20.15).
Closed 24-26 December
Public opening (shop):
Sunday to Tuesday: 10.00-18.30.
Wednesday, Thursday and Saturday: 10.00-19.00
Friday: 11.00-21.00.
Closed 25/26 December
Public opening (Upper Deck Café Bar):

Monday to Thursday: 10.00-21.30.
Fridays: 11.00-21.30.
Saturday: 10.00-21.30.
Sundays: 10.00-18.00
Closed 24-26 December, 1 January.
For group bookings please contact the Museum in advance, group rates are available for pre-booked parties
Facilities for disabled: A lift and ramps give access throughout the Museum. Facilities include a disabled toilet. Reduced admission for registered disabled visitors and person accompanying them
Membership details: Benefits of membership include discount on

purchases made at Museum shops at Covent Garden and Acton, discounted rate on talks and events. These are just some of the benefits

available. Details from the Friends of London Transport Museum on 020 7565 7298

| Museum | London Transport Museum Depot | London |

Member: HRA, TT

The Depot is a working museum store and treasure trove of over 370,000 objects. Attractions include rare road and rail vehicles, station models, signs, ticket machines, posters and original artwork

Contact: London Transport Museum, 39 Wellington Street, London WC2E 7BB

Depot location:
2 Museum Way, 118-120 Gunnersbury Lane, Acton, London W3 8BQ

Operating society/organisation:
Transport for London

Telephone:
020 7565 7299 (24hr recorded information)
020 7379 6344 (Administration, education service, group bookings, events and activities, corporate hospitality, mail order enquiries)

Fax: 020 7565 7250

Internet address:
e-mail: enquiry@ltmuseum.co.uk
Web site: www.ltmuseum.co.uk

Access by public transport: Bus (E3) or Underground to Acton Town station

Access by car: Parking on site is reserved for blue badge holders and must be requested in advance. Limited parking available in local area. Parking available for groups booking a private view

On site facilities: Museum shop (Depot open weekends only), lecture theatre, toilets

Public opening:
Pre-booked guided tours on the last Friday and Saturday of the month. Private views can be arranged for groups.
For group bookings, please contact the Museum in advance on 020 7565 7298. Group rates available for pre-booked parties of 10 or more

Locomotives and multiple-units

Name	No	Origin	Class	Type	Built
—	13	C&SLR	—		1890
—	ESL107	LT	—	Bo-Bo	1940
—	L35	LT	—	Bo-BoBE	1938
—	10012	LT	1938	DM	1938
—	012256	LT	1938	T	1939
—	12048	LT	1938	M	1939
—	11012	LT	1938	DM	1938
—	320	LT	Standard		1925-34
—	846	LT	Standard		1925-34
—	1789	LT	Standard		1925-34
—	3693	LT	Standard		1925-34
—	3327	LT	Standard		1925-34
—	4184	LT	Q	DM	1923
—	08063	LT	Q35	T	1935
—	4416	LT	Q38	DM	1938
—	4417	LT	Q38	DM	1938
—	22679	LT	R49	DM	1952
—	16	LT	Prototype	DM	1986
—	3530	LT	1972	DM	1972
—	3763	LT	1983	DM	1983
—	—	MR*	—	TC	1887

*Metroploitan railway Jubilee coach body

Industrial locomotives

Origin	Builder	Type	Built
Wotton Tramway†	A/Porter (807)	0-4-0TG	1872

Rolling stock: freight
City & South London Railway ballast wagon, No 63 of 1921
Metropolitan Railway milk van of 1890

†on loan to Buckinghamshire Railway Museum

Facilities for disabled: Disabled toilet, on the ground floor, ramps and wheelchair platforms to some areas and a lift to the first floor. Parking on site for blue badge holders must be booked in advance. The Museum offers a range of British Sign Language tours and talks, as well as object handling sessions. For further information, contact the Resource Desk on 020 7565 7298 or e-mail enquiry@ltmuseum.co.uk

Membership details: Details from the Friends of London Transport Museum on 020 7565 7296. Benefits include free entry to the Depot Open Weekends (whilst the Museum in Covent Garden is undergoing refurbishment), discount on purchases made at London Transport Museum shops in Covent Garden and Acton, discounted rate on talks and events. These are just some of the benefits available

Miniature Railway — Longleat Railway — Wiltshire

Contact: J. E. Hayton
Headquarters: Longleat Railway, Warminster, Wilts BA12 7NW
Telephone: 01985 845408
Internet address: *Web site:* www.longleat.co.uk
Car parking: On site
Access by public transport: Main line stations at Frome or Warminster
On site facilities: Too numerous to list, but include: grounds and gardens, safari park, historic house, Lord Bath's murals, safari boats, pets corner, etc
Souvenir shops: throughout the attraction
Length of line: 1.25 miles, 15in gauge
Opening times: House open all year (except Christmas Day). All attractions open daily from mid-February to early November. Railway operates from March to November 10.00 (up to) 18.00 (might be earlier during off-peak season).
Please contact for opening times/dates of specific attractions.
Special events: Santa trains — end November and December (weekends)
Facilities for disabled: On each train

Locomotives

Name	No	Builder	Type	Built
Lenka	4	Longleat	4-4DHR	1984
Ceawlin	5	Longleat*	2-8-2DH	1989
John Hayton	6	Exmoor Steam Railway	0-6-2	2004
Flynn	7	Keef (79)	0-6-0DH	2007

*rebuilt from Severn-Lamb 2-8-0DH dating from 1975

Rolling stock

11 passenger coaches and 3 works wagons

Steam Centre — Lynton & Barnstaple Railway — Devon

Member: HRA

The Lynton & Barnstaple Railway in North Devon is one of the world's most famous and picturesque narrow gauge lines. Passengers can now travel along part of the original route within the Exmoor National Park above the Heddon Valley near Parracombe. Awarded the HRA Annual Award for Small Groups 'for successfully re-creating the ambience of the legendary L&BR and for successfully running trains on the original trackbed at Woody Bay 69 years after the railway closed'

General Manager: Martyn Budd
Location/headquarters: Lynton & Barnstaple Railway, Woody Bay Station, Martinhoe Cross, Parracombe, Devon EX31 4RA
Telephone: 01598 763487
Internet address: *Web site:* www.lynton-rail.co.uk
Contact: Tony Nicholson, 10 Castle Heights, Lynton, Devon EX35 6JD
Chairman L&BR Trust: Peter Miles

Main station: Woody Bay
Other stations: Killington Lane, Chelfham
OS references:
Woody Bay SS 684464
Killington Lane SS 671458
Chelfham SS 610357
SatNav postcodes:
Woody Bay EX31 4RA
Chelfham EX31 4RP
Car park: Woody Bay station only
Access by public transport: First Buses service 300 (Minehead-Ilfracombe), 309 and 310 (both Barnstaple-Lynton) all stop at Woody Bay station; the 310 largely follows the original route of the railway and also stops at Chelfham

Length of line: Currently 1 mile, 1ft 11.5in gauge
On site facilities: Shop and tearoom at Woody Bay station
Passenger services: Most days between Easter and the end of October
Facilities for disabled: Toilets and access to trains and refreshments/shop
Membership details: Available from Woody Bay station
Membership journal: *Lynton & Barnstaple Railway Magazine* — three times a year

Locomotives

Name	No	Builder	Type	Built
Gertrude	—*	A/Barclay (1578)	0-6-0T	1918
Axe	—	K/Stuart (2451)	0-6-0WT	1915
Sid	—	Maffei (4127)	0-4-0WT	1925
Pilton	—*	Drewry (2393)	0-6-0DM	1952
Heddon Hall	—	Hunslet (6660)	4wDH	1965
Titch	—	M/Rail (8729)	4wDM	1941

*under restoration off-site

Mangapps Farm Railway Museum

Mangapps re-creates the atmosphere of a rural light railway, featuring a large museum collection, strong in items of East Anglian interest, railway signalling and goods rolling stock. Other features include original station buildings from Mid-Suffolk Light, Great Eastern and Midland & Great Northern Railways

Superintendent of the Line: John Jolly

Commercial Manager: June Jolly

Location: Mangapps Farm Railway Museum, Southminster Road, Burnham-on-Crouch, Essex CM0 8QQ. (Entrance on B1021, 1 mile north of Burnham)

Telephone: (01621) 784898

Fax: (01621) 783833

Internet address: *Web site:* www.mangapps.co.uk

Access by public transport: Burnham station approx 1 mile

On site facilities: Station, car park, souvenir shop, toilets, amenity and picnic areas

Refreshment facilities: Teas and light refreshments

Length of line: Three-quarter-mile

Public opening: Weekends and Bank Holidays all year (except closed November and Christmas/New Year period) and daily during summer school holidays.

Steam trains operate first Sunday June to September, Bank Holiday Sundays and Mondays and special event days. Diesel trains run on all other days

Opening times: Weekends (however, closed 26 December to 31 January), Bank Holidays (except Christmas) daily during August —

Locomotives and multiple-units

Name	No	Origin	Class	Type	Built
—	2018	BR	03	0-6-0DM	1958
—	03089	BR	03	0-6-0DM	1960
Lucie	03081	BR	03	0-6-0DM	1960
—	03399	BR	03	0-6-0DM	1961
—	D2325	BR	04	0-6-0DM	1961
—	51381	BR	117	DTS	1961
—	75033	BR	302	DTS	1958
—	75250	BR	302	DTS	1958
—	22624	LT	R38	DMS	1938
—	1030	LT	1959	DM	1959
—	2044	LT	1959	T	1959

Industrial locomotives

Name	No	Builder	Type	Built
Minnie	—	F/Walker (358)	0-6-0ST	1878
Brookfield	—	Bagnall (2613)	0-6-0PT	1940
Empress	—	Bagnall (3061)	0-6-0ST	1954
Toto	—	Barclay (1619)	0-4-0ST	1919
—	8	Barclay (2157)	0-4-0ST	1943
Hastings	—	Hunslet (469)	0-6-0ST	1888
Elland	No 1	H/Clarke (D1153)	0-4-0DM	1959
—	Army 226	Drewry (2180)	0-4-0DM	1945
—	11104	Drewry (2252)	0-6-0DM	1948
—	DS1169	R/Hornsby (207103)	4wDM	1941
—	—	S/Henshaw (7502)	4wDM	1966

Rolling stock

LNER Gresley and BR Mk1 coaching stock, extensive stock of goods wagons)

11.30-17.00

Special events: Santa Specials — pre-Christmas weekends in December

---

Mid-Hants Railway 'Watercress Line'

Member: HRA

Originally built as the Winchester to Alton link, the Mid-Hants Railway became known as the Watercress Line through regularly carrying this local produce to London markets. Now restored, the line runs from its main line connection at Alton through rolling countryside to its terminus at Alresford. Large and powerful locomotives work impressively over the steeply inclined route, known to railwaymen as 'the Alps'.

Headquarters: Mid-Hants Railway LTD, Alresford Station, Alresford, Hants SO24 9JG

Telephone: 01962 733810

Fax: 01962 735448

Talking timetable: 01962 734866

Internet addresses: *e-mail:* info@watercressline.co.uk

Web site: www.watercressline.co.uk

Main station: Alresford

Other public stations: Ropley, Medstead & Four Marks, Alton

OS reference: Alresford SU 588325, Ropley SU 629324

SatNav postcodes: Alresford SO24 9JG, Alton GU34 2PZ

Car park: Alresford, pay & display (free Sundays & Bank Holidays).

Alton station pay & display

Access by public transport:
SouthWest Train services — just over 1hr from London, Waterloo. Alternatively, travel to Winchester station and catch a bus from nearby City Road.
Bus services – operated by Stagecoach (National Travel line 0871 200 2233 or www.traveline.org.uk)

Refreshment facilities: Buffet service on most trains; 'West Country' buffet, picnic area at Alresford; T. Junction picnic area at Ropley; tea/coffee available at Alton when information office open

Catering facilities: The 'Countryman Pullman' pre-booked Sunday lunch trains, Christmas specials, and some evening trains. The 'Watercress Belle' operates on certain Saturday evenings March-December. Early booking is essential, please telephone to confirm seat availability for both trains. Real Ale trains run selected Saturday evenings featuring beers from local breweries and light snacks to purchase

Souvenir shops: Alresford, Alton and Ropley

On site facilities: Picnic area, children's play area and viewing facilities at Ropley. Interpretative display in Alresford shop. Picnic area at Alresford

Depot: Ropley. Locomotive yard open on operating days 10.30-16.30

Length of line: 10 miles

Passenger trains: Phone Talking Timetable (01962 734866), or visit web site to confirm details. Bank Holidays and weekends January to October; Tuesdays to Thursdays May to September (inc), daily in August, school half term in February, October half term 'Wizard Week', Steam Galas, Day out with Thomas at Easter and August. Santa Specials in December (bookings commence October) Online booking at: www.watercressline.co.uk

Journey time: Round trip 1hr 40min max

Special events: Spring Steam Gala — 13-15 March; Mother's Day — 22 March; Day out with Thomas — 4-13 April; St George's Day Event — 25/26 April; Watercress Festival— 17 May; Diesel Gala — 23-31 May; War on the Line — 13/14 June; Father's Day —

21 June; Bus Rally — 19 July; Day out with Thomas — 8-16 August; Autumn Steam Gala —

11-13 September; Members and Shareholders Day — 26 September; Sponsored Walk (no trains running)

Locomotives

Name	No	Origin	Class	Type	Built
—	30499	LSWR	S15	4-6-0	1920
—	30506	LSWR	S15	4-6-0	1920
Harry A. Frith	E828	SR	S15	4-6-0	1923
Lord Nelson	850	SR	LN	4-6-0	1926
—	31625	SR	U	2-6-0	1929
—	31806	SR	U	2-6-0	1926
—	31874	SR	N	2-6-0	1925
Wadebridge	34007	SR	WC	4-6-2	1945
Bodmin	34016	SR	WC	4-6-2	1945
Swanage	34105	SR	WC	4-6-2	1950
Canadian Pacific	35005	SR	MN	4-6-2	1945
—	41312	LMS	2MT	2-6-2T	1952
—	45379	LMS	5MT	4-6-0	1937
Bittern	60019	LNER	A4	4-6-2	1937
—	73096	BR	5MT	4-6-0	1956
—	75079	BR	4MT	4-6-0	1956
—	76017	BR	4MT	2-6-0	1954
—	92212	BR	9F	2-10-0	1959
—	08032	BR	08	0-6-0DE	1954
—	D3358	BR	08	0-6-0DE	1957
—	12049	BR	11	0-6-0DE	1948
—	D5353	BR	27	Bo-Bo	1961
—	33053	BR	33	Bo-Bo	1961
—	D6593	BR	33	Bo-Bo	1962
—	45132	BR	45	1Co-Co1	1961
—	51363	BR	117	DMBS	1959
—	51405	BR	117	DMS	1959
—	55003	BR	122	DMBS	1958
—	59510	BR	117	TCL	1959
—†	60124	BR	205	DMBS	1957
—†	60824	BR	205	DTCL	1957

†unit No 205025

Industrial locomotives

Name	No	Builder	Type	Built
—	4	Fowler (22889)	0-4-0DM	1939
Thomas	1	Hunslet (3781)	0-6-0T	1954
Douglas	10	Hunslet (2890)	0-6-0	1943
—	62-521*	Djuro Djakovic	0-6-0T	1954

*based on 'USA' tank design, to be renumbered 30076

Stock

30 ex-BR Mk 1 coaches; 2 ex-BR Mk 2 coaches used for accommodation; 3 ex-BR Mk 1 Pullman Cars; 3 ex-SR coaches; 1 ex-LSWR coach; 3 steam cranes; numerous goods vehicles

Owners

30076 Project 62 Group
30499 and 30506 the Urie Locomotive Society
E828 the Eastleigh Railway Preservation Society
850 on loan from the national Railway Museum
34105 the 34105 Light Pacific Group
35005, 45379, 75079, D3358, D6593 and Class 205 the Mid-Hants Railway
76017 the Standard 4 Locomotive Group
08032 on loan from Aggregate Industries
DMU vehicles the L721 Group
34007 the Wadebridge (34007) Ltd

England

— 7 November; Santa Specials —
5/6, 12/13, 19-24 December;
Chistmas Leave —
26/27 December; New Year —
1-3 January 2010
Facilities for disabled: Toilets at
Ropley, the old goodshed at
Alresford station and Alton.
Passengers in fixed wheelchairs can
be carried in the brake compartment
on most trains. Ramps are provided
to ease entry to trains. Ask
SouthWest Trains staff at Alton to
cross foot crossing
Membership details: Membership
Secretary, c/o above address.
E-mail:
mhr.membership@btconnect.com

Timetable Service — Mid-Norfolk Railway — Norfolk

Member: HRA

A scheme to preserve part of the
former Great Eastern line from
Wymondham to Wells-next-the-
Sea. The section from
Wymondham to Dereham has been
purchased and opened for
passenger and freight traffic since
May 1999. Clearance work is now
completed on the Dereham-North
Elmham section. The Mid-Norfolk
Railway Preservation Trust also
operates County School station as a
tea room and visitor centre during
the summer months

Headquarters: The Railway

Locomotives and multiple-units

Name	No	Origin	Class	Type	Built
—	D8069	BR	20	Bo-Bo	1961
—	31235	BR	31	A1A-A1A	1960
Sister Dora	31530	BR	31	A1A-A1A	1961
—	31538	BR	31	A1A-A1A	1959
—	37003	BR	37	Co-Co	1960
Aldeburgh Festival	47596	BR	47	Co-Co	1966
Ramillies	50019	BR	50	Co-Co	1968
Oystermouth	56040	BR	56	Co-Co	1978
—	73210	BR	73	Bo-Bo	1966
—	51226	M/Cam	101	DMBS	1958
Matthew Smith	51434	M/Cam	101	MBS	1958
—	51499	M/Cam	101	DMBS	1959
—	51503	M/Cam	101	DMC	1959

Station, Station Road, Dereham,
Norfolk NR19 1DF
Main station: Dereham
Telephone: (01362) 690633
Talking timetable: (01362) 851723
(answerphone)
Fax: (01362) 698487
Internet address:
Web site: www.mnr.org.uk
e-mail: info@mnr.org.uk
Car park: At Dereham
Museum: Small relics museum at
Dereham
Souvenir shop: Dereham
Refreshment facilities: Railway
Buffet at Dereham (March-
December) and tea room at County
School station (summer only)
Access by public transport: Bus
from Norwich and King's Lynn.
National Express East Anglia trains
to Wymondham
Period of public operation:
Weekends and Bank Holidays
28 March to 25 October.
Wednesdays 6 May to 30
September. Thursdays 23 July to 27
August. Sundays 15, 22 March
Special events: Mother's Day
Specials — 22 March; Diesel Gala
— 28/29 March; Vintage Transport
Day — 21 June; Santa Specials —
5/6, 12/13, 19/20, 23/24 December.
Mince Pie Specials — 27 December
and 1 January 2010
Special facilities: Operational main

Name	No	Origin	Class	Type	Built
—	55009	Gloucester	122	DMBS	1958
—	59117	M/Cam	101	TC	1958
—	56301*	Gloucester	100	DTC	1957
—	68004	BR	MLV / 419	DMVL	1959

*in use as static shop and tea room at County School station

Industrial locomotives

Name	No	Builder	Type	Built
—§	GET 2	Bagnall (8368)	0-4-0DM	1962
—§	GET 8	R/Royce (10272)	0-6-0DM	1967
—§	GET 11	Brush (804)	0-6-0DE	1978
—§	11103	Drewry (2583)	0-4-0DM	1956

§privately owned, stored at Hardingham and viewable from trains, no public
access

Locomotive notes: D8069, 31235, 31538, 47596, 50019 and 73210, also
various DMUs are in service

Rolling stock: 9 BR Mk 2 coaches, 10-ton rail-mounted crane, selection of
freight wagons, operational and stored at Hardingham

Owners

50019 and 68004 the Class 50 Locomotive Association
47596 the Stratford 47 Group
31235 the Colne Valley Enterprises Ltd
D8069 the Type One Association
GET the Great Eastern Traction group
37003 the Class 37 Locomotive Group
56040 the Class 56 Group

line connection for charter, freight
trains etc. Line used for training
purposes eg: low adhesion driving
techniques. Film location

Membership details: Membership
Secretary c/o Dereham Station
Membership journal: *The
Blastpipe* (four times a year)

Museum — Mid-Suffolk Light Railway — Suffolk

Member: HRA
The Mid-Suffolk Light Railway,
known affectionately as 'The
Middy', was a classic case of a
railway built late on in the great
railway age that never paid its way.
It effectively went broke before it
opened but still managed to struggle
on for 50 years. This example of a
quirky English history is
remembered in Suffolk's only
railway museum
Location: Wetheringsett, Nr
Stowmarket, Suffolk IP14 5PW
OS reference: TM 129659
Operating organisation: Mid-
Suffolk Light Railway Company
Telephone: 01449 766899
Internet address: *Web site:*
www.mslr.org.uk

Industrial locomotives

Name	No	Builder	Type	Built
Little Barford	—	Barclay	0-4-0ST	1939
—	1604	H/Clarke (1604)	0-6-0ST	1928
—	304470	R/Hornsby (304470)	0-4-0DM	1951

Rolling stock

GER 2-compartment brake third, GER 6-compartment brake third, GER
3-compartment first, 1 GER ventilated van, 1 GER non-ventilated van,
1 GER 5-plank wagon1 LMS van, 1 GWR van, private owner coal wagon
(rebuilt from BR open wagon), LNER brake van, NER milk van body, 2
GER 5 compartment third bodies, GER ventilated van body. GER steel
outside frame ventilated van, GER horsebox body, conflat (to provide
underframe for horsebox), replica contractor open wagon

Car park: On site
Access by public transport: Some
local buses from Ipswich to Diss set
down and pick up on the A140

Ipswich-Norwich road near to the
museum. Local buses from
Stowmarket to Wetheringsett.
Services tend to be infrequent and

England

the timetables are subject to change at short notice. Details of services can be obtained from Traveline 0870 608 2608 or www.traveline.org.uk
On site facilities: Souvenir shop, refreshments, railway walk (not when trains are running), railwayana and photographic exhibition, toilets (including disabled), visits to restoration works, real ale bar in summer when steam train running and picnic area
Period of public opening: Usually open on Sundays and Bank Holidays from Easter to end

September, plus Wednesdays in August (11.00-17.00)
Special events: Steam days: 3/4 May, 7 June, 2 July, 2, 9, 13, 16, 23, 30/31 August, 27 September, 27 December. Santa Specials 6, 13, 20 December
Special notes: Museum dedicated to Mid-Suffolk Light Railway. Original MSLR restored buildings and artefacts. Reproduction MSLR ticket on entry. *Railway World* award winner in 1994 and HRA award winner in 2002 and 2007. Driver experience detai;s shown on web site. Trains are available for

photographic charters etc. Site venue for wedding receptions
Facilities for disabled: Most of the site is accessible for disabled users. A wheelchair is available on request and there is wheelchair access to the demonstration passenger train. Toilets are accessible to wheelchair users
Membership details: Membership Secretary, Poachers Cottage, Church Hill, Stowmarket, Suffolk IP14 4SQ
Society journal: *Making Tracks —* quarterly Newsletter

Steam Centre	Middleton Railway	Leeds

Member: HRA
This is a preserved section of 'the world's oldest working railway', authorised by the first railway Act of Parliament in 1758, and also the first standard gauge railway to be taken over by volunteers in 1960
Headquarters: Middleton Railway Trust Ltd, Moor Road, Hunslet, Leeds LS10 2JQ
Telephone: 0113 271 0320
Internet addresses: *e-mail:* info@middletonrailway.org.uk
Web site: www.middletonrailway.org.uk
Main station: Moor Road, Hunslet
OS reference: SE 302309. If using satellite navigation please be aware there are two Moor Roads in LS10
Car park: Moor Road (free)
Access by public transport: Nearest main line station, Leeds City. Bus service No 61 from Aire Street (next to Leeds City station) to Tunstall Road (then 150yd walk)
Directions by car: Next to M621, junction 5. There have been major road alterations around the Middleton Railway.
From the south: M621 northbound and exit at jct 5. Turn right at the top of the slip road and take the marked exit at the roundabout. The railway is 50yd on the right
From the west: M621 southbound and exit at jct 6. Turn left at the end of the slip road, and left at the next set of traffic lights into Moor Road. Bear right at the mini

Locomotives

Name	No	Origin	Class	Type	Built
—	1310	NER	Y7	0-4-0T	1891
—	68153	LNER	Y1	0-4-0VB	1933
—	385	DSB	HsII	0-4-0WT	1893
John Alcock	7051	LMS	—	0-6-0DM	1932
(Olive)	RDB998901	BR	—	4wDM	1950

Industrial locomotives

Name	No	Builder	Type	Built
John Blenkinsop	—	Peckett (2003)	0-4-0ST	1941
—	—	Peckett (2103)	0-4-0ST	1948
—	—	Bagnall (2702)	0-4-0ST	1943
Henry de Lacy II	—	H/Clarke (1309)	0-4-0ST	1917
Mirvale	—	H/Clarke (1882)	0-4-0ST	1955
Manchester Ship Canal No 67	—	H/Clarke (1329)	0-6-0T	1921
—	11	Hunslet (1453)	0-4-0ST	1925
Picton	—	Hunslet (1540)	2-6-2T	1927
—	1684	Hunslet (1684)	0-4-0T	1931
Brookes No 1	—	Hunslet (2387)	0-6-0T	1941
Windle	—	Borrows (53)	0-4-0WT	1909
Matthew Murray	—	M/Wardle (1601)	0-6-0ST	1903
Lucy	—	Cockerill	0-4-0VBT	1890
Sir Berkeley†	—	M/Wardle (1210)	0-6-0ST	1891
—	6	H/Leslie (3860)	0-4-0ST	1935
Carroll	—	H/Clarke (D631)	0-4-0DM	1946
Mary	—	H/Clarke (D577)	0-4-0DM	1932
—	DL15	H/Clarke (D1343)	0-4-0DM	1965
Grace	—	H/Clarke (D1345)	0-6-0DM	1967
—	—	Hunslet (1786)	0-4-0DM	1935
—§	—	Hunslet (6273)	4wDH	1965
Flying Scotsman§§	—	Hunslet (8505)	4wDH	1981
—	—	Fowler (3900002)	0-4-0DM	1945
Conway	—	Kitson (5469)	0-6-0ST	1933
Austin No 1	—	Peckett (5003)	0-4-0DM	1961
—	—	Thomas Hill (138C)	0-4-0DH	1963
—*	D2999	Brush (91)/ Beyer Peacock (7856)	0-4-0DE	1958

roundabout and railway is 150yd on the left

Souvenir shop: Moor Road

Museum: Engine House is open weekends, Wednesdays and Bank Holidays Easter to the end of November

Length of line: 1.25 miles (extension pending)

Period of public operation: Weekends and Bank Holiday Mondays Easter to end of November, plus Santa trains in December.

Trains run at 40min intervals. Heritage diesels: Saturdays 13.00-16.20. August Wednesdays 13.00-16.20.

Heritage steam: Sundays and Bank Holiday Mondays 11.00-16.20 except special events which may have their own timetable.

2009 prices: adult £4.50; child £2.50; family tickets are available. Special events may attract different prices

Special events: Easter Trains — 11-13 April; Bluebell Walk — 3/4 May; Children's gala — 16/17 May; 250th Celebrations — 6/7 June; Model Railway Exhibition — 4/5 July; Wednesday opening in August trains from 14.00 with heritage diesel traction; September Steam Gala — 19/20

Name	No	Builder	Type	Built
—	—	G/Batley (420452)	4wDE	1979

*on loan from BSC Orb Works, Newport
†on 10 year loan from Vintage Carriages Trust, but may be away on hire at times
§3ft gauge
§§2ft 2in gauge

Note: Nos 6, 11, 1310, 68153 and *Sir Berkeley* are under repair in the workshops and may not be accessible to the public

Stock

2 CCTs converted for passenger use Nos 1867 and 2048; CCT as stores van No 2073. Various goods vehicles; 5-ton Booth rail crane; 1 3-ton Smith steam crane; 1 3-ton Isles steam crane; 7.5-ton steam crane

Owners

1310, 385 the Steam Power Trust
RDB998901 the EM2 Locomotive Society
Flying Scotsman and Hunslet 8505 on loan from National Mining Museum

September; November Ghost Trains — 31 October, 1 November; Santa trains with steam traction — 5/6, 12/13, 19/20, 24 December; Mince Pie Specials — 1 January 2010

Facilities for disabled: Good access with additional assistance by prior arrangement. Disabled toilets, reserved car parking spaces

Special notes: Operating in every year since 1758, the railway still operates under its original Act of Parliament. The first railway to successfully use steam locomotives commercially from 1812. Part of South Leeds Heritage Trail, highlighting former locomotive works in the area, and other historic places

Special facilities: Charter trains, birthday parties on non-special event running days; catering facilities; training/conference room; education facilities

<table>
<tr><td>Timetable Service</td><td>Midland Railway — Butterley</td><td>Derbyshire</td></tr>
</table>

Member: HRA, TT

The Midland Railway — Butterley is a rapidly developing Preservation Scheme with a difference. The massive 57 acre Museum site and 35 acre Country Park enabled it to become 'More Than Just a Railway' as its publicity says. The seven road Matthew Kirtley Museum allows much of the historic collection to be on display and most of the locomotives to be stored and displayed under cover. A miniature railway (3.5 and 5in gauge) and a 1-mile narrow gauge line (2ft gauge) carries passengers through the Country Park; Brittain Pit Farm Park, with its wide variety of livestock; and of course there is a 3.5-mile standard gauge line

Locomotives and multiple-units

Name	No	Origin	Class	Type	Built
—	158A*	MR	—	2-4-0	1866
Princess Margaret Rose	46203	LMS	8P	4-6-2	1935
Duchess of Sutherland	6233	LMS	8P	4-6-2	1938
—	44027†	LMS	4F	0-6-0	1924
—	45491	LMS	5MT	4-6-0	1943
—	47564	LMS	3F	0-6-0T	1928
—	47327	LMS	3F	0-6-0T	1926
—	47357	LMS	3F	0-6-0T	1926
—	47445	LMS	3F	0-6-0T	1927
—	53809	SDJR	7F	2-8-0	1925
—	73129	BR	5MT	4-6-0	1956
—	80080	BR	4MT	2-6-4T	1954
—	80098	BR	4MT	2-6-4T	1955
—	92214	BR	9F	2-10-0	1959
—	92219	BR	9F	2-10-0	1959
—	D2858	BR	02	0-4-0DM	1959
—	D2138	BR	03	0-6-0DM	1960
—	08590	BR	08	0-6-0DE	1959
—	12077	BR	11	0-6-0DE	1950

complete with Midland signals, three restored signalboxes, Butterley station, the scenic delights of Butterley Reservoir and Golden Valley!

The Victorian Railwaymen's Church, the demonstration signalbox, and all the other many attractions that make up the Midland Railway — Butterley will be open throughout the year

Location: Midland Railway, Butterley Station, Nr Ripley, Derbyshire DE5 3QZ

OS reference: SK 403520

Operating society/organisation: Midland Railway Trust Ltd

Telephone: Ripley (01773) 747674, Visitor Information Line (01773) 570140.

Fax: (01773) 570271

Internet address:
e-mail: mr_b2004@btconnect.com
Web site:
www.midlandrailwaycentre.co.uk

Car park: Butterley station on B6179 1 mile north of Ripley

On site facilities: Museum, award winning country park, Brittain Pit Farm Park, souvenir shops, miniature railway, narrow gauge railway, garden railway, model railways

Refreshment facilities: Butterley station buffet, Johnson Buffet (Swanwick), on-train bars and extensive 'Wine and Dine' trains, 'The Midlander' (details from above address).
'Midday Midlander' Sunday lunch trains will run on selected Sundays — these need to be booked in advance

Length of line: Standard gauge 3.5 miles, narrow gauge 0.8-mile

Public opening: In 2009 trains run every Saturday, Sunday and Bank Holiday Monday EXCEPT 14 November
Trains will also run every day 14-22 February, 4-14 April, 23-31 May, 22 July to 3 September, 25 October to 1 November, 22-24 December
Golden Valley Light Railway:
Trains will run every weekend and Bank Holiday Monday April to October, and every day 23-31 May, 22 July-3 September. Special steam days — check for details.
Butterley Park Miniature Railway:
Trains will run Sundays and Bank Holidays Easter to September.
Journey time: Approximately 1hr

Name	No	Origin	Class	Type	Built
—	20001	BR	20	Bo-Bo	1957
—	20205	BR	20	Bo-Bo	1967
—	20227	BR	20	Bo-Bo	1968
—	D7671	BR	25	Bo-Bo	1967
Boadicea	31418	BR	31	A1A-A1A	1959
—	33018	BR	33	Bo-Bo	1960
—	33201	BR	33	Bo-Bo	1962
—	37190	BR	37	Co-Co	1964
Aureol	40012	BR	40	1Co-Co1	1959
Great Gable	D4	BR	44	1Co-Co1	1959
Royal Tank Regiment	45041	BR	45/1	1Co-Co1	1962
—	45108	BR	45/1	1Co-Co1	1961
—	45133	BR	45/1	1Co-Co1	1961
—	46045	BR	46	1Co-Co1	1963
—	47401	BR	47	Co-Co	1963
—	47761	BR	47	Co-Co	1963
—	D1516	BR	47	Co-Co	1963
Sir Edward Elgar	50007	BR	50	Co-Co	1967
Western Lady	D1048	BR	52	C-C	1962
Electra	27000	BR	EM2	Co+Co	1953
—	50015	BR	114	DMBS	1956
—	50019	BR	114	DMBS	1956
—	51073	BR	119	DMBC	1958
—	51188	BR	101	DMBS	1958
—	51341	P/Steel	117	DMBS	1959
—	51353	P/Steel	117	DMBS	1959
—	51395	P/Steel	117	DMS	1959
—	51398	P/Steel	117	DMS	1959
—	51567	BR	108	DMSL	1959
—	51973	BR	108	DMBS	1958
—	53170	BR	101	DMC(L)	1957
—	53253	BR	101	DMC(L)	1957
—	55513	BR	141	DMS	1983
—	55533	BR	141	DMS(L)	1983
—	55966	BR	127	DPU	1959
—	55976	BR	127	DPU	1956
—	56006	BR	114	DTC	1956
—	56015	BR	114	DMBSO	1956
—	56484	BR	108	DTC	1960
—	59486	P/Steel	117	TCL	1960
—	59521	P/Steel	117	TCL	1960
—	59575	M/Cam	111	TRBSL(L)	1957
—	59609	BR	127	TC	1959
—	79018	BR	—	MBS	1954
—	79612	BR	—	DTC	1954
—	29666	M/Cam	—	TC	1931
—	29670	M/Cam	—	TC	1931
Iris	M79900	BR	—	MBS	1956

*may arrive on loan from the National Railway Museum during 2009
†may return to the National Railway Museum during 2009

Locomotive notes: In service 92214, 47327 (as *Thomas*), 6233, 53809, 80098, 73129, 46045, 08590, Class 114, *Iris* and 127 DMU, D4, 33201, 37190, 46045, 47401, 50007, D2138, 40012, 12077, 45133 and D7671. Under restoration: 44027, 45491, 47445, 80080. Awaiting repairs or stored: 46203, D1517, 92219. Boiler and frames only 47564. Static display: 158A, 27000.

Industrial locomotives

Name	No	Builder	Type	Built
Gladys	—	Markham (109)	0-4-0ST	1894
Stanton	24	Barclay (1875)	0-4-0CT	1925
Whitehead	—	Peckett (1163)	0-4-0ST	1908

England

Special events: Day out with Thomas — 7/8, 14/15 March; Mother's Day Lunch Train — 22 March; Diesel Multiple Unit Gala — 28/29 March; Easter Trains — 4-19 April; Diesel Locomotive Gala — 25, 29 April; Victorian Gala and Vintage Train — 2-4 May; Diesel and Steam Weekend — 9/10 May; Day out with Thomas — 23-27 May; 1940s Weekend and 65th Anniversary of D-Day — 6/7 June; Free for Disabled Weekend — 13/14 June; Father's Day Lunch Train — 21 June; English Electric Weekend — 27/28 June; Teddy Bears Weekend (free for children with their teddy) — 4/5 July; Narrow Gauge Railway Gala, Garden Railway and Modellers Weekend, Princess Royal Locomotive Trust Patrons Weekend featuring 6233 — 11/12 July; Road Rally — 12 July; Indietracks Music Festival — 25/26 July; Half price for the over 60s — 27-31 July; Anything Goes Weekend — 1/2 August; Day out with Thomas — 5-9 August; Paddington Bear Weekend — 15/16 August; Vintage Train Weekend — 21-23 August;Works Open Day Event — 29-31 August; 1940s Indian Summer Event — 3/4 October; Day out with Thomas — 10/11 October; Wizards and Spooks Event — 24 October-1 November; Halloween Fright Night — 31 October; Fireworks Night — 7 November; Santa Specials — 21/22, 28/29 November, 3, 5/6, 10, 12/13, 17, 19, 20, 22, 23/24 December; Day out with Thomas — 27-31 December.

Note: Day out with Thomas dates subject to confirmation

All Day out with Thomas are © Gullane (Thomas) Ltd 2007 and are licensed by Gullane (Thomas) Ltd a HIT Entertainment Company. Midday Midlander lunch trains run on selected dates – these need to be booked in advance

Facilities for disabled: Toilets, special coach, access to shop and cafeteria

Special facilities: The railway is licensed for weddings, civil partnership ceremonies, and baby naming ceremonies. There is a woodland burial ground in the country park adjacent to the railway. Trains can be chartered for special meals, educational visits or

Name	No	Builder	Type	Built
Victory	—	Peckett (1547)	0-4-0ST	1919
Lytham St Annes	—	Peckett (2111)	0-4-0ST	1949
Brown Bailey	4	N/Wilson (454)	0-4-0ST	1894
Castle Donnington	1	RSH (7817)	0-4-0ST	1954
George	—	RSH	0-4-0ST	19??
Henry	—	RSH	0-4-0ST	19??
Neepsend		Sentinel (9370)	4wVBT	1947
Andy	2	Fowler (16038)	0-4-0DM	1923
—	RS9	M/Rail (2024)	0-4-0DM	1921
—	RS12	M/Rail (460)	0-4-0DM	1912
Boots	2	Barclay (2008)	0-4-0F	1935
Castle Donnington	2	Barclay (416)	0-4-0DM	1957
High Marnham	—	Barclay (441)	0-4-0DM	1949
Boots	—	R/Hornsby (384139)	0-4-0DE	1955
—	—	H/Clarke (D1152)	0-6-0DM	1959
Albert Fields	—	H/Clarke (D1114)	0-6-0DM	1958
Princess Elizabeth*	6201	H/Clarke (D611)	4-6-2DM	1938
Princess Margaret Rose*	6203	H/Clarke (D612)	4-6-2DM	1938

*21in gauge

Golden Valley Light Railway
2ft gauge unless otherwise shown

Name	No	Builder	Type	Built
—	—	Deutz (10249)	4wDM	1932
—	—	M/Rail (5906)	4wDM	1934
Tubby	—	M/Rail (8667)	4wDM	1941
Pioneer	—	M/Rail (8739)	4wDM	1942
—	—	M/Rail (8756)	4wDM	1942
Campbell Brick Works	—	M/Rail (60S364)	4wDM	1968
—	—	Lister (3742)	4wDM	1931
—	—	M/Rail (11246)	4wDM	1963
—	2	O&K (7529)	0-4-0WT	1914
—	—	O&K (5215)	4wDM	1936
Wheal Jayne	19	BEV	4wBE	1985
—	—	Ruston (7002/0567/6)	4wDM	1966
Lyddia	—	Ruston (191646)	4wDM	1938
Berryhill	—	Ruston (222068)	4wDM	1943
Hucknall Colliery	3	Ruston (480678)	4wDM	1961
—	—	Hunslet (7178)	4wDH	1971
Calverton Colliery	22†	H/Clarke (1117)	0-6-0DM	1958
—	—	Lister (53726)	4wDM	1963
—	—	SMH (40SD529)	4wDM	1983
—	NG24	B/Drewry (3703)	4wBE	1974
Calverton No 7	7	Hunslet (8911)	4wDM	1980
Ellison	—	SMH (102T20)	4wDH	1979
Pearl 2	—	T. D. A. Civil (1)	0-4-2T	1997

Locomotive notes: In service: *High Marnham, Boots, Castle Donnington No 1, Castle Donnington No 2,* NG24, Ruston 222068, SMH (40SD529 & 102T20), *Calverton Colliery No 22,* Lister, Deutz 10249, *Albert Fields,* M/Rail 60S364, *Princess Margaret Rose.* Under restoration: *Andy,* O&K 7529, *Lytham St Annes, Castle Donnington No 1.* Awaiting repairs or stored on display: RS9, Hunslet 7178, M/Rails 5906/11246. Static display: *Gladys,* 4, *Boots No 2,* Sentinel 9370, *Welbeck Colliery, Victory,* RS12, *Stanton No 24, Brown Bailey* (as Oswald the talking engine)

Stock
Numerous carriages, wagons and cranes. Museum display includes MR Royal saloon, MR 4-wheeled coach, MR brake third, LD&ECR all third, BR horsebox, LMS travelling Post Office, L&YR family saloon, MR motor carvan, MR bogie brake third, restored freight vehicles, LMS 50-ton steam crane, and much more

almost anything else. Footplate Experience and Railway Experience courses are run. The large museum site is also used for exhibitions and displays. The railway also has an impressive track record in the restoration of diesel multiple-units and coaches for other lines

Membership details: Membership Secretary, at above address

Membership journal: *The Wyvern* — quarterly

Marketing names: 'More than just a Railway'; Golden Valley Light Railway (narrow gauge); Butterley Park Miniature Railway (miniature line)

Owners

44027 on loan from the National Railway Museum
47357, 47327, 47445, 47564, 73129 Derby City Council
46203, 6233, 80080, 80098 the Princess Royal Class Locomotive Trust
D4, 45041 and 46045 the Peak Locomotive Preservation Co Ltd
D7671 Derby Industrial Museum
33201 the Birmingham Railwaymen's Crompton Workgroup
45108 the Peak Locomotive Group
Class 141 unit the Llangollen Railcar Group
51073 the Railcar Enterprises
51341, 51353, 51395, 51398, 59486, 59521 the Swanage Railway

Museum	Monkwearmouth Station Museum	Tyne & Wear

The Museum is one of Britain's finest neo-classical stations and was built in 1848 to commemorate the election of George Hudson as MP for Sunderland. Restored features include the booking office, unchanged since it was installed in 1866, waiting shelter on the west platform and siding area

Location: North Bridge Street, Sunderland SR5 1AP
Telephone: (0191) 567 7075
OS reference: NZ 396576
On site facilities: Car parking on

Rolling stock
NER brake van 1915, LNER CCT van 1939

museum forecourt, shop. Self-service refreshment dispenser
Access by public transport: 10min walk from Sunderland Central station. Served by several bus routes from Sunderland city centre, Newcastle and South Shields
Public opening: Daily 1 January-31 December (except New Year's Day, Christmas Day, Boxing Day

[please check for Good Friday and Easter Sunday opening times]).
Monday to Saturday 10.00-17.00.
Sunday 14.00-17.00. Free admission
Access for disabled: Ramped access, suitable for wheelchair users

---

Miniature Railway	Moors Valley Railway	Dorset

Location: Moors Valley Country Park, Horton Road, Ashley Heath, Nr Ringwood, Dorset BH24 2ET
General Manager:
Mr J. A. W. Haylock
Telephone: (01425) 471415
Internet address: *e-mail:*
shop@moorsvalleyrailway.co.uk
Web site:
www.moorsvalleyrailway.co.uk
Car parking: On site
Access by public transport: Wilts & Dorset bus X34, from Bournemouth/Ringwood to Ashley Heath

Locomotives — 7.25in gauge

Name	No	Builder	Type	Built
Horace	2	Haylock	0-4-2DH	1999
Talos	3	Marsh	0-4-2T	1978
Tinkerbell	4	Marsh	0-4-2T	1968
Sapper	5	Marsh/Haylock	4-6-0	1982
Medea	6	Narogauge Ltd	2-6-2T	1981
Aelfred	7	Narogauge Ltd	2-6-4T	1985
Jason	9	Narogauge Ltd	2-4-4T	1989
Offa	10	Narogauge Ltd	2-6-2	1991
Zeus	11	Narogauge Ltd	2-6-2	1991
Pioneer	12	Narogauge Ltd	4-6-2	1992
Horton	14	Narogauge Ltd	2-4-0	1991
William Rufus	15	Narogauge Ltd	2-4-0+0-4-2	1997
Robert Snooks	16	Manktelow	0-4-4T	1999

On site facilities: Picnic areas, lakeside walks, adventure playground, railway shop and refreshments all set in the beautiful Moors Valley Country Park. Car park and toilets (including disabled)

Depots: Adacent to main station

Length of line:7.25in gauge; 1 mile long

Period of public operation: Weekends all year; daily all school holidays and Spring Bank Holiday to mid-September. Santa Specials in December

Special events: Railway Open Day — 29 March; Tinkerbell Rally — 2/3 May; Grand Summer Gala — 6/7 June; American Weekend

Name	No	Builder	Type	Built
Hartfield	17	Colbourn	2-4-4T	1999
Thor	18	Jefford	4-6-2	2005
Athelstan	19	Couling	2-8-0	2006
Vixen	22	Narogauge Ltd	0-4-0+0-4-0DH	2005
Perseus	24	Ash	0-4-2T	2006
Emmet*	20	Haylock	0-4-0T	2003

*2ft gauge

Rolling stock
36 passenger vehicles, selection of wagons

— 4/5 July; Hornby/Bachmann /LGB Weekend — 25/26 July; Model Railway Weekend — 12/13 September; Tank Engine Day — 8 November; Santa Specials — 6, 13 December (bookable in advance)

Fare: Single and return journeys; day rovers; Midday Specials (Sundays only). Party rates available

---

Museum — Moseley Railway Trust — Staffordshire

Member: HRA

Postal address: 11 Ashwood Road, Disley, Stockport, Cheshire SK12 2EL

Site address: Apedale Heritage Centre, Loomer Road, Chesterton, Newcastle-under-Lyme, Staffs ST5 7RR

SatVav Postcode: ST5 7LB

Telephone: 0845 094 1953

Internet address: *Web site:* www.mrt.org.uk

Site includes: Apedale Heritage Centre, Country Park, car parking, refreshments, toilet. Open daily 10.30-16.00. Mine tours weekends and Bank Holidays

Railway under construction. It is currently planned to commence passenger trains during 2009, but please see the railway press and web site for details. Visitors are welcome, please contact via the Chairman or web site for details

Length of line: 470m, under construction, 2ft gauge

Membership details: Brian Budd, Eversley, 1 The Sidings, Whaley Bridge, High Peak SK23 7HE

Membership journal: *Moseley Matters* (quarterly)

Industrial locomotives (2ft gauge)

Name	No	Builder	Type	Built
Billet	1	W/Rogers (C6717)	4wBE	1963
Cable Mill	2	W/Rogers (C6716)	4wBE	1963
81A 186	3	M/Rail (8878)	4wDM	1944
Stanhope	4**	K/Stuart (2395)	0-4-2ST	1917
—	5*	K/Stuart (3014)	0-6-0WT	1916
—	6	M/Rail (9104)	4wPM	1941
—	7	Hunslet (1215)	4-6-0T	1916
—	7	M/Rail (8663)	4wDM	1941
Electra	12†	Brook Victor (565)	4wBE	1970
—	13	M/Rail (11142)	4wDM	1960
Knothole Worker	14	M/Rail (22045)	4wDM	1959
—	15 *	Hunslet (7448)	4wDM	1976
Margaret	16	Hunslet (9056)	4wDH	1982
LCWW 81-03	18	H/Hunslet (6299)	4wDM	1964
—	20	M/Rail (8748)	4wDM	1942
—	21	M/Rail (8669)	4wDM	1941
—	22	Lister (3834)	4wPM	1931
—	23*	Lister (52031)	4wDM	1960
—	24	Hunslet (1974)	4wDM	1939
—	25	Hunslet (6007)	4wDM	1963
Twusk	26	H/Hunslet (6018)	4wDM	1961
Annie	27	R/Hornsby (198297)	4wDM	1939
—	28	Ruston (198228)	4wDM	1940
Vanguard	29	R/Hornsby (195846)	4wDM	1939
Friden	30*	R/Hornsby (237914)	4wDM	1946
—	31	R/Hornsby (189972)	4wDM	1938
—	33	M/Rail (7033)	4wPM	1936
—	34	R/Hornsby (164350)	4wDM	1933
—	35	Wickham (4131)	4wPMR	1947
Commercial	36	R/Hornsby (280865)	4wDM	1949
—	37	R/Hornsby (260719)	4wDM	1948
Kenneth	38	R/Hornsby (223749)	4wDM	1944
—	39	M/Rail (1111)	4wPM	1918

Name	No	Builder	Type	Built
Sludge	40	Simplex (40SD516)	4wDM	1979
—	41	M/Rail (5821)	4wDM	1934
—	42	M/Rail (7710)	4wDM	1939
—	43	Simplex (104063G)	4wDM	1976
Chaumont	44	Hudson (LX1002)	4wDH	1968
87008	45	R/Hornsby (179870)	4wDM	1936
—	47	M/Rail (1369)	4wPM	1918
R12/ND6458	48	R/Hornsby (235725)	4wDM	1943
—	49	O/Koppel (4470)	4wPM	1931
—	50	Deutz (10050)	4wDM	1931
—	51*	Baguley (646)	0-4-0PM	1918
LAWR	52	Baguley (1695)	0-4-0PM	1928
—	53	Hibberd (2306)	4wDM	1940
Yard No 54	54†	Hibberd (2196)	4wPMR	1940
—	58	H/Clarke (D558)	4wDM	1938
—	59	O/Koppel (4588)	4wPM	1932
—	60	M/Rail (6035)	4wPM	1937
—	61	M/Rail (1320)	4wDM	1918
MCWW P396	62	R/Hornsby (497542)	4wDM	1963
—	64	R/Hornsby (256314)	4wDM	1949
—	65	R/Hornsby (223667)	4wDM	1943
—	66	Pikrose (B0366V)	4wBE	1993
—	67	W/Rogers (D6912)	4wBE	1964
—	68*	Brook Victor (608)	2w-2BE	1971
Crystal	70*†	W/Rogers (K7070)	4wBE	1970
—	71*	Clayton (5843)	4wBE	1971
Lady Anne	72	Clayton (B0922B)	4wBE	1975
—	74	O/Koppel (3444?)	4wDM	1930
—	78	M/Rail (5038)	4wPM	1930
—	79††	Ruhrthaler (3909)	4wDH	1969
—	80	L/Blackstone (52610)	4wDM	1961
(87004)	81	M/Rail (2197)	4wDM	1923
—	83	Rhiwbach Quarry	2-2wPM	c1935
—	84	Howard (984)	4wPM	1931
—	86	Hibberd (2586)	4wDM	1941
—	—	H/Clarke (1238)	0-6-0WT	1916

*stored off site, due to arrive 2009
**in operation on West Lancs Railway
†2ft 6in gauge
†† 750mm gauge

The Museum of Science and Industry

Museum   Manchester

Member: HRA

Based in the buildings of the world's oldest surviving passenger railway station (dating from 1830), the Museum has colourful 'hands-on' galleries that amuse, amaze and entertain. Visitors can find out about our industrial past, and walk through a Victorian sewer complete with sounds and smells

Location: Liverpool Road, Castlefield, Manchester (off Deansgate near Granada TV)

OS reference: SJ 831987

Locomotives

Name	No	Origin	Class	Type	Built
Pender	3††	IoMR	—	2-4-0T	1873
Novelty	Replica of 1829				1986
	locomotive using some original parts				
—	3157†	PR	—	4-4-0	1911
—	2352§	SAR	GL	4-8-2+2-8-4	1929
Ariadne	1505 (27001)	BR	EM2 (77)	Co-Co	1954
Hector	26048	BR	EM1 (76)	Bo-Bo cab only	1952
Planet*	—	Replica	—	2-2-0	1992

Industrial locomotives

Name	No	Builder	Type	Built
—	258	E/Electric (1378)	4wBE	1944

England

101

Operating society/organisation:
The Museum of Science and Industry in Manchester, Liverpool Road, Castlefield, Manchester M3 4FP
Telephone: (0161) 832 2244
Internet address: *e-mail:* marketing@msim.org.uk
Web site: http://www.msim.org.uk
Car parks: On site, plus parking in the area (Museum car park £5, subject to change)
Access by public transport: Manchester Victoria, Piccadilly, Oxford Road and Deansgate main line stations. GM bus 33. G-Mex Metrolink station
On site facilities: Oldest passenger railway station, listed buildings containing exhibitions about science, industry, aviation, space, water supply and sewage disposal, gas and electricity. Xperiment the 'hands-on' science centre and the 'Out of this world' space gallery. World's largest collection of working steam mill engines in the Power Hall, demonstrated every afternoon. The Collections Centre has research facilities and access to reserve collections. Museum shop, restaurant, Learning, Conference Centres and coffee bar

*full scale model of 1830-built locomotive
††ex-Isle of Man Railways, 3ft gauge, sectioned (B/Peacock 1255)
†ex-Pakistan Railways, 5ft 6in gauge (V/Foundry 3064)
§ex-South African Railways, 3ft 6in gauge (B/Peacock 6693)

Rolling stock
Reproduction M&BR 1st class carriage c1840 using original fragments
2 full scale working models L&MR 2nd class carriages c1835
1914 L&YR ambulance carriage rebuilt 1923 as Medical Examination Car, LMS No 10825 (under restoration, assembled in 1917 from 1916 made modules)
B782903 4-wheeled covered goods van, BR (Wolverton), 1961
B783709 4-wheeled covered goods van, BR (Wolverton), 1962
3-plank loose coupled goods wagon, GCR (Chatham), c1890
Wickham Type 27 trolley (ex MoD No 9037) on loan from Marsh Trackworks

Owner
Novelty on loan from the National Railway Museum, York

Note:
Full scale (working) model — reproduction made to other than original specification
Replica — reproduction made by original company in original way
Reproduction — item made in original way by other than original company

Public opening: Daily except 24-26 December, including Saturdays and Sundays, 10.00-17.00. Entrance in Lower Byrom Street. Admission free to permanent galleries, although prices still apply for special exhibitions. Please ring for details. Groups can book a visit by calling (0161) 833 0027
Special notes: Good wheelchair access, toilets for the disabled, lecture and conference facilities

Museum — National Coal Mining Museum for — West Yorkshire

Member: Registered Museum
Museum Director: Dr M. L. Faull
Address: National Coal Mining Museum for England, Caphouse Colliery, New Road, Overton, Wakefield, West Yorkshire WF4 4RH
Operating society/organisation: National Coal Mining Museum for England Trust Ltd
Charity number: 517325
Telephone: 01924 848806
Fax: 01924 840694
Internet addresses:
e-mail: info@ncm.org.uk
Web site: www.ncm.org.uk
OS reference: SE 253164
Car park: Free - on site
Access by public transport:
Bus: Service 128 between Wakefield and Dewsbury serves

Locomotives

Name	No	Origin	Class	Type	Built
—	D2284*	BR	04	0-6-0DM	1960

*currently on loan to Heritage Shunters Trust, Peak Rail

Standard gauge industrial locomotives

Name	No	Builder	Type	Built
Acton Hall No 3	—	Peckett (1567)	0-6-0ST	1920*
—	47	T/Hill (249V)	0-6-0DH	1978*
—	44	Hunslet (6684)	0-6-0DH	1968*
—	40	Hunslet (7307)	0-6-0DH	1973

Narrow gauge and underground locomotives
3ft gauge

Name	No	Builder	Type	Built
—	BEM403	Hunslet (3614)	0-4-0DMF	1948*

2ft 6in gauge

Name	No	Builder	Type	Built
Alicia	—	H/Clarke (DM746)	0-4-0DMF	1951*
—	—	R/Hornsby (480679)	4wDMF	1961*
Deborah	2	H/Clarke (DM1356)	0-4-0DMF	1965+
—	—	H/Clarke (DM1433)	0-6-0DMF	1955+

England

the museum entrance. No 232 from Huddersfield or Wakefield stops adjacent and is slightly less convenient

Refreshment facilities: Licensed café providing hot and cold food

On site facilities: Souvenir shop

Running lines:
2ft 6in gauge operated locomotive line providing a transport link between Caphouse Colliery and Hope Pit
2ft 3in gauge rope-hauled demonstration 'paddy' line

Period of public operation: The museum is open daily 10.00-17.00 (except closed 24-26 December and 1 January 2010)

Special events:
Major exhibitions for 2009 are: Littleton Colliery photographic exhibition — until 26 April; Exhibition of Oliver Kilbourn Paintings — 18 May until 27 September; Working World of Tom McGuiness, a miner and his art — 12 October until 10 January 2010. Other events planned for 2009 are: See How They Run (demonstrations of mining machines) — 8 March; Miners' Gala — 6 June; Santa Underground — every weekend from 21 November and December until Christmas

Special facilities: Underground tours, conference centre, education facilities 'The Learning Curve'

Facilities for disabled: Toilets, full access to all galleries, audio loop, wheelchairs can be accommodated underground with prior booking

Name	No	Builder	Type	Built
Kirsten	0592	GMT (0592)	4w-4wDMF	1981
Stephanie	0593	GMT (0593)	4w-4wDMF	1981*
Anna	—	GMT	4w-4wDMF	1984*
—	1	Clayton (3538)	4w-4wBEF	1989+
2ft 4in gauge				
—	—	Atlas (2463)	4wBEF	1945
—	—	R/Hornsby (375347)	4wDM	1954
2ft 3in gauge				
Caphouse Flyer	—	Hunslet (8832)	4wDEF	1978
2ft 2in gauge				
—	—	Hunslet (7530)	4wDF	1977*
2ft 1.5in gauge				
—	—	R/Hornsby (379659)	4wDM	1955*
2ft gauge				
Fryston No 2	—	H/Clarke (DM655)	0-4-0DMF	1949

*not currently on public display
+in use on Caphouse-Hope railway

Locomotives on loan to other railways
Standard gauge

Name	No	Builder	Type	Built
The Welshman	—	M/Wardle (1207)	0-6-0ST	1890
Airedale	—	Hunslet (1440)	0-6-0ST	1923
Antwerp	—	Hunslet (3180)	0-6-0ST	1944
Wheldale	—	Hunslet (3186)	0-6-0ST	1944
Progress	—	RSH (7298)	0-6-0ST	1946
—	9	YEC (2521)	0-6-0ST	1952
Monkton No 1	—	Hunslet (3788)	0-6-0ST	1953
—	20	H/Clarke (D1152)	0-6-0DM	1958
3ft gauge				
—	BEM402	Hunslet (8505)	0-4-0DMF	1981
2ft 3in gauge				
Houghton Main Flyer	—	Hunslet (7274)	4wDM	1973
2ft 2in gauge				
Flying Scotsman	—	Hunslet (6273)	4wDM	1965
2ft gauge				
—	—	R/Hornsby (441424)	4wDMF	1961

Carriages and wagons
The museum's collection contains several varieties of standard gauge coal trucks, various narrow gauge manriding cars, coal-carrying cars and coal tubs. There are also two steam cranes

Locomoties on loan
The Welshman and 9 the Chesterfield Locomotive Action Group, Barrow Hill Roundhouse
Airedale, Wheldale, Monkton No 1 the Embsay & Bolton Abbey Steam Railway
Antwerp the North Yorkshire Moors Railway
Progress the Tanfield railway
20 the Midland Railway Centre, Butterley
BEM402 and *Flying Scotsman* the Middleton Railway
Houghton Main Flyer the Corris Railway
R/Hornsby (441424) the Chasewater Railway

National Railway Museum

Member: HRA, TT, MLSOG
Location: National Railway Museum, Leeman Road, York YO26 4XJ
OS reference: SE 594519
Operating society/organisation: Part of the National Museum of Science and Industry
Telephone: 08448 153 139
Internet addresses: *e-mail:* nrm@nmsi.ac.uk
Web site: www.nrm.org.uk
Car park: Available on site, charge applies. Coach parking is available — pre-booking required
Access by public transport: The museum is within a few minutes' walking distance of the railway station and city centre. No 2 Green Line park & ride bus operates to the door. A road-train operates between the Museum and the city centre (seasonal)
On site facilities: Museum shop, restaurant and toilets (all with baby changing facilities). Miniature railway rides (subject to availability), outdoor play areas, children's interactive learning centre, conference centre and reference centre. Search Engine Library and archive facility opened December 2007
Public opening: Daily 10.00-18.00. Closed 24-26 December. Admission is free for all. The museum reserves the right to charge for special events
Facilities for disabled: Most areas of the museum are accessible. Wheelchairs may be borrowed from the entrances. Disabled parking is available at the museum's City entrance
Special notes: The museum opened

1975 and has welcomed over 20 million visitors. It has received numerous awards including the prestigious 'European Museum of the Year' award in 2001.

As the world's largest railway museum, it offers the visitor three extensive exhibition halls. The Great Hall, the Station Hall and The Works house the world's premier collection of railway related material.

In the Great Hall there is an impressive array of locomotives around the turntable (demonstrated daily). Icons such as *Mallard* and the Japanese Bullet Train (the only one on display outside Japan) can also be found in the hall, along with the story of British Rail and a display dedicated to the movement of Mail by Rail.

A new exhibition in The Works is dedicated to the story of the most famous locomotive in the world, *Flying Scotsman*, which was saved for the nation in 2004. Once the current major overhaul of the locomotive is complete (late 2009) it will spend time both on main line operations as part of the museum's working fleet, and from time to time in the exhibition. Work in the museum's workshop on *Flying Scotsman* and other rolling stock can be viewd from the balcony galleries in The Works. Exhibitions on railway works and controlling the network can also be found on the balcony galleries, as can a live link to York's IECC signalbox. There is an external viewing area overlooking the mouth of York station. The Warehouse, also in The Works, is the museum's open store

and is an Aladdin's cave of railway treasures.

The Station Hall illustrates the concept of travel by train — for passengers and freight. Several trains are drawn up at platforms and range from superb Royal carriages to humble freight wagons. Access is possible to some footplates and carriages opened on request by Explainers. A range of talks and tours is also on offer, and staff are on hand to guide younger visitors in the Interactive Learning Centre, accessible via the South Yard.

As a venue for conferences, corporate events, private parties and weddings the museum acts as a spectacular backdrop.

For details ofthe museum's support group contact The Secretary, Friends of the National Railway Museum, c/o the above address. For information on becoming a museum volunteer call 01904 685737 and speak to the Volunteering Manager.

The museum's new library and archive facility, Search Engine, open from December 2007, houses the reference library, photographic and drawing collection in a brand new facility in The Grand Hall. Consult the NRM web site for more information.

The tables which follow indicate the whereabouts (display, on loan, in store) of the National Railway Collection. It must be emphasised that the appearance of any particular item on public display cannot be guaranteed. To confirm the exact location of a specific item, enquirers should contact the museum before visiting

Locomotives — Steam

Name	No	Origin	Builder	Class	Type	Built
Agenoria	—	Shutt End Colliery	Foster/Raistrick	—	0-4-0	1829
Coppernob	3	FR	Bury, Curtis & Kennedy	—	0-4-0	1846
Pet	—	LNWR	Crewe	—	0-4-0ST	1865
Aerolite	66	NER	Gateshead	X1(LNER)	2-2-4T	1869
—	1	GNR	Doncaster	—	4-2-2	1870
Bauxite	2	Hebburn Works	B/Hawthorn	—	0-4-0ST	1874

England

Name	No	Origin	Builder	Class	Type	Built
—	1275	NER	Gateshead	—	0-6-0	1874
Boxhill	82	LBSCR	Brighton	A1	0-6-0T	1880
Gladstone	—	LBSCR	Brighton	—	0-4-2	1882
Wren	—	LYR	B/Peacock	—	0-4-0ST	1887
—	1008	LYR	Horwich	—	2-4-2T	1889
Hardwicke	790	LNWR	Crewe	—	2-4-0	1892
—	1621	NER	Gateshead	M	4-4-0	1893
—	245	LSWR	Nine Elms	M7	0-4-4T	1897
—	673	MR	Derby	—	4-2-2	1899
Handyman	—*	—	H/Clarke (573)	—	0-4-0ST	1900
—	737	SECR	Ashford	D	4-4-0	1901
—	87	GER	Stratford	J69	0-6-0T	1904
—	2818	GWR	Swindon	2800	2-8-0	1905
Lode Star	4003	GWR	Swindon	'Star'	4-6-0	1907
Flying Scotsman	4472	LNER	Doncaster	A3	4-6-2	1923
King George V	6000	GWR	Swindon	'King'	4-6-0	1927
Cheltenham	925	SR	Eastleigh	V/Schools	4-4-0	1934
Rocket (replica)	—		R. Stephenson	—	0-2-2	1934
—	5000	LMS	Crewe	5MT	4-6-0	1935
—	607	Chinese Govt Rlys	Vulcan	KF7	4-8-4	1935
Mallard	4468	LNER	Doncaster	A4	4-6-2	1938
—	C1	SR	Brighton	Q1	0-6-0	1942
Winston Churchill	34051	SR	Brighton	BB	4-6-2	1946
Ellerman Lines	35029	BR(SR)	Sectioned	MN	4-6-2	1949
Frank Galbraith	5	Tees-Side Bridge & Engineering Co	Sentinel	—	4wTG	1957
Iron Duke (broad gauge replica)	—	GWR	RESCO	—	4-2-2	1985

*3ft gauge

Locomotives — Electric

Name	No	Origin	Builder	Class	Type	Built
—	1	NSR	Bolton & Sons	—	0-4-0WE	1917
—	809	GPO	Green Bat	—	2w-2E	1931
—	26020	BR	Gorton/Metrovick	76	Bo-Bo Electric	1951
—	RA.36	TML	Hunslet	—	4wBE/WE	1990
Royal Scot	87001	BR	Crewe	87	B0-B0	1973

Locomotives — Diesel

Name	No	Origin	Builder	Class	Type	Built
—	—	WD	Drewry	—	0-4-0DM	1934
—	—	Yorkshire Water Authority	R/Hornsby (187105)	—	4wDM	1937
—	08911	BR	Horwich	08	0-6-0 DE	1962
—	D8000	BR	E/Electric	20	Bo-Bo	1957
—	5500	BR	Brush	31	A1A-A1A	1957
—	D200	BR	E/Electric	40	1Co-Co1	1958
—	03090	BR	—	03	0-6-0DM	1960
—	D2860	BR	YEC	02	0-4-0 DH	1960
King's Own Yorkshire Light Infantry	55022	BR	E/Electric	55	Co-Co	1961
Western Fusilier	D1023	BR	Swindon	52	C-C	1963
—	41001	BR	Crewe	41	Bo-Bo	1972
Prince William	47798	BR	Crewe	47	Co-Co	1965

Locomotives on loan
Livingston Thompson from the Ffestiniog Railway

Rolling Stock Powered Units — Electric

1916	LNWR Motor Open Third Brake No 28249
1925	SR Motor Third Brake No S8143S
1937	SR Motor Third Open Brake No S11179S
1941†	LMS Class 502 BMS No 28361
1941†	LMS Class 502 DTC No 29896
1975	Birmingham Airport Maglev passenger car
1976	Series 'O' Shinkasen No 2214
	BR Class 423/4VEP DT No 76875
	BR Class 414/2HAP MBS No 61275
	BR Class 414/2HAP DTC No 75395

Rolling Stock Powered Units — Diesel

1959	BR DMU Class 108 Nos 51562 & 51922

Rolling Stock — Departmental

1890	GNR Locomotive Tender No 1002
1899	GWR Hand Crane No 537
1906	NER Dynamometer Car No 902502
1907	NER Steam Breakdown Crane No CME 13
1907	Match Truck No DE942114
1926	LNER Match Truck No DE320952
1931/2	LNER Petrol-driven platelayers' trolley No 960209
1936	GWR Ballast Wagon No 80659
1955	GEC 12.5-ton Coles Crane
1969	BR Plasser Tamping & Liner No 73010
1989	Molhouser side discharge muck car ASDR 3105 (Channel Tunnel)

Rolling Stock — Passenger

1834	B&WR 1st & 2nd composite
1834	B&WR 2nd class
1834	B&WR 3rd class
1842	L&BR Queen Adelaide's Saloon
1850	NER Brake End (body only)
1851	ECR 1st class No 1
1860	Cornwall Rly broad gauge coach (body only)
1861	NBR Port Carlisle branch 'dandy car'
1869	LNWR Queen Victoria's Saloon
1885	MR 6-wheel composite brake No 901
1885	WCJS 8-wheel TPO No 186
1887	GNR Brake Van No 848
1897	Lynton & Barnstaple Rly brake composite No 6992
1898	ECJS 3rd class No 12
1899	Privately owned Duke of Sutherland's Saloon No 57A
1900	LNWR (ex-WCJS) Dining Car LMS 76
1902	LNWR King Edward's Saloon No 800
1902	LNWR Queen Alexandra's Saloon No 801
1903	LSWR Tricomposite brake No 3598

1908	ECJS Royal Saloon No 395
1913	Pullman Car Co 1st class parlour car *Topaz*
1914	MR Dining car No 3463
1930	L&MR 1st *Huskinson* (replica)
1930	L&MR 1st *Traveller* (replica)
1930	L&MR 2nd (replica)
1930	L&MR 2nd (replica)
1936	CIWL Night Ferry sleeping car No 3792
1937	LNER Buffet Car No 9135
1937	LMS corridor 3rd class brake No 5987,
1938	GJR TPO (replica)
1941	LMS Royal Saloon 799 (armoured car)
1945†	GWR Royal Saloon No 9007
1955	BR Lavatory composite No E43046
1962	BR Mk II 2nd brake corridor No 35468
1969	BR Mk IIb 2nd open No 5455

Rolling Stock — Freight & Non Passenger Carrying

1815	Little Eaton (Derby Canal) Gangroad Wagon
1815	Peak Forest Canal Tramway Wagon No 174
1816	Grantham Canal Tramway Truck
1828	Dandy Cart
1840	Stratford & Moreton Tramway Wagon
1894	LSWR Brake van No 99
1908	LNWR Open carriage truck No 11275
1912	GNR 8-ton van No E432764
1917	GCR Box Van
1917	LNWR Box Van
1920	LSWR Lowmac, No DE563024, NYMR
1924	LMSR Van
1931	GWR Fruit Van No 112884
1931	Stanton Iron Works 12-ton wagon
1933	LMSR 20-ton Goods Brake Van No 295987
1935	SR Bogie goods brake van No 56297
1935	PLM Train Ferry Van No 475014
1936	LMSR 3 plank open wagon No 472867
1937	GWR Siphon bogie milk van No 2775
1937	LMSR Milk Tank Wagon No 44057
1937	2 x Yorkshire Water Authority side-tipper wagons
1944	LMS Lowmac No M700728
1944	GWR 13-ton open wagon No DW143698
1949	BR Bogie bolster D No B941000
1950	BR 20-ton Weltrol No B900805
1951	ICI Liquid chlorine tank wagon No 47484
1951	BR 8-ton cattle wagon No B893343
1962	BR Speedfreight container No BA 4324B
1966	Milk Marketing Board 6-wheel tank No 42801
1989	TML side-tipping muck cart No R T239

†stored at MoD Kineton

Items away from the NRM
Locomotives

Original type/No/Name	Location	Builder	Built
Wylam Colliery	Science Mus	—	1813
Hetton Colliery 0-4-0	Locomotion	G. Stephenson	1822
SDR 0-4-0 *Locomotion*	Darlington	R. Stephenson & Co	1825
L&MR 0-2-2 *Rocket*	Science Mus	R. Stephenson & Co	1829
L&MR 0-2-2 *Novelty*	Museum of Science & Technology (Manchester)	Braithwaite & Ericsson	1829
SDR 0-6-0 No 24 *Derwent*	Darlington Nth Rd Mus	A. Kitching	1845

England

Original type/No/Name	Location	Builder	Built
GJR 2-2-2 *Columbine*	Science Mus	Crewe	1845
Wantage Tramway 0-4-0WT No 5 *Shannon*	Didcot Rly Ctr	G. England	1857
LNWR 0-4-0ST 1439	Ribble Valley	Crewe	1865
MR 2-4-0 No 158A	Locomotion	Derby	1866
South Devon Rly 0-4-0WT *Tiny*	South Devon Rly	Sara	1868
LSWR 2-4-0WT No 30587	Bodmin	B/Peacock	1874
NER 2-4-0 No 910	Locomotion	Gateshead	1875
NER 2-4-0 No 1463	Darlington Nth Rd Mus	Gateshead	1885
C&SL No 1	LT Museum	B/Peacock	1890
S&MR 0-4-2WT *Gazelle*	Col Stephens Rly Mus	Dodman	1893
GER 2-4-0 No 490	Bressingham	Stratford	1894
Rhodesia Railways 4-8-0 No 993	Tyseley	Sharp Stewart	1896
GWR 0-6-0 No 2516	Steam	Swindon	1897
TVR 0-6-2T No 28	Vale of Glamorgan Council	TVR	1897
GNR No 990 *Henry Oakley*	Bressingham	Doncaster	1899
LSWR 4-4-0 No 120	Bodmin	Nine Elms	1899
MR 4-4-0 No 1000	Severn Valley (Engine House)	Derby	1902
GER 0-6-0 No 1217	Barrow Hill	Stratford	1905
LT&SR 4-4-2T No 80 *Thundersley*	Bressingham	R. Stephenson	1909
GCR 2-8-0 No 102	Great Central	Gorton	1911
WD No 1377 (2ft Gauge)	LBR	Simplex	1918
GCR 506 *Butler Henderson*	Barrow Hill	Gorton	1920
NSR No 2	Locomotion	Stoke	1922
GWR 4-6-0 No 4073 *Caerphilly Castle*	Steam	Swindon	1923
LMS 0-6-0 No 4027	Midland Rly Ctr (tbc)	Derby	1924
GWR 2-2-2 *North Star* (replica)	Steam	R. Stephenson	1925
SR 4-6-0 No 777 *Sir Lamiel*	GCR	N/British	1925
SR 4-6-0 No 850 *Lord Nelson*	Mid-Hants Railway§	Eastleigh	1926
LNER 2-6-0 No 4774 *Green Arrow*	Locomotion	Doncaster	1937
RSH(7063) 0-4-0ST	Locomotion		1942

England

107

GWR 0-6-0PT No 9400	Steam	Swindon	1947
BR 4-6-2 No 70013 *Oliver Cromwell*	Great Central/main line	Crewe	1951
BR No 92220 *Evening Star*	Steam	Swindon	1960
BR Bo-Bo No E3036	Barrow Hill	N/British	1960
BR Co-Co No D6700	NYMR	E/Electric	1960
replica 0-4-0 Rocket	†	Locomotion Enterprises	1979

†private site
*expected to return to NRM
§expected to be a permanent loan, commencing 2009

Powered Units

NER	electric parcels van No 3267, G. Stephenson Mus
GWR	diesel railcar No 4, Steam
BR	Class 101 vehicle Nos 51192/54352 East Lancs

Departmental Stock

1932	LMS Ballast plough brake van No 197266, Embsay
1949	BR(LMS) Dynamometer car No 3, No 45049, Barrow Hill

Passenger Stock

1846	SDR 1st & 2nd composite No 31, Beamish
1850	NER 4-wheel coach body, Darlington
1910	GCR Open 3rd class No 666, Nottingham
1925	GWR 3rd class dining car No 9653, Severn Valley Rly
1925	LMS 3rd class vestibule No 7828 *(on loan to LMS Carriage Association)*
1934	GWR Buffet Car No 9631, Steam,
1936	LNER 3rd Open, No 13254, NYMR
1941	LMS Royal saloon No 798, Glasgow Museum of Transport
1960	Pullman Car Co 1st class Parlour car No 326 *Emerald,* Carnforth
1960	Pullman Car Co 1st class Kitchen car No 311 *Eagle,* Bluebell
1985	GWR 3rd (broad gauge replica), Didcot

Freight & Non Passenger Carrying Stock

1850	South Hetton Colliery Chaldron Wagon No 1155, D Bahn Museum, Nuremberg
1898	CR well trolley bogie crocodile, Bo'ness
1902	NER 20-ton wooden hopper wagon No 4551, Tyne & Wear
1909	GWR Girder Wagon Set (Pollen E) Nos DW84997, 84998, 84999, 85000, Didcot
1912	LBSCR Open wagon No 27884, Yeovil
1912	LSWR Gunpowder van No KDS61209, Yeovil
1914	GWR Shunters' truck No W94988, Steam
1922	LBSCR cattle truck No 7116, Isle of Wight Steam Rly
1928	ICI Nitric acid tank wagon No 14, Yeovil
1941	LNER 20-ton brake van, No 246710, NYMR
1948	BR(SR) 12-ton shock absorbing wagon No 14036, NYMR
1950	BR 12-wheel well wagon, No KDB901601, East Lancs
1955	BR 16-ton mineral wagon No B227009, Middleton
1959	BR Fish van No B87905, Hull

Museum — National Waterways Museum — Glos

The museum completed a Lottery update of the galleries and site in 2001

Location: Gloucester Docks — signposted 'Historic Docks'
OS reference: SO 826183
Operating society/organisation: National Waterways Museum, The Waterways Trust, Llanthony Warehouse, Gloucester Docks, Gloucester GL1 2EH
Tel: (01452) 318200
Fax: (01452) 318202
Internet address: *e-mail:* bookingsnwm@thewaterwaystrust.org
Web site: www.nwm.org.uk
Car parks: Pay & display outside

Industrial locomotives

Name	No	Builder	Type	Built
—	1	A/Barclay (2126)	0-4-0F	1942

Ex-Gloucester Corporation, Castle Meads Power Station, Gloucester Docks. Now on static display

Rolling stock
William Balmforth of Rodley crane, c1880. Small collection of GW, Midland, LMS and BR vans with local connections. Sharpness Docks open wagons and Gloucester-built flat wagon, Manchester Ship Canal (ex-GWR) Toad brake van

museum. Free coach parking
Access by public transport: Main line Gloucester station, 1 mile

On site facilities: Tea room, souvenir and specialist bookshop (canal-related with some railway

literature). School room/children's holiday activities. Working demonstrations vary. Tug driving and blacksmith courses. Trip boats and other museums in docks
Facilities for disabled: Full facilities, lifts, ramps, toilets. All indoor displays, quaysides and tea room accessible. Floating exhibits not accessible
Public opening: Summer (April-October) — daily, 10.00-17.00, Winter (November-March) — daily, 11.00-16.00, except closed on 25 December.
Special events: Preservation, modellers' & craft events; leisure learning courses (send for further information)
Membership details: 'Friends' support organisation. Membership Secretary, c/o Museum address, Volunteers active in restoration/fundraising. Winter Meetings programme
Membership journal: *Llanthony Log* — quarterly

Nene Valley Railway

Timetable Service — Cambs

Member: HRA, TT

This unique railway's collection includes locomotives and coaches from 10 countries and two continents. It is a regular location for TV and film makers — from films like *Goldeneye* with Pierce Brosnan as 007 to ITV's *London's Burning*. The railway and the pleasant Cambridgeshire countryside have doubled for locations as diverse as Russia and Spain

Locomotives

Name	No	Origin	Class	Type	Built
City of Peterborough	73050	BR	5MT	4-6-0	1954
—	D9504	BR	14	0-6-0DH	1964
—	D9516	BR	14	0-6-0DH	1964
—	D9523	BR	14	0-6-0DH	1964
—†	31271	BR	31	A1A-A1A	1961
—	37518	BR	37	Co-Co	1962
Atlantic Conveyor	D306	BR	40	1Co-Co1	1960
—	47270	BR	47	Co-Co	1965
—	64.305-6	DB	64	2-6-2T	1936
—	7173	DB	52	2-10-0	1943
—	656	DSB	F	0-6-0T	1949

General Manager:
Cris Rees
Headquarters: Nene Valley
Railway, Wansford Station,
Stibbington, Peterborough, Cambs
PE8 6LR
Telephone: Stamford (01780)
784444; Talking Timetable (01780)
784404
Main station: Wansford
Other public stations: Yarwell,
Orton Mere, Ferry Meadows,
Peterborough NVR (15min walk
from city centre)
OS reference: TL 903979
Car park: Wansford, Orton Mere,
Ferry Meadows, Peterborough NVR
Access by public transport: Buses
from Peterborough to Orton Mere
and Ferry Meadows
Refreshment facilities: Wansford,
bar coach on most trains
Souvenir shops: Wansford
Exhibition: Wansford
Depot: Wansford
Length of line: 7.5 miles
Passenger trains: Yarwell
Junction-Wansford-Ferry Meadows-
Orton Mere-Peterborough NV
Period of public operation:
Sundays from mid-February;

Name	No	Origin	Class	Type	Built
—	101	SJ	B	4-6-0	1944
—	1178	SJ	S	2-6-2T	1914
—	3.628	Nord	3500	4-6-0	1911
—	5485	PKP	Typ	0-8-0T	1961
—	51401	BR	117	DMS	1959
—	51347	BR	117	DMBS	1959
—	59508	BR	117	TCL	1959

†on loan from Midland Railway

Industrial locomotives

Name	No	Builder	Type	Built
Toby	—	Cockerill (1626)	0-4-0VBT	1890
Yvonne	—	Cockerill (2945)	0-4-0VBT	1920
Muriel	—	E/Electric (1123)	0-4-0DH	1966
Derek Crouch	—	H/Clarke (1539)	0-6-0ST	1924
Thomas	—	H/Clarke (1800)	0-6-0T	1947
Jacks Green	—	Hunslet (1953)	0-6-0ST	1939
—	75006	Hunslet (2855)	0-6-0ST	1943
—	—	R/Hornsby (294268)	4wDM	1951
Doncaster	—	YEC (2654)	0-4-0DE	1957
—	11	Rebuilt Hill	4wD	1963
Stanton No 50	—	YEC (2670)	0-6-0DE	1958
Barabel	—	R/Royce (10202)	0-4-0DH	1967
—	DL83	R/Royce (10271)	0-6-0DH	1967

Stock
15 BR Mk 1 coaches; Wagons Lits sleeping car, Italian-built; Wagons Lits
dining car, Belgian-built; 6 coaches from Denmark; 1 coach from France;
4 coaches from Belgium; 1 steam rail crane; SR Travelling Post Office;
TPO coach M30272M; 20 12-ton Vanfits plus items of freight stock

England

weekends from Easter to end of October; Wednesdays from May, plus other midweek services in summer. Santa Specials at end of November and throughout December (telephone for details)
Special events: Take place throughout the year including Thomas' Weekend, Gala Weekend and Vintage Rail/Mail Weekend

(telephone for details). The shop, café, bookshop, model railway and exhibition are open on operating days and the locomotive yard is open all year for viewing. NVR is also the home of *Thomas* the children's favourite engine
Facilities for disabled: Ramp access to all stations and shops. Full toilets in Wansford station, souvenir

shop. Disabled persons and helpers are eligible for concessionary fares. Passengers can be assisted on and off trains
Membership details: Bill Forman, c/o above address
Membership journal: *Nene Steam* — 4 times/year
Marketing name: Britain's International Steam Railway

Timetable Service	North Bay Railway	North Yorkshire

Member: HRA
This 20in gauge railway opened in 1931 is almost a mile long, with all the features of a main line railway including a tunnel, bridges, signals stations and gradient boards reproduced to scale. The steam outline locomotives are based on Sir Nigel Gresley's Class A1 design for the LNER.
Location: Northstead Manor Gardens, Scarborough
Headquarters: Peasholme Park Station, Northstead Manor Gardens, Scarborough YO12 6PF
Telephone: General enquiries: 01723 383636
Internet addresses:
e-mail: info@nbr.org.uk
Web site: www.nbr.org.uk
Main public station:
Peasholme Park

Locomotives

Name	No	Builder	Type	Built
Neptune	1931	H/Clarke (D565)	4-6-2DH s/o	1931
Robin Hood	570	H/Clarke (D570)	4-6-4DH s/o	1932
Triton	1932	H/Clarke (D573)	4-6-2DH s/o	1932
Poseidon	1933	H/Clarke (D582)	4-6-2DH s/o	1933

Stock
12 bogie coaches

Other public stations:
Scalby Mills
Car parks: Nearby pay & display
Access by public transport: The railway is within walking distance of the main line stations and local bus services
Refreshment facilities: At both stations, full meals, licensed at Peasholme Park
Journey time: 8 minutes

Length of line:
0.875 mile, 1ft 8in gauge
Period of public operation: Daily, April until end October, then weekends and school holidays at other times
Facilities for disabled: Full
Special events: Santa Specials in December

Steam Centre	North Ings Farm Museum	Lincolnshire

The museum contains agricultural equipment, tractors and railway items
Contact: Tim Hall or Malcolm Phillips (joint owners)
Headquarters: North Ings Farm Museum, Fen Road, Dorrington, Lincoln LN4 3QB
Telephone: 01526 833100
Internet address: *e-mail:* info@northingsfarmmuseum.co.uk
Web site: www.northingsfarmmuseum.co.uk
Car parks: At the museum entrance
Access by public transport:

Locomotives

Name	No	Builder	Type	Built
Swift	—	Marshall	0-4-0VBT	1970
—	—	R/Hornsby (200744)	4wDM	1940
—	—	R/Hornsby (371937)	4wDM	1956
—	—	R/Hornsby (375701)†	4wDM	1954
—	—	R/Hornsby (421433)	4wDM	1959
—	—	M/Rail (7403)	4wDM	1939
—	—	M/Rail (7493)	4wDM	1940
—	—	O&K	4wDM	1932
—	—	Lister Railtrack*	4wDM	—
—	—	H/Hunslet (7120)	4wDM	1969

†dismantled
*constructed from spare parts

Nearest main line station
Ruskington, 3 miles
Refreshment facilities: Only
available by prior arrangement
Length of line:
600yd, 2ft gauge
Period of public operation: Open
first Sunday, April to October.
10.00-17.00
Facilities for disabled: Toilet,

Owners
M/Rail (7403) and R/Hornsby (200744) on loan from Narrow Gauge Railway Museum Trust

wheelchairs can be accommodated
on the train. Part of the museum is
not easily accessible for
wheelchairs

| Timetable Service | ## North Norfolk Railway (The Poppy Line) | Norfolk |

Member: HRA, TT

Part of the former Midland & Great Northern Joint Railway, other elements of the LNER have crept in in the guise of the 'B12' and the newly restored Quad Art set. GER 'J15' is now in service. Guest locomotives can be viewed at various times throughout the year. The line runs through beautiful coast, wood and heathland scenery with a nature trail running along its side between Weybourne and Kelling Heath

Managing Director: Hugh Harkett

Headquarters: North Norfolk Railway plc, Sheringham Station, Sheringham, Norfolk NR26 8RA

Telephone: Sheringham (01263) 820800

Fax: (01263) 820801

Internet address: *Web site:* www.nnrailway.co.uk

Main station: Sheringham

Other public stations: Weybourne, Kelling Halt, Holt

OS reference: Sheringham TG 156430, Weybourne TG 118419

Car parks: Sheringham (public), Weybourne, Holt

Access by public transport: By train to Sheringham station (National Express East Anglia)

Refreshment facilities: Sheringham, Weybourne, Holt

Souvenir shops: Sheringham, Weybourne, Holt

Depot: Weybourne

Length of line: 5.25 miles

Passenger trains: Steeply graded (1 in 80), Sheringham-Weybourne-Holt

Period of public operation: Most days from 1 April to end October. Weekends in December plus Christmas week

Locomotives and multiple-units

Name	No	Origin	Class	Type	Built
—	65462	GER	J15	0-6-0	1912
—	69621	GER	N7	0-6-2T	1924
—	61572*	LNER	B12	4-6-0	1928
—	68088*	LNER	Y7	0-4-0T	1923
92 Squadron	34081	SR	BB	4-6-2	1948
—	90775	MoS	WD	2-10-0	1943
—	D2280	BR	04	0-6-0DM	1960
Camulodunum	D3940	BR	08	0-6-0DE	1960
—	D3935	BR	08	0-6-0DE	1961
—	12131	BR	11	0-6-0DE	1952
—	D5207	BR	25	Bo-Bo	1962
—	5580	BR	31	A1A-A1A	1960
—	31207	BR	31	A1A-A1A	1960
Mirage	D6732	BR	37	Co-Co	1962
—	47367	BR	47	Co-Co	1965
—	51228	M/Cam	101	DTSL	1958
—	54062	M/Cam	101	DMBS	1957
—	79960	W&M	—	Railbus	1958
—	79963§	W&M	—	Railbus	1958
—	LEV1	BR/Leyland	—	Railbus	1978
—	Car 91†	M/Cam	5BEL	DMPBS	1932

*under restoration
§on loan to Mangapps Farm Railway
†ex-'Brighton Belle' Pullman Car, converted to locomotive-hauled

Industrial locomotives

Name	No	Builder	Type	Built
Ring Haw	—	Hunslet (1982)	0-6-0ST	1940
Wissington*	—	H/Clarke (1700)	0-6-0ST	1938
—	—	Bagnall (2370)	0-6-0F	1929

*under restoration

Stock
3 ex-LNER coaches, GNR Quad Art set (in service, but not on a daily basis), 7 ex-BR coaches, 3 coach King's Cross suburban set; Gresley buffet, Wisbech & Upwell Tramway coach, 2 CCT wagons, small number of wagons, Southern Railway PMV, LNER BYP, Colman's Mustard Van

Owners
Wissington, 65462, 61572, 31207 and 90775 the Midland & Great Northern Railway Society
69621 East Anglian Railway Museum
5580 A1A Locomotives
47367 The Stratford Class 47 Group
LEV1 on loan from National Railway Museum

England

QUADS OUT!

North Norfolk Railway has the train of the year!

MORE SPECIAL EVENTS THAN EVER IN 2009!

Feb 27–Mar 1, Mar 7/8	Big steam gala to commemorate M&GN closure in 1959
May 23 – 25	Altogether Now! Hands-on children and family event
July 4 – 11	Quad-Art week. Quad-Art set in daily service
July 5	Vintage Transport Day
July 17, 18 & 19	8th North Norfolk Railway Beer Festival
Sept 4, 5 & 6	Grand Steam Gala
Sept 19 & 20	The famous '40s Weekend
Oct 24 & 25	Altogether Now! Hands-on children and family event
December	Santa Specials

There's no more important heritage train in Britain than the 84-years-old teak-bodied Gresley Quad-Art set – now back in all its glory on the NNR.

Magnificently restored at Carnforth with the help of a Heritage Lottery Fund grant, the Quads will be out at special events on the NNR in 2009 – including daily service in Quad-Art Week, July 4th -11th.

With its spectacular seaside setting, its superb loco stud (including WD 2-10-0 90775, J15 0-6-0 65462, B12 4-6-0 61572 and N7 69621, plus guest engines in the summer) and its three enchanting stations, the North Norfolk Railway is now one of Britain's foremost heritage railways.

NEW! *The North Norfolkman* Sunday lunch trains on March 22, April 26, May 3, June 7, July 12, August 2, 16 and 23.
NEW! *The North Norfolkman* evening dinner trains on June 13, July 4, August 8.
Murder Mystery wine and dine trains on June 27, Sept 12 and 26, Oct 10 and 24, Nov 28.

Visit www.nnrailway.co.uk or call 01263 820 800

NORTH NORFOLK RAILWAY
Sheringham Station, Norfolk NR26 8RA

LIVE STEAM – LIVING HISTORY

Special events: Special Steam Gala, 50th Anniversary of M&GN Closure — 27 February-1 March, 7/8 March; Altogether Now! Hands-on children and family event — 25-27 May; Vintage Transport Day — 12 July; 8th Poppy Line Beer Festival — 17-19 July; Grand Steam Gala — 4-6 September; The Famous '40s Weekend — 19/20 September; Altogether Now! Hands-on children and family event — 24/25 October; Santa Specials (advanced booking only) — 5/6, 12/13, 19/20, 22-24 December; Santa School Specials (advance booking only) — 8/9 December; Mince Pie Specials — 26 December-3 January 2010;

Special facilities: Weybourne station is licensed for weddings. Special dining trains can be booked for corporate and party entertaining. Online booking available on www.nnrailway.co.uk

William Mariott Museum: This museum is now open in a replica M&GN goods shed at Holt station. Artefacts and ephemera commemorating the man who built the railway and ran it for almost 40 years. Open on steam operating days

Facilities for disabled: All stations have level access. Wheelchair access to most trains, and to gift shop and buffet at Sheringham. Disabled parking at Holt station

Membership details: Midland & Great Northern Joint Railway Society, Mr D. Bickell, c/o Sheringham Station, Sheringham, Norfolk NR26 8RA

Membership journal: *Joint Line* — quarterly

Timetable Service — North Yorkshire Moors Railway — North Yorkshire

Member: HRA, TT

This 18-mile line runs through the picturesque North York Moors National Park and is host to an extensive collection of main line locomotives

General Manager: Philip Benham

Headquarters: Pickering Station, Pickering, North Yorkshire YO18 7AJ

Telephone: Pickering (01751) 472508 for passenger enquiries, charter and diner bookings

Internet address:
e-mail: info@nymr.co.uk
Web site: www.nymr.co.uk

Main station: Pickering

Other public stations: Whitby Grosmont, Goathland, Levisham, Pickering

OS reference: Pickering NZ 797842, Levisham NZ 818909, Goathland NZ 836013, Grosmont NZ 828053

Car parks: Grosmont, Goathland, Levisham, Pickering

Access by public transport: Northern Rail services linking Middlesbrough with Grosmont and Whitby
Bus services include Leeds-York-Malton-Goathland-Whitby; Helmsley-Pickering-Scarborough

Refreshment facilities: Available on most trains and at Grosmont, Goathland and Pickering. Tea bar at Levisham most weekends

Souvenir shops: Pickering,

Locomotives and multiple-units

Name	No	Origin	Class	Type	Built
George Stephenson	44767§	LMS	5MT	4-6-0	1947
Eric Treacy	45428*	LMS	5MT	4-6-0	1937
—	49395	LNWR	7F	0-8-0	1918
—	2392	NER	P3	0-6-0	1923
—	63395*	NER	T2	0-8-0	1918
Sir Nigel Gresley	60007	LNER	A4	4-6-2	1937
Lord of the Isles	62005	LNER	K1	2-6-0	1949
—	69023§	LNER	J72	0-6-0T	1951
—	3814**	GWR	2884	2-8-0	1940
—	5224	GWR	4200	2-8-0T	1930
—	6619	GWR	5600	0-6-2T	1928
—	825	SR	S15	4-6-0	1927
—	30830††	SR	S15	4-6-0	1927
Repton	30926	SR	V	4-4-0	1934
Hartland	34101**	SR	WC	4-6-2	1950
—	75029	BR	4MT	4-6-0	1954
—	80135††	BR	4MT	2-6-4T	1956
Dame Vera Lynn	3672††	MoS	WD	2-10-0	1943
—	2253††	USATC	S160	2-8-0	1943
—	D2207	BR	04	0-6-0DM	1953
—	08556	BR	08	0-6-0DE	1959
—	08850	BR	08	0-6-0DE	1961
Helen Turner	D5032††	BR	24	Bo-Bo	1959
—	D5061*	BR	24	Bo-Bo	1960
Sybilla	D7628	BR	25	Bo-Bo	1965
—	D6700	BR	37	Co-Co	1960
Lion	50027	BR	50	Co-Co	1968
—	51511	BR	101	DMC	1959
—	53204	BR	101	DMBS	1957
—	59539	BR	101	TSL	1958

*undergoing major overhaul at Grosmont, due to traffic 2009
§undergoing major overhaul off-site
**undergoing major overhaul at Grosmont, not in traffic
††awaiting overhaul

Goathland, Grosmont, Grosmont MPD and Whitby.

Artist in Residence: Chris Ware is based at Levisham station whose studio is open when trains are running

Locomotive Depot: Grosmont

Length of line: 18 miles (Pickering-Grosmont), 24 miles (Pickering-Whitby)

Passenger trains: Steam-hauled services Grosmont-Pickering. Pullman evening dining service and 'Moorlander' Sunday lunch service run regularly. Saloons are also available for special occasions (eg wedding parties, conferences, etc) *Note:* NYMR trains operate to/from Whitby throughout the season. Ring for details

Special events: Spring Steam Gala — 1-4, 8-10 May; Swinging Sixties — 13/14 June; Vintage Vehicle Weekend — 11/12 July; Family Wekend — 1/2 August; Tedy Bears' Picnic — 12/13 September; Heritage Diesel Gala — 18-20 September; Autumn Steam Gala — 2-4 October; The Railway at War — 16-18 October; Wizard Weekend — 31 October/1 November; Santa Specials —

Industrial locomotives

Name	No	Builder	Type	Built
—	29*	Kitson (4263)	0-6-2T	1904
—	5††	R/Stephenson (3377)	0-6-2T	1909
Antwerp	—††	Hunslet (3180)	0-6-0ST	1944
Neil D. Barker	12139	E/Electric (1553)	0-6-0DE	1948
—	16	Drewry	0-4-0DM	1941
—	2	R/Hornsby (421419)	4wDM	1958
—	3*	R/Hornsby (441934)	4wDM	1960
Ron Rothwell	1	Vanguard (129V)	0-4-0DM	1963
—	2	Vanguard (131V)	0-4-0DM	1963

*on loan to Middleton Railway
††awaiting overhaul

Stock
5 pre-Grouping, 12 pre-Nationalisation, 32 x BR Mk 1, 4 x Pullman, 5 other BR coaches, 2 x Camping Coach, 1 x BR Mk 3 sleeper, 11 x brake vans, 4 x diesel cranes, 2 x 45-ton steam cranes, 88 other vehicles

Owners
825 and 30830 the Essex Locomotive Society
62005, 63395 and 69023 the North Eastern Locomotive Preservation Group
60007 Sir Nigel Gresley Locomotive Preservation Trust
Antwerp the National Mining Museum
5 and 29 Lambton Locomotives Trust
D5032 T. J. Thomson & Co
D5061 the Class 24 Society
50027 the Class 50 Support Group
3814, 6619, 34101 and 44767 private
75029 the North Yorkshire Moors Historical Railway Trust
49395 and D6700 on loan from National Railway Museum
5224 on loan from LNWR

115

5/6, 12/13, 18-21 December
Period of public operation: Daily 16 March-1 November, Santa Specials and other Xmas services in December/January and New Year

Facilities for disabled: The NYMR welcomes disabled visitors and special attention will gladly be provided if advance notice is given

Special notes: Operates through North York Moors National Park and to Whitby

Steam Centre — Northampton & Lamport Railway — Northants

Member: HRA

Part of the Northampton to Market Harborough branch originally opened in 1859 and finally closing in 1981. That year a group was formed with the intention of re-opening the branch. Trains restarted in 1995 with 0.75 mile of running line and sidings. When completed to Lamport the line will be 6 miles long

Headquarters: Pitsford & Brampton Station, Pitsford Road, Chapel Brampton, Northampton NN6 8BA

Location: About 5 miles north of Northampton, Pitsford Road off A5199 (formerly A50) or A508

Chairman: Dr Colin Wilson

Operating company: Northampton Steam Railway Ltd

Telephone: 01604 820327. Sundays and weekday afternoons, recorded announcements other times

Internet address: *Web site:* www.nlr.org.uk

Access by public transport: None

On site facilities: NLR souvenir shop, buffet coach, toilets, second-hand bookshop

Length of line: 1.3 miles, extension to bridge 14 now open

Public opening:
Every Sunday and Bank Holiday Monday from 2 March to 26 October.
Santa Specials, Saturday and Sunday from 7-21 December.
Plus some Saturdays during special events

Special events: Please contact for details

Locomotives and multiple-units

Name	No	Origin	Class	Type	Built
Bickmarsh Hall	5967	GWR	'Hall'	4-6-0	1937
—	3862	GWR	2884	2-8-0	1942
—	31289	BR	31	A1A-A1A	1961
—	37679	BR	37	Co-Co	1963
The Royal Artilleryman	45118	BR	45	1Co-Co1	1962
—	47205	BR	47	Co-Co	1965
—	51359*	BR	117	DMBS	1959

*expected to move to the East Lancs Railway

Industrial locomotives

Name	No	Builder	Type	Built
Colwyn	45	Kitson (5470)	0-6-0ST	1933
Westminster	1378	Peckett (1378)	0-6-0ST	1914
—	2104	Peckett (2104)	0-4-0ST	1948
Vanguard	5374	Chrzanow (5374)	0-6-0T	1959
Bunty	146C	Fowler (4210018)/ rebuilt T/Hill	0-4-0DH	1950 1964
—	21	Fowler (4210094)	0-4-0DH	1955
—	1	R/Hornsby (275886)	4wDM	1949
Sir Gyles Isham	764	R/Hornsby (319286)	0-4-0DM	1953

Stock

Coaches: 1 x BR Mk 1 TSO; 1 x BR Mk 1 CK; 1 x BR Mk 1 RBR; 1 x Mk 2 TSO; 1 x BR Mk 1 NAV; 2 x SR PMV; 1 x GWR Toad; 1 x LMS CCT; 1 x BR 20-ton brake

Owner

Colwyn the Colwyn Preservation Society

Facilities for disabled: Limited access

Special notes: All stock is visible along the side of the line. Carriages are available for birthday parties etc on operating dates except certain special events, and complete trains are also available for hire during weekdays for school or special events. Please contact the railway for details

Membership details: Membership Secretary, Pitsford & Brampton Station, Pitsford Road, Chapel Brampton, Northampton NN6 8BA

Membership journal: *Premier Line* — 4 times a year

Northamptonshire Ironstone Railway Trust

The museum is a working display as well as a collection of historic memorabilia. Many of the items that are currently being renovated are housed in a shed that accommodates the museum display
Location: Hunsbury Hill Industrial Museum, Hunsbury Hill Country Park, Hunsbury Hill Road, Camp Hill, Northampton
OS reference: SP 735584
Operating organisation: Northamptonshire Ironstone Railway Trust Ltd
Telephone: 01604 702031
Contact: W. Nile, 14 Lyncrest Avenue, Dunston, Northampton (Tel: 01604 757481)
Access by public transport: Northampton Transport bus routes, 24, 25 to Camp Hill from Greyfriars bus station
On site facilities: Light refreshments, shop, toilets. Children's play areas and picnic areas
Length of line: 2.25 miles with yard, engine shed and workshops, 2 stations and level crossing
Public opening: Museum and shed/yard for viewing most weekdays and weekends. Train service from Easter Sunday to end of September on Sundays and Bank Holiday Mondays plus December for Santa Specials. Parties can be catered for on weekdays by appointment
Times of opening: 10.00 to 16.00 for viewing with train service from 13.00 to 17.00 on Sundays and Bank Holidays
Facilities for the disabled: Passenger coach can accommodate wheelchairs

Multiple-units

Name	No	Origin	Class	Type	Built
—	13004	SR	4DD	DMBS	1949
—	70284	BR	4CEP / 411	TS	1956
—	70296	BR	4CEP / 411	TS	1956
—	69304	BR	4BIG / 422	TSRB	1965
—	14352†	BR	415 / 4EPB	DMS	1954
—	15396†	BR	415 / 4EPB	TS	1954
—	14351†	BR	415 / 4EPB	DMS	1954

†unit No 415176

Industrial locomotives

Name	No	Builder	Type	Built
Vigilant†	—	Hunslet (287)	0-4-0ST	1882
Belvedere◊	—	Sentinel (9365)	0-4-0TG	1946
Musketeer◊	—	Sentinel (9369)	0-4-0TG	1946
Hylton	—	Planet (3967)	0-4-0DH	1961
Charles Wake	—	Fowler (422001)	0-4-0DH	1965
Lois	—	Fowler (422033)	0-4-0DH	1965
—	16	Hunslet (2087)	0-4-0DM	1940
Muffin	46	R/Hornsby (242868)	4wDM	1946
Sir Alfred Wood	53	R/Hornsby (319294)	0-6-0DM	1953
—*	87	Peckett (1871)	0-6-0ST	1934
Northampton†	1	Bagnall (2565)	0-4-0ST	1934
Cherwell**	—	Bagnall (2654)	0-6-0ST	1942
—	—	Grafton	Steam crane	1934

* metre gauge on loan to Irchester Country Park
◊ static display
† being rebuilt
**3ft gauge

Owners
13004, unit No 415176 the Bulleid Preservation Enterprises
70284/70296 Northampton Social Services

Special notes: Museum to the Ironstone Industry of Northamptonshire, the museum houses photographs, documents and other items connected with the ironstone industry. The railway is laid on the old trackbed of the quarry system and partly on a new formation with remains of the quarry face and cuttings available for exploration
Membership details: Mr R. Coleman, c/o above address

Nottingham Transport Heritage Centre

Member: HRA
Along with access to nearly 10 miles of the ex-Great Central

Railway main line in Nottinghamshire, the Centre is host to a road and rail transport heritage

vehicle collection. The railway has a main line connection just south of Loughborough (Midland) station and regular freight trains use the line as far as the British Gypsum works at East Leake.

Plans are in place to reconnect this section with the Great Central Railway at Loughborough. See www.bridgingthegap.co.uk
Location: Signposted on the A60 Loughborough road just south of Ruddington traffic lights, 5 miles south of Nottingham and 7 miles north of Loughborough
Operating society/organisation: Great Central (Nottingham) Ltd, Mere Way, Ruddington, Nottingham NG11 6NX
Telephone: (0115) 940 5705
Fax: (0115) 940 5905
Internet address:
E-mail: mail@nthc.co.uk
Web site: www.nthc.co.uk
Access by public transport: Buses from Nottingham city centre and Broad Marsh via Nottingham railway station. Nottingham City Transport (0115) 9506070, Trent Barton (01773) 712265
On site facilities: Car park, shop and cafeteria, picnic areas and country park walks. 700m-long triple-gauge passenger-carrying miniature railway. Model railway layouts
Length of line: 8 mile round trip to Rushcliffe Halt by steam train. 18 mile round trip to Loughborough junction by diesel (monthly and galas)
Facilities for disabled: Access to most areas, accessible toilets
Public opening: Sundays and Bank Holidays Easter Sunday to late October, plus Santa weekends in December.
Open 10.30-17.00

Locomotives and multiple-units

Name	No	Origin	Class	Type	Built
—	13180	BR	08	0-6-0DE	1955
—	13290	BR	08	0-6-0DE	1956
—	D7629	BR	25	Bo-Bo	1965
—	D8007	BR	20	Bo-Bo	1957
—	D8154	BR	20	Bo-Bo	1966
—	37009	BR	37	Co-Co	1961
—	47292	BR	47	Co-Co	1966
—	47765	BR	47	Co-Co	1964
—	56097	BR	56	Co-Co	1981
—	73110 (E6016)	BR	73	Bo-Bo	1962
—	51138	BR	116	DMBS	1958
—	51151	BR	116	DMS	1958
—	53645	BR	108	DMBS	1958
—	53926	BR	108	DMBS	1959
—	59389	BR	108	TS	1958
—	1631	USATC	S160	2-8-0	—

Industrial locomotives

Name	No	Builder	Type	Built
Julia	54	H/Clarke (1682)	0-6-0ST	1937
Corby	56	RSH (7667)	0-6-0ST	1950
Ruddington	63	RSH (7761)	0-6-0ST	1954
Dolobran	—	M/Wardle (1762)	0-6-0ST	1910
Rhyl	—	M/Wardle (2009)	0-6-0ST	1921
Arthur	—	M/Wardle (2015)	0-6-0ST	1921
Marblaegis	—	R/Hornsby	0-4-0DM	1947
Quag	1	R/Hornsby (371971)	0-4-0DM	1954
Staythorpe	D2959	R/Hornsby (449754)	0-4-0DE	1961
Churchill	423	R/Hornsby (459518)	0-4-0DM	1961
Ubique	15097	M/Rail (1930)	4wPM	1919
Morris	15099	M/Rail (2028)	0-4-0DM	1932

Rolling stock: 9 BR Mk 1s, 8 BR Mk 2s including 6 ex-Gatwick express coaches, GCR coach (body) CBL No 1663 (oldest surviving GCR coach, built 1903), 4 Barnum coaches, 2 MS&LR 6-wheel coaches, 1 'Internation' concept coach (used as display area and will not run), 1 LNER 45-ton steam breakdown crane, various goods wagons

(first train from 11.00)
Special events: See web site or phone for details

Membership details: LNER/GC Heritage Trust, c/o above address
Society journal: 3 times per year

Attraction — Old Kiln Light Railway — Surrey

The Old Kiln Light Railway is located in the grounds of the Rural Life Museum which houses the largest countryside collection in the south of England
Location: Rural Life Centre, Reeds Road, Tilford, Farnham, Surrey GU10 2DL
Telephone: (01252) 795571 (museum)

Industrial locomotives (2ft gauge)

Name	No	Builder	Type	Built
Pamela	—	Hunslet (920)	0-4-0ST	1906
Elouise	—	O&K (9998)	0-4-0ST	1922
Eagle	—	M/Rail (5713)	4wDM	1936
Phoebe	—	M/Rail (8887)	4wDM	1944
—	—	M/Rail (8981)	4wDM	1946
—	—	M/Rail (5297)	4wPM	1931
Norden	—	Ruston (392117)	4wDM	
Emily	—	Hibberd (2528	4wDM	

England

Internet address: *Web site:* www.rural-life.org.uk
On site facilities: Free parking, picnic areas, shop, café
Access by road:
The museum is 3 miles south of Farnham, just off the A287 and midway between Frensham and Tilford villages
Length of line: Half mile, under extension, 2ft gauge
Public opening:
Summer: 11 March to 31 October, 10.00-17.00, Wednesday to Sunday and Bank Holidays Monday. Winter opening: Wednesdays and Sundays only, 11.00-16.00
The railway operates on Sundays
Special events (generally transport related): Steam Toy Rally — 11 April; Model Railway Exhibition — 2 May; Village at War — 9/10 May; Dad's Army —

Name	No	Builder	Type	Built
Sam	—	Hunslet	4wDM	1944
Red Dwarf	—	Ruston (181820)	4wDM	1936
Sand Rock	—	Ruston (177639)	4wDM	
—	—	Hunslet (7010)	4wDM	1971
–	—	Hunslet (7011)	4wDM	1971
–	—	Hunslet (7012)	4wDM	1971
–	—	Hunslet (7012)	4wDM	1971
Sue	—	Wickham (3031)	4wDM	1941
Liz	—	Wickham (3287)	2w-2PMR	1943

Stock
Glyn Valley replica coach, Baguley open coach, RNAD van, brake van

13 May to 5 August; Bus & Coach Rally — 24 MAy; Miniature Traction Engine Rally — 13/14 June; Citroen & Renault Car Rally — 5 July; Rustic Sunday — 26 July; CSVAC Stationary Engine Rally — 1/2 August; Ford Mk II Car Rally — 9 August; Weyburn Engineering — 9 August to 25 October; Classic Vehicle Gathering — 20 September; Steam & Vintage Weekend — 26/27 September; Land Rover Rally — 11 October; Santa Specials — 5/6, 12/13 December
Disabled facilities: Good access to all areas

Oswestry Railway Centre
(Cambrian Railways Society)

Steam Centre | Shropshire

Member: HRA
The Gobowen to Llanddu line is some 8.25 miles long and is currently owned by Network Rail. Shropshire County Council is negotiating with Network Rail to buy the line. Leases have been agreed for the Cambrian Railways Trust to lease the former main line (Oswestry to Llynclys) and the Cambrian Railways Society to lease the branch (Llynclys to Llanddu), from SCC. Under this arrangement the CRT will restore and run the main line, the CRS will be the museum body for the project, will be responsible for the Oswestry station area and will restore and run the branch.

The CRS is currently operating on three sites:
• The Oswestry Railway Centre, located in the former goods yard adjacent to the station. This is home to the Cambrian Railways Museum which has been awarded Phase II status by the Museums & Galleries Commission as being a museum of national importance. Also on site is the CRS engine shed and workshop, the fully restored Oswestry South

Industrial locomotives

Name	No	Builder	Type	Built
—	1	H/Clarke (D843)	0-4-0DM	1954
Adam	1	Peckett (1430)	0-4-0ST	1916
—	3	Hunslet (D3526)	0-6-0DM	1947
Oliver Velton	6	Peckett (2131)	0-4-0ST	1951
—	8	Barclay (885)	0-6-0ST	1900
—	322	Planet (3541)	4wDM	1952
Alpha	—	Planet (3593)	0-4-0DH	1962
Scottie	—	R/Hornsby (412427)	0-4-0DM	1957
Norma	3770	Hunslet (3770)	0-6-0ST	1952
Telemon	—	Drewry/Vulcan (2568)	0-4-0DM	1955

Stock
1 GWR auto-trailer, 1 BR TSO, 1 BR BSK, 1 BR RBR, 1 GWR brake van; 2 LMS brake vans, 1 BR brake van, 4 tank wagons, 3 open wagons, 2 tank wagon 4-wheel chassis (tanks removed, ex-Machynlleth fuel point), 2 box vans, 2 flat wagons, also ex-BR on track plant 98306 (GP TRAMM)

Owners
Telemon and *Scottie* the Cambrian Diesel Group
322 Private

Signalbox and a 400yd long running line, on which trains can be run for party bookings.
• Weston Wharf. This is a society-owned goods shed and sited on the outskirts of Oswestry.
• The Nantmawr branch, this 1.5 mile long line starts at the end of the Network Rail line at Llanddu and was purchased in 2004
Location: Oswestry station yard, Oswald Road, Oswestry, Shropshire SY11 1RE
OS reference: SJ 294297

Operating society/organisation:
Cambrian Railways Society Ltd,
Oswald Road, Oswestry, Shropshire
SY11 1RE
Telephone: (01691) 671749
Internet address: *Web site:*
www.cambrianrailwayssociety.co.uk
Car park: In Society's depot
Access by public transport:
By rail — Gobowen station is 2.5
miles north.

By bus — 2min walk from
Oswestry bus station.
Please note that there is no
Gobowen-Oswestry bus service on
Sundays
Length of line: 400yd, opened
7 December 1996, the Light
Railway Order having been granted
Public opening: Cambrian
Railways Museum is open:
Monday-Saturday 09.00-16.00.

Sunday 11.00-16.00.
Trains will normally only run for
group bookings or on special
events, please contact to confirm
On site facilities: Refreshment
room — the 'Whistle Stop' (open
on special days in former
Llansantffraid signalbox) and picnic
area

Timetable Service	Paignton & Dartmouth Steam Railway	Devon

Member: HRA

The Paignton & Dartmouth Steam Railway is the holiday line with steam trains running for seven miles in Great Western tradition along the spectacular Torbay coast to Churston and through the wooded slopes bordering the Dart estuary to Kingswear. The scenery is superb, with seascapes right across Lyme Bay to Portland Bill on clear days. Approaching Kingswear is the beautiful River Dart, with its fascinating craft, and on the far side, the 'olde worlde' town of Dartmouth and Britannia Royal Naval College, Butterwalk, Bayard's Cove and Dartmouth Castle

General Manager: Andrew Pooley
Headquarters: Paignton Queen's Park station, Paignton, Devon TQ4 6AF
Telephone:
Paignton (01803) 555872
Main station: Paignton Queen's Park (TQ4 6AF)
Other public stations:
Goodrington, Churston, Kingswear (for Dartmouth)
OS reference: SX 889606
Car parks: Paignton municipal car park, Goodrington, Dartmouth (ferry to Kingswear)
Access by public transport:
Adjacent to both Paignton main line station and bus station
Refreshment facilities: Paignton and Kingswear
Depot: Churston (TQ5 0LN)
Length of line: 7 miles
Passenger trains: Paignton-

Locomotives and multiple-units

Name	No	Origin	Class	Type	Built
Hercules	4277	GWR	5205	2-8-0T	1920
Warrior	4555	GWR	4500	2-6-2T	1924
Trojan	4588†	GWR	4575	2-6-2T	1927
Goliath	5239	GWR	5205	2-8-0T	1924
Lydham Manor	7827	GWR	7800	4-6-0	1951
Braveheart	75014	BR	4MT	4-6-0	1951
Titan	D2192	BR	03	0-6-0DM	1962
Samson	D3014	BR	08	0-6-0DE	1954
Mercury	D7535	BR	25	Bo-Bo	1965
—	59003*	BR	116	TS	1957
—	59004*	BR	116	TS	1957
—	59488*	P/Steel	117	TCL	1959
—	59494*	P/Steel	117	TCL	1959
—	59503*	P/Steel	117	TCL	1959
—	59507*	P/Steel	117	TCL	1959
—	59513*	P/Steel	117	TCL	1959
—	59517*	P/Steel	117	TCL	1959

*converted to locomotive-hauled vehicles
Note: Locomotives out of service are not available for viewing
†may not be on site for all of 2009

Stock
11 ex-BR Mk 1 coaches; 1 Pullman observation coach

Kingswear, views of Torbay and Dart estuary, 495yd tunnel, 3 viaducts
Period of public operation: Easter to October and Santa Specials in December
Facilities for disabled: Limited, special ramp to take wheelchairs onto trains. Disabled toilets at Paignton and Kingswear
Special events: Santa Specials — please see timetable and press for details. Combined river excursions available
Special facilities: Private charters,

details on request. Timeline exhibition coach at Kingswear
Special note: The railway also operates excursion vessels on the River Dart. Combined river excursions available, Boat trains and Round Robin tickets. Round Robin — single journey to Kingswear, 1hr 30min boat cruise to Totnes and bus back to Paignton

Peak Rail plc

Member: HRA

In 1968 the railway between Matlock and Buxton, through the Peak National Park, was closed and lifted. This was once part of the Midland Railway's route between Manchester Central and London. In 1975 efforts were started to reopen the line. Services between Matlock and Darley Dale commenced in 1991

Location: *Registered Office:* Matlock Station, Matlock, Derbyshire DE4 3NA

OS reference: Matlock SK 060738

Operating society/organisation: Peak Rail plc, Matlock Station, Matlock, Derbyshire DE4 3NA

Telephone: (01629) 580381

Internet address: *Web site:* www.peakrail.co.uk

Car parks: Matlock station, Darley Dale, Rowsley South station

Length of line: 4 miles — Matlock Riverside-Rowsley South. A 2ft gauge railway is now operational at Rowsley

On site facilities: Shop at Matlock. Shop and buffet at Rowsley South. Picnic area and riverside walk

Public opening: Sundays throughout the year, Saturdays April to October. Midweek during summer. Timetable varies

Facilities for disabled: Darley Dale and Rowsley. Matlock Riverside unsuitable for disabled passengers. Specially adapted carriage is fully accessible to wheelchair users (not available on DMU services)

Period of public operation: Not advised, see timetable supplement

Special events: Please contact for details

Locomotives and multiple-units

Name	No	Origin	Class	Type	Built
—	48624	LMS	8F	2-8-0	1943
—	D2953	BR	01	0-4-0DM	1956
—	D2854	BR	02	0-4-0DH	1960
—	D2866	BR	02	0-4-0DH	1961
—	D2868	BR	02	0-4-0DH	1961
—	03027	BR	03	0-6-0DM	1958
—	03099	BR	03	0-6-0DM	1960
—	D2139	BR	03	0-6-0DM	1960
—	D2199	BR	03	0-6-0DM	1961
—	D2229	BR	04	0-6-0DM	1955
Alfie	D2272	BR	04	0-6-0DM	1960
—	D2284	BR	04	0-6-0DM	1960
—	D2324	BR	05	0-6-0DM	1959
Dorothy	D2337	BR	04	0-6-0DM	1961
—	D2587	BR	05	0-6-0DM	1959
—	06003	BR	06	0-6-0DM	1959
—	07013	BR	07	0-6-0DE	1961
Geoff L. Wright	D3023	BR	08	0-6-0DE	1953
—	12061	BR	11	0-6-0DE	1949
—	D9500	BR	14	0-6-0DH	1965
—	D9502	BR	14	0-6-0DH	1964
—	D9525	BR	14	0-6-0DH	1964
—	31270	BR	31	A1A-A1A	1961
Penyghent	D8	BR	44	1Co-Co1	1959
Jimmy Milne	47635	BR	47	Co-Co	1964
Renown	50029	BR	50	Co-Co	1968
Repulse	50030	BR	50	Co-Co	1968
—	97654	BR	—	0-6-0DM	1959

Industrial locomotives

Name	No	Builder	Type	Built
The Duke	2746	Bagnall (2746)	0-6-0ST	1944
—	64	Brush (803)	0-6-0DE	1978
Royal Pioneer	150	RSH (7136)	0-6-0ST	1944
Zebedee	—	RSH (7597)	0-6-0ST	1949
Vulcan	—	V/Foundry (3272)	0-4-0ST	1918
Castlefield	—	H/Clarke (D1388)	0-6-0DH	1970
—	20	R/Hornsby (432479)	0-4-0DM	1959
Rotherham	—	YEC (2480)	0-4-0DM	
Bigga	—	Fowler (4200019)	0-4-0DM	1947
—	—	Drewry (2552)	0-6-0DM	1953

Rolling stock — coaches: 2 BR Mk 1 RMB, 1 BR Mk 1 SLF, 3 BR Mk 1 TSO, 2 BR Mk 1 SO, 3 BR Mk 1 SK, 1 BR Mk 1 BSK, 2 BR Mk 1 BG, 1 BR Mk 1 GUV, 1 BR Mk 2 SO, 1 BR Mk 2 BSO, 1 BR Mk 2 BFK, 1 LMS TK, 2 LMS BCK, 1BTK, 1 Bullion coach, 3 parcels vans

Rolling stock — wagons: 1 5 plank, 1 LMS 5 plank, 3 match wagons, 1 LNER flat wagon, 1 LMS 5 plank tube, 1 LMS 2 plank tube, 1 BR Grampus 20-ton ballast, 1 LNER flat, 1 LMR water bowser, 1 Plasser & Theurer tamper, 2 LMS fish vans, 2 Austrian ferry wagons, 1 SR parcels van, 1 Shell tank wagon, 1 Esso tank wagon, 2 tank wagons, 2 LNER 2 plank dropsides, 3 BR 12-ton box vans, 1 12-ton van (wooden underframe), 2 BR Pallet vans, 1 Charles Roberts covered van, 1 LNER crane, 2 LMS brake vans, 1 BR brake van, 1 MR brake van, 1 BR Sturgeon rail wagon, 1 BR Lowmac, 1 BR Weltrol, 1 BR Salmon, 2 BR Dogfish ballast hoppers

Owners
50029 and 50030 The Renown Repulse Restoration Group
D8 the North Notts Loco Group
Vulcan the Vulcan Loco Trust
7597 Peak Rail and Peak Railway Association
Classes 01 to 14 the Heritage Shunters Trust
12061 on loan to the Heritage Shunters Trust

Derbyshire Dales Narrow Gauge Railway
Industrial narrow gauge locomotives (2ft gauge)

Name	No	Builder	Type	Built
—	—	M/Rail (5853)	4wDM	1934
—	—	M/Rail (22070)	4wDM	1960
—	—	R/Hornsby (264252)	4wDM	1952
—	85049*	R/Hornsby (393325)	4wDM	1956
—	85051*	R/Hornsby (404976)	4wDM	1956
—	—	R/Hornsby (487963)	4wDM	1963

*plant numbers carried by former British Railways locomotives

---

Miniature Railway	**Perrygrove Railway**	Glos

Member: Britain's Great Little Railways (corporate member of HRA)
Headquarters: Perrygrove Railway, Coleford, Gloucestershire GL16 8QB
Contact: Michael Crofts
Telephone/Fax: 01594 834991
Internet address:
Web site: www.perrygrove.co.uk
OS reference: SO 579094
Main station: Perrygrove (GL16 8QB)
Other public stations: Rookwood, Heywood, Oakiron
Car park: Parking at Perrygrove for 60 cars plus 2 coach bays
Access by public transport:
Network Rail: Lydney (7 miles).
Dean Forest Railway: Parkend (3 miles).
Buses (all Stagecoach services) from: Gloucester — 30/31;
Lydney — 721;
Cinderford — 30/31;
Monmouth — H35;
Ross on Wye — H35;
Ruardean — 746.
Enquiries: 01452 425610
Refreshment facilities: Light refreshments in Perrygrove station café
Souvenir shops: Small shop at Perrygrove
Museum: Heywood Collection of

Locomotives (15in gauge)

Name	No	Builder	Type	Built
Spirit of Adventure	—	ESR (295)	0-6-0T	1995
Ursula	—*	J. Waterfield	0-6-0T	
Lydia	—	Alan Keef (22)	2-6-2T	2008
Workhorse	—	Simplex (1064)	0-4-0DM	1963
Jubilee	—	Hunslet (9337)	0-4-0DH	1994

*based on Heywood locomotive of 1916

Stock
Modern: 3 carriages, 16 goods wagons
Vintage: 2 carriages*, 2 brake vans, 11 goods wagons

*Includes saloon carriage built by Sir Arthur Heywood for the Duke of Westminster's private railway at Eaton Hall in 1904, and a replica of the Duffield Bank Dining Carriage

minimum gauge railways on display at Perrygrove
Depot: All sheds are at Perrygrove. Tours are encouraged under supervision when staff are available
Length of line: 0.75 miles, 15in (381mm) gauge
Period of public operation:
Every Saturday and Sunday from Easter to end of October.
Daily local school holidays
Special events:
Summer Gala — 26 June 2009;
Enthusiast Afternoon coincides with the annual open day at Alan Keef Ltd (please see web site to confirm date)— usually first or second Saturday in September;
Christmas trains operate, advance booking essential: 01594 834991
Facilities for disabled: All disabilities catered for. About 75% of the site is accessible to wheelchairs, although some of the woodland paths are rough. There is space for a wheelchair on the train
Membership details: Volunteers welcome
Membership journal: Diary pages on web site

Steam Centre — Plym Valley Railway — Devon

Member: HRA

A scheme dedicated to the restoration of services over the former GWR Marsh Mills-Plym Bridge line, a distance of 1.5 miles

Location: 5 miles from centre of Plymouth, Devon, north of A38. From Marsh Mills roundabout, take B3416 to Plympton, follow signs for Coypool park & ride

Internet addresses:

Web site: www.plymrail.co.uk

OS reference: SX 517564

Operating society/organisation: Plym Valley Railway Co Ltd, Marsh Mills Station, Coypool Road, Marsh Mills, Plymouth, Devon PL7 4NW

Access by public transport: Buses from Plymouth, Nos 20, 20A, 21, 22A, 51 stop close to site

On site facilities: Shop and refreshments at Marsh Mills, Coypool (Sundays only)

Public opening: Sundays from 11.00, and other selected days. Trains are scheduled to operate: April, May, June, July, August, September, October, November, December. Please contact for actual dates.

13.00-16.00 at regular intervals

Length of line: Half-mile currently

Locomotives and multiple-units

Name	No	Origin	Class	Type	Built
—	D2046	BR	038	0-6-0DM	1958
—	13002	BR	08	0-6-0DE	1953
William Cookworthy	37207	BR	37	Co-Co	1963
—	51365	BR	117	DMBS	1960
—	51407	BR	117	DMS	1960

Industrial locomotives

Name	No	Builder	Type	Built
Byfield No 2	—	Bagnall (2655)	0-6-0ST	1941
Albert	—	Barclay (2248)	0-4-0ST	1948
—	—	T/Hill (125V)	4wDH	1963
—	—	Hibberd (3281)	4wDM	1948

Rolling stock: 1 x BR Mk 1 coach, 4 x BR Mk 2 coaches, 1 LBSCR compartment coach (body only), 2 x BR GUVs, 3 x brake vans, various wagons. Self-propelled Smith & Rodley diesel crane of 1956

in use for passenger rides

Special events: Please contact for details

Disabled facilities: Ramps available for less able visitors giving access to shop, café and trains

Special notes: Visitors are advised that, at the moment, the railway and two locomotives are still under restoration. 2 working locomotives and DMU. The line was extended beyond the first bridge in 2003.

Train rides behind *Albert* or No 13002 on some Sundays (normally 2nd in the month) to Lee Moor Crossing

Membership details: Membership Secretary, Plym Valley Railway, Marsh Mills Station, Coypool Road, Marsh Mills, Plymouth, Devon PL7 4NW

Membership journal: *Plym Valley Railway News* — 3/year

Marketing name: The Woodland Line

Museum — Railworld — Cambs

Member: HRA

Railworld is a 'Sustainable Transport Centre' and a '21st Century Rail Showcase'. It has a superb model railway, 'hands-on' exhibits to delight children and film shows. In addition it has a museum which is mainly about Peterborough's railway history. There are also 'Age of Steam' exhibits and a database of over 7,000 names of local railworkers since the 1840s (50p extra access charge — by appointment)

Location: Situated alongside the Town station of the Nene Valley Railway.

Walk — 15min walk from train and

Locomotives

Name	No	Origin	Class	Type	Built
—	996	DSB	4MT	4-6-2	1950

Industrial locomotives

Name	No	Builder	Type	Built
—	804	Alco (77778)	Bo-Bo	1949
Nutty*	5	Sentinel (7701)	4wVBT	1929
—†	740	O&K (2343)	0-6-0T	1907

*2ft 6in gauge (off-site at present)

† 2ft gauge (off-site at present)

remainder standard

Other stock: Britain's RTV 31 Hovertrain vehicle, Presflo 2-axle flyash wagon (No B874076 of 12965) and a 2-axle 8,650gal tank wagon (No 55223 of 1966). Birmingham International Airport Maglev car No 01 of 1984 supplied by Metro-Cammell, operational 1984-1995 — the world's first train without wheels in commercial service

bus stations, Stagecoach route 1
(every 10min).
By car — turn off A1139 at jct 5,
signs to City Centre, follow brown
and white 'Little Puffer' signs to
Oundle Road into Council's long
stay car park, drive through to
Railworld. The Railworld car park
is free to visitors.
By bike — situated on the 'Green
Wheel' cycle route.
By boat — alongside river quay
OS reference: TL 189981
Operating society/organisation:
Railworld, Oundle Road,
Peterborough, Cambridgeshire
PE2 9NR

Charity number: 291515
Contact: Peter Fearn CEO
Telephone and Fax:
01733 344240 and 01733 319362
Internet address: *e-mail:*
info@railword.net
Web site: www.railworld.net
On site facilities: Buffet open
weekends March to October.
Picnic area. Model railway
Public opening: Daily March-
October 11.00-16.00. Also Monday
to Friday November-March 11.00-
16.00
Special events: National Science
and Engineering Week — 6-15
March; Peterborough Green

Festival — 24 May-7 June
Access for disabled: Reasonable
wheelchair access
Admission charge: Adult £5, Child
£2.50, Concessions £4, Family £13
(2A+4C)
Membership details: C/o above
address
Membership journal: *Friends of
Railworld* — biannually
Special notes: Railworld is a no
smoking site

Ravenglass & Eskdale Railway

Cumbria

Member: HRA
From the coast through two of
Lakeland's loveliest valleys to the
foot of England's highest mountain,
small steam engines haul trains in
the heart of the national park
General Manager:
Trevor Stockton
Headquarters: Ravenglass &
Eskdale Railway, Ravenglass,
Cumbria CA18 1SW
Telephone: (01229) 717171
Fax: (01229) 717011
Internet address: *e-mail:*
steam@ravenglass-railway.co.uk
Web site: www.ravenglass-
railway.co.uk
Main station: Ravenglass
Other public stations: Muncaster
Mill, Irton Road, The Green,
Beckfoot, Eskdale (Dalegarth)
OS reference: SD 086964
Car parks: All stations
Access by public transport: Main
line services to Ravenglass; bus
service from Whitehaven
Refreshment facilities:
Ravenglass, Dalegarth. Bar meals at
'Ratty Arms'
Picnic areas: At both termini
Souvenir shops: Ravenglass,
Dalegarth
Museum: Ravenglass
Length of line: 7 miles, 15in gauge
Passenger trains: Steam- or diesel-
hauled narrow gauge trains

Locomotives

Name	No	Builder	Type	Built
River Irt	—	Heywood	0-8-2	1894
River Esk	—	Davey Paxman (21104)	2-8-2	1923
River Mite	—	Clarkson (4669)	2-8-2	1966
Northern Rock	—	R&ER	2-6-2	1976
Bonnie Dundee	—	K/Stuart (720)*	0-4-2	1901
Shelagh of Eskdale	—	R&ER/Severn-Lamb	4-6-4D	1969
				rebuilt 1998
Quarryman	—	Muir-Hill (2)	0-4-0P/Paraffin	1928
Perkins	—	Muir Hill (NG39A)	0-4-4DM	1929
Lady Wakefield	—	R&ER	B-B	1980
Synolda	—	Bassett-Lowke	4-4-2	1912
—	—	Greenbat (2782)	0-4-0BE	1957
Cyril	—	Lister	0-4-0DM	1987
Douglas Ferreira	—	TMA Engineering	Bo-Bo	2005

*rebuilt to 15in gauge 1981, stored off site

Ravenglass-Dalegarth
Period of public operation: Daily
late March-early November.
Limited winter service November-
March
Family ticket: All day travel at
reduced price
Facilities for disabled: Special
coaches for wheelchair passengers.
Advance notice preferred.
Wheelchair access to toilets, café
and museum at Ravenglass; toilets,
shop and café at Eskdale
(Dalegarth)
Special notes: At Ravenglass the
R&ER has two camping coaches
and the company also operates the

'Ratty Arms' public house formed
by conversion of the former BR
station buildings. During the high
summer, mid-July through August,
four steam locomotives are
normally in use Monday-Thursday
Membership details:
Mr N. Dickinson, 3 Clifton Terrace,
Ravenglass, Cumbria CA18 1SE
Membership journal: *The R&ER
Magazine* — quarterly
Marketing names: 'la'al Ratty' —
Cumbrian dialect for little narrow
track, now a watervole
stationmaster!

Member: HRA

Preston Docks have had a railway infrastructure since 1850, and when the final tar trains ran in 1995, it looked like that tenancy had come to an end. However, Steamport Southport began negotiations with Preston Borough Council, and during 1999, the group formerly based at the old engine shed in Southport moved to their new home on the dockside at Preston.

Due to the main line traversing the swing bridge in the Marina, the timetable will be dictated by the tide — the only preserved steam line to have such a feature.

Heritage passenger and modern freight operations blend together as restored diesel locomotives handle bulk bitumen trains on behalf of Total Bitumen. This traffic has switched from road transport since the railway reopened

Location: Off Chain Caul Way, Riversway, Preston Docks, Preston, Lancs

SatNav Postcode: PR2 2PD

OS reference: SD 504295

Operating society/organisation: Steamport Southport Ltd, 3 Lincoln Drive, Old Road, Liverpool L10 3LJ

Telephone: 01772 728800

Internet address: *e-mail:* enquiries@ribblesteam.org.uk *Web site:* www.ribblesteam.org.uk

Car park: On site

Main station: Chain Caul Road

Access by public transport: By train — to Preston (www.nationalrail.co.uk). By bus — Preston Bus 88c orbital Preston to Larches; Stagecoach 75 Preston to Poulton. Buses stop on Peddars Way between McDonalds and roundabout on Navigation Way. By road — follow the signs for Riversway Docklands, use the A583

On site facilities: Buffet, museum and workshop.

Length of lines: 1.5 miles

Public opening: Generally weekends and Bank Holidays from Easter to end of September. 10-13, 19, 26 April; 2-4, 9/10,

Locomotives and multiple-units

Name	No	Origin	Class	Type	Built
—	46441	LMS	2MT	2-6-0	1950
—	1097	LYR	—	0-4-0ST	1910
—	D2148	BR	03	0-6-0DM	1960
—	03189	BR	03	0-6-0DM	1961
—	D2595	BR	05	0-6-0DM	1959
—	D9539	BR	14	0-6-0DH	1965
—	601 / 671	NSR	—	0-6-0DE	1956

Industrial locomotives

Name	No	Builder	Type	Built
—	272	G/Ritchie (272)	0-4-0T	1894
Daphne	—	Peckett (737)	0-4-0ST	1899
The King	—	Borrows (48)	0-4-0WT	1906
Lucy	—	Avonside (1568)	0-6-0ST	1909
Efficient	—	Barclay (1598)	0-4-0ST	1918
MDHB No 26	—	Avonside (1810)	0-6-0ST	1918
—	1883	Avonside (1883)	0-6-0ST	1922
Alexander	—	Barclay (1865)	0-4-0ST	1926
Heysham No.2	—	Barclay (1950)	0-4-0F	1928
Derbyshire	—	Barclay (1969)	0-4-0ST	1929
Gasbag	—	Sentinel (8024)	4wVBT	1929
Hornet	—	Peckett (1935)	0-4-0ST	1937
Linda	—	H/Leslie (3931)	0-6-0ST	1938
Kinsley	—	Hunslet (1954)	0-6-0ST	1939
North Western Gas Board	—	Peckett (1999)	0-4-0ST	1941
Walkden	—	Hunslet (3155)	0-6-0ST	1944
St Monans	—	Sentinel (9373)	4wVBT	1947
Agecroft No.2	—	RSH (7485)	0-4-0ST	1948
No. 6	—	Barclay (2261)	0-4-0ST	1949
Respite	—	Hunslet.(3696)	0-6-0ST	1950
Shropshire	—	Hunslet (3793)	0-6-0ST	1953
Glasshoughton No.4	—	Hunslet (3855)	0-6-0ST	1954
Hotto	—	Howard (965)		1930
Mighty Atom	—	H/Clarke (D628)	0-4-0DM	1943
Sparky	—	H/Clarke (D629)	0-4-0DM	1945
Persil	—	Fowler (4160001)	0-4-0DM	1950
Margaret	—	H/Clarke (D1031)	0-4-0DM	1956
BICC	—	NBL (27653)	0-4-0DH	1957
D2870	—	YEC (2667)	0-4-0DH	1960
Energy	—	Sentinel (10165)	4wDH	1965
Stanlow	—	T/Hill (160V)	0-4-0DH	1966
Enterprise	—	Sentinel (10282)	4wDH	1968
Progress	—	Sentinel (10283)	4wDH	1968
—	—	Barclay (D615)	0-4-0DH	1977
'YellowBat'	—	E/Electric (EE788)	4wBE	1930
Greenbat	—	G/Batley (2000)	4wBE	1945

Rolling stock

The railway holds one of the largest collections of industrial standard gauge locomotives, currently 42 strong. In addition there are over 60 other items of rolling stock, including BR Mk 1 passenger coaches in regular service, 305 Engineer's coach built at York in 1902 for the North Eastern Railway, pre and ex-BR and private owner tank wagons, coverd vans, 16- and 20-ton mineral and coal wagons, brake vans, Dogfish and other railway maintenance plant including TRAMM DR98404 and rail-mounted

16/17, 23-25, 30/31 May, 6/7, 13/14, 20/21, 27/28 June; 4/5, 11/12, 18/19, 25/26 July; 1/2, 5, 8/9, 12, 15/16, 19, 22/23, 26, 29-31 August; 5/6, 12/12, 19/20, 26/27 September; 3/4 October.
See web site for details
Open from 10.30. Trains hourly 11.00-16.00.
Return trip c40min
Unlimited travel on day of admission
Special events: Litle & Large Steam Weekend — 16/17 May; Trains & Boats (Preston's Riverway

7.5-tonne crane DRT81201. 75% of locomotives and 60% of other rolling stock are usually in public view. Items move around regularly as maintenance takes place. Barclay 0-6-0 diesel 615 has recently arrived from th e Tanfield Railway

Festival) — 25/26 July; Diesel Weekend — 3/4 October; Santa Special dates to be confirmed. Additional events will be advertised on the web site
Facilities for disabled: Full access in museum and onto platform, limited on trains
Membership details:

RSR Memberships, Ribble Steam Railway, Chain Caul Way, Ashton-on-Ribble, Preston PR2 2PD
Membership journal: *The Ribble Pilot* — 3 copies a year
Special note: The railway is not open or accessible at any other times than those advertised. Access will be refused outside these times

---

| Timetable Service | Romney, Hythe & Dymchurch Railway | Kent |

Member: HRA

This line was built in 1926/27 as a one-third size miniature main line, and is by far the longest and most fully equipped 15in gauge railway in the world. It carries not only daytrippers and holidaymakers but also children to and from the local school at New Romney.

Headquarters: Romney, Hythe & Dymchurch Railway, New Romney Station, Kent TN28 8PL
Telephone: (01797) 362353/363256
Fax: 01797 363591
Internet addresses: *e-mail:* info@rhdr.org.uk
Web site: http://www.rhdr.org.uk
OS reference: TR 074249
Main station: New Romney
Other public stations: Hythe, Dymchurch, St Marys Bay, Romney Sands, Dungeness
Car parks: Hythe, Dymchurch, New Romney, Dungeness
Access by public transport:
Folkestone Central station (South Eastern Trains) and then bus to Hythe (4 miles) or Rye station (Southern) and then bus to New Romney (8 miles)
Refreshment facilities: Cafeterias at New Romney and Dungeness, picnic areas at Dymchurch, New Romney and Dungeness. Also licensed observation coach on certain trains
Souvenir shops: Hythe, New Romney and Dungeness (plus Dymchurch in main season)
Model Railway Exhibition: New

Locomotives

Name	No	Builder	Type	Built
Green Goddess	1	Davey Paxman	4-6-2	1925
Northern Chief	2	Davey Paxman	4-6-2	1925
Southern Maid	3	Davey Paxman	4-6-2	1926
The Bug	4	Krauss (8378)	0-4-0TT	1926
Hercules	5	Davey Paxman	4-8-2	1926
Samson	6	Davey Paxman	4-8-2	1926
Typhoon	7	Davey Paxman	4-6-2	1926
Hurricane	8	Davey Paxman	4-6-2	1926
Winston Churchill	9	YEC (2294)	4-6-2	1931
Doctor Syn	10	YEC (2295)	4-6-2	1931
Black Prince	11	Krupp (1664)	4-6-2	1937
John Southland	12	TMA Birmingham	Bo-Bo	1983
Captain Howey	14	TMA Birmingham	Bo-Bo	1989
—	PW1	M/Rail (7059)	4wDM	1938
—	PW2	RH&DR	4wPM	1965
Redgauntlet	PW3	Jacot/RH&DR	4wPM	1963
Trembly*	—	Lister (37658)	4wDM	1952

*on loan fitted with a *Toby* body for Day out with Thomas events

Stock
40 saloon bogie coaches; 12 open bogie coaches; 5 luggage/brake saloons; 1 parlour car; 1 mess coach; 40 assorted wagons

Romney, with displays of old, and not so old, toys; plus two large operating model railways. Open all operating days and selected other days
Depot: New Romney
Length of line: 13.5 miles, 15in gauge
Passenger trains: Train frequency depends on the time of year: maximum frequency is 40 minutes, more frequent on certain special event days
Period of public operation: Trains run daily from 28 March to 1

November. Also weekends and school holidays in February and March. Out of season the school train departs New Romney to Hythe with limited public accommodation, please telephone 01797 362353 (Monday-Friday, term times only)
Special events: Mother's Day — 22 March; Kent Great Day Out — 28 March; Easter Bunny Specials — 11/12 April; 1940s Weekend — 9/10 May; Romney Evening Music Event — 23 May; Heritage Tour Evening Train — 13 June; Return of *Green Goddess* Celebrations —

13/14 June; Summer Solstice Breakfast Train — 21 June; Father's Day with Model Exhibitions— 21 June; Basil the Bug — 4/5 July; Romney Marsh Wildlife Breakfast Safari Train — 13 July; RNLI Dungeness Lifeboat Station Open Day — 23 August; Basil the Bug — 5/6 September; Romney Steam & Diesel Gala — 3/4 October; Wizards & Witches Specials — 31 October; Santa Specials —5/6, 12/13, 19-24 December (pre-booking essential);

Welcome to New Year's Open Days — 1-3 January 2010.
Special notes: Senior citizen concessions any day except Bank Holidays and advertised special events. Family tickets available. Parties can be catered for at New Romney and Dungeness cafés and Jazz trains. Evening dining train service on selected summer Saturdays
Special facilities: Special trains can be run at most times by prior arrangement.

Facilities for disabled: Ramps and level crossings at all stations for easy access. Special wheelchair coach available on any train by prior arrangement. Stair lift between café and Model Railway Exhibition. Disabled toilets at Hythe, Dymchurch, New Romney and Dungeness
Membership details: RH&DR Association, 26 Norman Close, Battle, East Sussex TN33 0BD
Membership journal: *The Marshlander* — quarterly

Diesel Centre | Rother Valley Railway | East Sussex

Member: HRA
The original section of what was to become known as the Kent & East Sussex Railway was thought to be lost to preservation for ever following decisions of Transport Minister, Barbara Castle, in the late 1960s. However, more enlightened attitudes in recent years mean that work is now in hand to reinstate the missing link between Robertsbridge and the K&ESR at Bodiam
Location/headquarters: Robertsbridge Station, Robertsbridge, East Sussex TN32 5DG
Telephone: 01580 881833
Internet addresses: *Web site:* www.rvr.org.uk
Operating society/organisation: Rother Valley Railway Ltd, 3-4 Bower Terrace, Maidstone, Kent ME16 8RY, and the Rother Valley Railway Supporters Association
OS reference: TQ 734235
Access by public transport: SouthEastern Trains on Charing

Industrial locomotives

Name	No	Builder	Type	Built
Titan	43	Vulcan/Drewry	0-4-0DM	1955
—	D77	Vulcan/Drewry	0-4-0DM	1947
—	97701	Matisa	0-4-0DE	1975

Rolling stock
Ex-SR brake van, ex-SR Maunsell brake third, ex-SR Maunsell open third, ex-BR Mk 1 TSO, ex-SR GBL, BY, and PMV vans, Trout hopper wagon, 2 tank wagons, open wagon, Lowmac, Permaquip Panex track machine and a Thos Smith 5-ton rail crane

Cross and Tunbridge Wells to Hastings service call at Robertsbridge station. Arriva bus services 4 and 5 on Maidstone-Hastings service call at High Street, Robertsbridge
Car parks: Robertsbridge station and Station Road, Robertsbridge
On site facilities: Visitor centre housed in former VSOE lounge with souvenir shop and buffet. Rolling stock under restoration, picnic area
Facilities for disabled: Access to the visitor centre, buffet, shop and

all public areas
Length of line: Standard gauge — c400yd at present. When restored, length to Bodiam will be 3.5 miles, with end-on connection to K&ESR
Public opening: Every Sunday and Bank Holiday (except Christmas and Boxing Day). 09.00-17.00 (dusk if earlier)
Special events: Annual model railway exhibition. Brake van rides will commence as soon as resources permit
Journal: *The Phoenix* — quarterly

Miniature Railway | Royal Victoria Railway | Hampshire

Location: Royal Victoria Country Park
Headquarters: Royal Victoria Railway, Royal Victoria Country Park, Netley, Southampton

SO31 5GA
Contact: Peter Bowers
Telephone: 023 8045 6246
Internet address: *Web site:* www.royalvictoriarailway.co.uk

SatNav users: Do NOT use the postcode to locate the RVR. Please follow the brown signs marked Royal Victoria Country Park
Main station: Netley

Car parking: On site £1.20
Access by public transport:
By rail: SouthWest Trains to Netley, follow signs to Royal Victoria Country Park.
By road: Exit M27 at jct 8 and follow brown tourist signs to Royal Victoria Country Park, approx 3 miles
On site facilities: Small souvenir shop. Museum on site for Royal Victoria Hospital
Depots: At main station, engine and carriage sheds and turntable, possibly largest for 10.25in gauge railway
Length of line: 1 mile, 10.25in gauge
Period of public operation:
All local school holidays except 3 days before Xmas and closed Christmas Day. Weekends all year
Special events: Please check web site
Facilities for disabled: Most areas accessible

Locomotives

Name	No	Builder	Type	Built
Maurice the Major	1	P. Bowers	Bo-Bo	1995
Basil the Brigadier*§	2	Kitson	2-6-0-0-6-2	1935
Trevithick	3	R. Marsh	0-6-2	1976
Isambard Kingdom Brunel	4	D. Curwen	2-6-0	1977
Peter the Private	5	Curwe/Bowers	2-6-0	2009
Western Independence	D1000	D. Curwen	Co-Co	1964
Western Explorer§	D1002	Severn Lamb	Co-Co	1968
Western Thunderer	D1011	D. Curwen	Co-Co	1964
Royal Scot*§	6100	B/Lowke	4-6-0	1938
Royal Scot*§	6100	E. Dove	4-6-0	c1950

*historic locomotive
§on site awaiting restoration

Rolling stock
2 Triang Pullman coaches, 4 Triang toastrack coaches, 2 4-car articulated units (2 covered, 2 open carriages), various goods vehicles

Note: If wishing to view the historic locomotives please contact before making journey

---

<table>
<tr><td>Timetable Service</td><td><h1>Rudyard Lake Railway</h1></td><td>Staffordshire</td></tr>
</table>

Member HRA, Britain's Great Little Railways.
The railway provides a 3 mile scenic return trip alongside the lake that gave Rudyard Kipling his name. Trains are always steam hauled and a two train service operates on busy days. The fleet of goods wagons is extensive and impressive and so goods trains also often feature. A further one mile extension is being planned
Contacts: Mike & Eileen Hanson, Directors
Headquarters: Rudyard Station, Rudyard, Nr Leek, Staffordshire ST13 8RS
Telephone: 01538 306704
Fax: 01995 672280
Internet address:
e-mail: info@rlsr.org
Web site: www.rlsr.org
Main station: Rudyard
OS reference SJ 955579
Other stations:
The Dam (SJ 953584), Hunthouse Wood (SJ 946598)
Car parking: On site, free at Rudyard
Access by public transport;

Locomotives

Name	No	Builder	Type	Built
Modred	2	T. Stanhope	4w	1969
Rudyard Lady	5	L. Smith	4-4w	1989
Waverley		D. Curwen	4-4-2	1952
Excalibur	6	Exmoor SR (293)	2-4-2T	1993
Merlin	7	Exmoor SR (296)	2-4-2T	1998
Pendragon	9	Exmoor SR (297)	2-4-2T	1994
King Arthur	8	Exmoor SR (324)	0-6-2T	2005
Sir Ernie	—	RLSR	2-2-2BE	2008

Rolling Stock
12 coaches
1 4w vans, 3 4w open, 1 4w crane, 1 4w brake van, 3 bogie ballast

Owner
Waverley — the Waverley Group

Special Notes
Driver training courses run throughout the year.
All trains allow carriage of prams, bikes, wheelchairs etc.
All locomotives should be in operation in 2009

Nearest mainline rail at Stoke on Trent, Macclesfield, Congleton. Bus services to Leek
On site facility: Short 7.25in gauge railway operates on special events

Souvenir shop: On trains
Refreshment facilities: Café at Dam Head, alight at Dam station
Length of Line: 1.5 miles, 10.25 inch gauge

England

Operation (2009):
Every Sunday and Bank Holiday: 4 January to 29 November, 11.00-16.00;
Every Saturday: 3 April to 31 October, 11.00-16.00.
Daily: 23-31 May, 22 July to 6 September, 24 October to 1 November.

School Holidays — daily
Special Events:
Easter Egg Specials — 10-13 April; Lollipop Specials — 2-4, 23-25 May, 29-315 August;
Steam Gala — 3/4 October; Halloween Special — 31 October/1 November; Santa Specials — 12/13 December

Disabled Facilities: Access to all stations but wheelchairs with occupant not allowed on trains, wheelchairs can however be carried. Disabled toilets at the Dam Head.
Membership details: Eileen Hanson at above address or via e-mail

Timetable Service — Ruislip Lido Railway — London

Member: HRA
The 12in gauge line is operated by enthusiast volunteers as an attraction within Ruislip Lido, a country park which is maintained by the London Borough of Hillingdon
Location: Ruislip Lido, Reservoir Road, Ruislip, Middlesex
SatNav Postcode : HA4 7TY
Operating society/organisation: Ruislip Lido Railway Society Ltd, Secretary, RLR, Suite 123, Rye House, 113 High Street, Ruislip, Middx HA4 8JN
Telephone: 01895 622595
Internet address: *Web site:* www.ruisliplidorailway.org
Car park: Available at Lido
Access by public transport: Ruislip Underground station (Metropolitan and Piccadilly lines) then by bus H13 or 331 nearby (daily). Lido is off the A4180 road
Refreshment facilities: Family pub/restaurant on site. Refreshments available in the Railway room. Picnic areas also available
Length of line: 1.25-mile single journey, 2.5 miles return. From Beach (sand) to car park and return
Public opening: The line is open at

Locomotives

Name	No	Builder	Type	Built
Robert	3	Severn-Lamb	B-2 DH	1973
Lady of the Lakes	5	Ravenglass & Eskdale Railway	B-B DM	1986
Mad Bess	6	RLRS	2-4-0ST+T	1998
Graham Alexander	7	Severn-Lamb	B-B DM	1990
Bayhurst	8	Severn-Lamb	B-B DH	2003
John Rennie	9	Severn-Lamb	B-B DH	2004

Locomotive notes: All locomotives are normally available for service. Limited steam-hauled service. *Mad Bess* underwent a 10-year overhaul during the latter months of 2008

Stock
6 open coaches; 9 closed coaches; miscellaneous service stock

weekends from 9 February to 30 November. Daily throughout July and August, also daily during Hillingdon school holidays. Sunday Santa Specials on 29 November, 6, 13, 20 December
  24-hour recorded train information service (01895) 622595. Full service leaflet on request to 0845 643 0182.
Group bookings 0845 643 0182
Journey time: Single 20min, return 40min
Facilities for disabled: Wheelchair passengers can travel on all trains

Special facilities: If any enthusiast wishes to take a look around the workshops, such requests can normally be accommodated if arranged beforehand.
Group bookings are welcome and special trains can be arranged
Membership details: Membership Secretary, RLR, Suite 123, Rye House, 113 High Street, Ruislip, Middx HA4 8JN
Membership journal: *Woody Bay News* — 3 issues per year

Steam Centre — Rutland Railway Museum — Rutland

Member: HRA
This museum is dedicated to portraying the ironstone quarrying history of the Midlands and has a wide range of authentic locomotives and rolling stock. Indeed, its

collection of quarry freight rolling stock is probably the most comprehensive in the country and regular demonstrations are a feature of the 'open days'.
Location: Cottesmore Iron Ore

Mines Siding, Ashwell Road, Cottesmore, near Oakham, Rutland — situated midway between villages of Cottesmore and Ashwell, approximately 4 miles north of Oakham (locally signposted)

OS reference: SK 886137
Secretary: Simon Layfield 07798
641105
Operating society/organisation:
Rutland Railway Museum,
Cottesmore Iron Ore Mines Siding,
Ashwell Road, Cottesmore, Nr
Oakham, Rutland LE15 7BX
Telephone: Oakham (01572)
813203
Internet address: *Web site:*
www.rutlandrailwaymuseum.org.uk
Car park: Free car park on site
Access by public transport:
Nearest main line station, Oakham.
Bus service, Paul James,
Nottingham-Melton Mowbray-
Ashwell-Oakham,
Corby/Peterborough-Oakham-
Ashwell (service 19).
On site facilities: Train rides, open-
air quarry feature, demonstration
freight trains, toilets, museum,
picnic sites, demonstration line with
lineside walk and viewing areas,
static displays of quarrying
equipment, large operational wagon
collection, steam and diesel
locomotives.
Museum shop and refreshments
available on open days
Length of line: Three-quarter-mile
Passenger trains: Regular service
operate on open days
Public opening: Open Sundays,
Easter to end of September (11.00-
17.00) and Thursdays (working
days, after noon).
   (Leaflets available, SAE please).
   School and private parties by
special arrangement
Special events: Please see web site
for details
Special facilities: Driver
Experience Days (pre-bookings
only).
Facilities for disabled: Site
relatively flat, but uneven surface.
Toilet access may cause some

Industrial locomotives

Name	No	Builder	Type	Built
Stamford	—*	Avonside (1972)	0-4-0ST	1927
Dora	—	Avonside (1973)	0-4-0ST	1927
Cranford No 2	—	Bagnall (2668)	0-6-0ST	1942
Firefly	—	Barclay (776)	0-4-0ST	1896
BSC No 2	—	Barclay (1931)	0-4-0ST	1927
Sir Thomas Royden	—	Barclay (2088)	0-4-0ST	1940
Belvoir	—	Barclay (2350)	0-6-0ST	1954
Uppingham	—	Peckett (1257)	0-4-0ST	1912
Elizabeth	—	Peckett (1759)	0-4-0ST	1928
Holwell	14	H/Leslie (3138)	0-6-0ST	1915
Singapore	—	H/Leslie (3865)	0-4-0ST	1936
—	24	Hunslet (2411)	0-6-0ST	1941
—	65	Hunslet (3889)	0-6-0ST	1964
—	8	Peckett (2110)	0-4-0ST	1950
—	7	Sentinel (9376)	4wVBT	1947
—	—	Barclay (352)	0-4-0DM	1941
—	20-90-01	Barclay (499)	0-4-0DH	1965
—	3	N/British (27656)	0-4-0DH	1957
Betty	8411/04	R/Royce (10201)	0-4-0DH	1964
—	—	R/Hornsby (305302)	4wDM	1951
—	—	R/Hornsby (306092)	4wDM	1950
—	110	R/Hornsby (411319)	4wDM	1958
—	3	R/Hornsby (421436)	0-4-0DE	1958
—	—	R/Hornsby (544997)	0-4-0DE	1969
—	—	YEC (2641)	0-6-0DE	1957
—	No 28	YEC (2791)	0-6-0DE	1962
—	1382	YEC (2872)	0-6-0DE	1962

*not on site

Locomotive notes: In service 7, AB (1931)

Stock
4 brake vans; 14 covered goods vans; 57 wagons (includes rakes of wagons as used in local ironstone and industrial railways); 3 rail cranes

difficulty for physically disabled
Special notes: The open-air
museum houses an extensive
collection of industrial locomotives
and rolling stock typifying past
activity in local ironstone quarries,
nationwide mines and factories. A
demonstration line approximately
three quarters of a mile long has
been relaid on the former MR
Cottesmore mineral branch

originally built to tap local
ironstone quarries), on which
restored locomotives and stock are
run
   Admission £4 per head (all
classes). Small charge for train
rides. Special charges for Santa
Specials
Membership details: Membership
Secretary, c/o above address

England

S&D Mendip Main Line Project (Midsomer Norton South Station)

Member: HRA

The S&D Mendip Main Line Project has secured a foothold on the northern part of the S&D where previous preservation attempts failed. The Somerset & Dorset Railway Heritage Trust (S&DRHT) has the central object of preserving the route and infrastructure wherever the opportunities arise, whether for heritage or conventional railways or, more simply, for public recreation and conservation. In practice, energies are being concentrated at Midsomer Norton, with the aim of extending the running line southwards up the notorious 1 in 53 grade to Chilcompton, and potentially northwards down to Radstock. The Trust is leasing former trackbed with the aim of securing a total run of nearly one mile within 3-5 years. Midsomer Norton station has become one of the few significant visitor attractions in this former coal-mining community, with the S&D legend attracting national and international attention

Main station: Midsomer Norton South

OS Reference: ST 664537

Officers: Chairman: John Baxter; Secretary: Peter Russell; Finance Director: Douglas Hill; Membership Secretary: Tim Deacon; Vice-President: Richard Stevens

Headquarters: Somerset & Dorset Railway Heritage Trust, Midsomer Norton Station, Silver Street, Midsomer Norton, BA3 2EY

Telephone: 01761 411221

Internet address:
e-mail: general@sdjr.co.uk
Web site: www.sdjr.co.uk

Car park: Limited parking on site. 200-place free car parking — 300yd towards town centre (OS ref: ST 666542). Somervale School (300yd west, weekends) and Norton Hill School (100yd east, Saturday and Sunday pm only)

Industrial locomotives

Name	No	Builder	Type	Built
David James Cook	—	E/Electric (D1120)	0-6-0DE	1966
—	(47192)	Sentinel	0-4-0VBT	1927

Ex-BR locomotives to be hired in for future main events and resident industrial steam locomotive expected on site during 2009

Rolling stock

Coaches — BR Mk 1 brake, BR Mk 1 sleeping car; BR Mk 3 buffet car, Mk 1 TSO and Mk 1 SK (both expected 2009)

Wagons — 2 ex-MoD box vans, LSWR box van, 3 brake vans (2 LMS, 1 SR Queen Mary, (GWR), milk tanker, Dogfish, Dace, Barbel, Sturgeon, Lafarge Cement internal box van, Kilmersdon Colliery coal wagon

Access by public transport:
Nearest rail stations Bath Spa (13 miles), Frome (13 miles), Trowbridge (15 miles). Bus (First) 173, 177/778, 179/779 connect with Bath/Bristol with drop offs near station (every day excluding public holidays); 184 connects with Frome (weekdays and Saturdays).
Updates on www.firstgroup.com

On site facilities: Sales/information area in main station building during opening times; toilets. Static buffet coach in sidings (light refreshments and meals). Museum building for static exhibits under development with expected opening 2009. Exhibits currently stored off site. Reconstructed signalbox being re-equipped during 2009. Goods shed workshop open for guided viewing

Length of line: Fifth of mile running line through station, plus sidings in goods yard. Extension underway over further fifth mile. Planned southward extension for approx two-thirds mile towards Chilcompton Tunnels

Opening times: Site, buildings and shop open Sundays and Mondays 10.00-17.00 throughout the year. Otherwise, normally only site open for viewing. Buffet service normally open Sundays; but may extend to other days during 2009. Train operations — phone to check. Steam train dates and times announced in press and on the web. Regular operations may start later in 2009

Special events: Please see railway/local press and web site. Midsummer at Midsomer — 20/21 June; Santa event — 12/13 December

Disabled access: Wheelchairs can access station forecourt, down platform, main building (via platform) and up platform via barrow crossing. Parking for disabled in station forecourt; phone to ensure space is reserved. Buffet coach, picnic area and museum accessed by gently ramped path

Membership details: Tim Deacon, 38 Bay Crescent, Swanage, Dorset BH19 1RB

Rates from 2009: Ordinary Adult (16+) £14, Junior or Senior Citizen £10; Senior Citizen Family £16; Family/Household £18; Corporate £22;

Life membership: (single member) £180; Family/Corporate £250; retired spouses/partners £150; retired single £100.

Visitor / membership / volunteering leaflets available on request or at station

Membership journal: *The S&D Telegraph* — 3 times per annum (free to members). Current and back numbers £2.95 each, (£2.50 before No 27), subject to availability

Museum — Science Museum — London

Built on land acquired with the profits from the Great Exhibition of 1851, the Science Museum was one of the first to include industrial archaeology. The railway exhibits are drawn from the collection based at the National Railway Museum. They form part of a major gallery, 'Making the Modern World', which opened in June 2000 on the site of the former Land Transport gallery

Location: South Kensington
OS reference: TQ 268793
Operating society/organisation: Science Museum, Exhibition Road, South Kensington, London SW7 2DD
Telephone: 020 7942 4000
Internet address: *Web site:* www.sciencemuseum.org.uk
Access by public transport: South Kensington Underground station

Catering facilities: Cafés on ground floor, hot meals, tea, coffee, sandwiches, etc. Picnic area in basement
On site facilities: Bookshop, toilets on most floors
Public opening: Daily 10.00-18.00. Closed 24-26 December
Special events: All organised by the National Railway Museum, York, which is part of the Science Museum. Telephone (01904) 621261 for details
Facilities for disabled: Toilets on most floors, ramp and lifts to all floors. Parties should contact before arrival if extra assistance is required
Special notes: Static exhibits only in 'Making the Modern World'

Locomotives

Name	No	Origin	Class	Type	Built
Rocket	—	Liverpool & Manchester Railway	—	0-2-2	1829
Columbine	—	Grand Junction Railway	—	2-2-2	1845
Puffing Billy	—	Wylam Colliery	—	0-4-0	1814

Locomotive note: Restored to static display condition

Timetable Service — Seaton & District Electric Tramway — Devon

Member: HRA, South West Tourism

A unique 2ft 9in gauge electric tramway, operating on the trackbed of the former Southern Railway branch line between Seaton and Seaton Junction in east Devon. Trams operate between Seaton, Colyford and Colyton. Panoramic views of the beautiful Axe Valley and estuary together with a host of wading birds and other wildlife

Location: Harbour Road Car Park, Seaton; Swan Hill Road, Colyford (next to White Hart Inn); Station Road, Kingsdon, Colyton
OS reference: SY 252904
Operating society/organisation: Modern Electric Tramways Ltd t/a Seaton Tramway, Car Depot, Harbour Road, Seaton, Devon EX12 2NQ
Telephone: 01297 20375
Fax: 01297 625626
Internet address:
e-mail: info@tram.co.uk
Web site: www.tram.co.uk
Access by public transport: Nearest railway station: Axminster. Buses: Axe Valley Mini Travel service 885 from Axminster; service 899 from Sidmouth. First Southern National service X53 from Weymouth, Exeter and Lyme Regis; service 20 from Taunton and Honiton. Bus enquiries 0870 608 2608 or www.devon.gov.uk/devonbus

Trams

No	Prototype based on	Type	Built
2	London Metropolitan Tramways	A	1964
4	Blackpool	'Boat'	1961
6	Bournemouth (later Llandudno & Colwyn Bay)	'open-top'	1954
7	Bournemouth (later Llandudno & Colwyn Bay)	'open-top'	1954
8	†—	—	1968
9	Blackburn/Plymouth	double-deck	2004
10	Blackburn/Plymouth	double-deck	2005
11	Blackburn/Plymouth	double-deck	2006
12	London Metropolitan Tramways	'Feltham'	1966
14*	London Metropolitan Tramways	A	1904
16*	Bournemouth		1921
17	Manx Electric Tramway	'toastrack'	1988
19*	Exeter Corporation	—	1906

†a larger version of the ex-Bournemouth design of cars 6 and 7
*rebuilds of heritage trams
9, 10, 11 are based on elements of designs from Plymouth and Blackburn

On site facilities: Gift shops at Seaton and Colyton. Restaurant, ice cream parlour and picnic area at Colyton
Length of line: 3 miles, 2ft 9in gauge
Period of public operation and departure times (2009):
Weekends: 28 February to 29 March, 10.00-16.00.
Daily: 4 April to 1 November, 10.00-17.00.
Weekends: 7 November to 19 December, 10.00-16.00.
  Santa Specials — in December,
enquire for details.
Private hire all year round for groups of 20+
Fares for 2009: Seaton to Colyton return fares — Adult £8.35, OAP £7.50, Child £5.85. Single fares, all day Rover, Friday explorer and Family ticket also available. Discounts for loyalty cardholders, families and parties of 12 or more
Facilities for disabled: Tramcar No 17 carries up to 10 wheelchairs. Please note that it has open sides and is therefore exposed to the weather. Trams 9, 10 and 11
accommodate 2 wheelchairs and depart frequently. Groups should book in advance. Please phone for times.
Disabled toilets at Seaton and Colyton
Special notes: Tram driving lessons available through the season except 26 July-6 September. Bird watching trips available February to May and September to December. Enquire for details. Service operated by open-top double-deck bogie cars (enclosed saloon cars during inclement weather)

Timetable Service | **Severn Valley Railway** | **Worcestershire**

Member: HRA, TT
The railway hosts more main line engines than any other preserved line in the country, enjoying the back-up of a large volunteer and professional workforce and extensive engineering workshops

and equipment. Railway travel like it used to be
General Manager: Nick Ralls
Headquarters: Severn Valley Railway Co Ltd, Railway Station, Bewdley, Worcs DY12 1BG
Telephone: Bewdley (01299)

403816; 24hr timetable — (01299) 401001
Internet address: *Web site:* http://www.svr.co.uk
Main stations: Bridgnorth, Bewdley, Kidderminster Town
Other public stations: Arley,

SPECIAL EVENTS FOR 2009

the line for all seasons

21 Feb 1960's TRANSPORT DAY
Visit our stations and see a variety of vehicles from the 1960's period.

6/7/8 March FESTIVAL OF STEAM
In it's new three day format for 2009 the Festival of Steam is a date to be noted in your diary now!

27/28 June & 4/5 July 1940's WEEKEND
A nostalgic look at Britain during World War II with period vehicles, costumes and re-enactments.

25/26/27 Sept AUTUMN STEAM GALA
The UK's premier steam railway event, with continuous running for three full days. Experience an extensive train service between Kidderminster & Bridgnorth throughout the weekend.

8/9/10 October DIESEL GALA
Our ever popular Diesel Gala returns to its October spot in 2009. Full diesel timetable operates on Thursday and Friday with a mix of diesel and steam traction on Saturday.

11 October CLASSIC CAR & BIKE DAY
Visit our stations and meet with the owners of these wonderful vehicles.

VISIT THE ENGINE HOUSE
VISITOR & EDUCATION CENTRE AT HIGHLEY

Other special events are planned, see our website for details

KIDDERMINSTER - BEWDLEY - BRIDGNORTH
Tel: 01299 403816   WWW.SVR.CO.UK

Highley, Hampton Loade, Northwood Halt, Country Park Halt

SatNav postcodes:
Bridgnorth — WV16 5DT
Bewdley — DY12 1BG
Kidderminster Town — DY10 1QX

OS reference: Bridgnorth SO 715926, Bewdley SO 793753

Car parks: At all main stations

Access by public transport: First Bus service 192 to Kidderminster and Bewdley and 125 & 297 to Bridgnorth. Rail service to Kidderminster (main line) with immediate connections to SVR station. Through tickets available from all manned main line stations

Refreshment facilities: At most stations, but not on all operating days and on most trains. Fully licensed bars at Bridgnorth and Kidderminster Town

Souvenir shops: Bridgnorth, Kidderminster Town

Depots: Bridgnorth (locomotives), Bewdley and Kidderminster (stock)

Model railways: At Kidderminster and Hampton Loade

Length of line: 16.5 miles

Passenger trains: Steam-hauled trains running frequently from Kidderminster Town to Bewdley and Bridgnorth. Diesel-hauled service on limited occasions as advertised

Period of public operation: Every weekend, Santa Steam Specials weekends in December. Daily service 2 May to 4 October, plus February, Easter and October local school holidays. Open for limited viewing at other times

Special events: Day out with Thomas — 9/10, 16/17 May; 1940s Weekends — 27/28 June, 4/5 July; Severn Valley in Bloom — 25/26 July; Seaside Special — 5/6 September; Autumn Steam Gala — 25-27 September; Diesel Gala — 8-10 October; Classic Car & Bike Day — 11 October; Santa Steam Specials — 5/6, 12/13, 19/20, 24 December; Festive Season service — 26 December-3 January 2010

Facilities for disabled: Facilities available, special vehicle available to carry wheelchairs by prior arrangement. Disabled people's toilets and ramp access to refreshment facilities at Kidderminster and Bridgnorth.

Locomotives and multiple-units

Name	No	Origin	Class	Type	Built
Gordon†	AD600	LMR	WD	2-10-0	1943
—†	1000	MR	4	4-4-0	1902
—	43106	LMS	4MT	2-6-0	1951
—	46443	LMS	2MT	2-6-0	1950
RAF Biggin Hill+	45110	LMS	5MT	4-6-0	1935
—†	47383	LMS	3F	0-6-0T	1926
—†	48773	LMS	8F	2-8-0	1940
—	42968	LMS	5P4F	2-6-0	1933
—	813	GWR	—	0-6-0ST	1901
—	2857	GWR	2800	2-8-0	1918
—	5164	GWR	5101	2-6-2T	1930
—	4150	GWR	5101	2-6-2T	1947
—	5764	GWR	5700	0-6-0PT	1929
—	7714	GWR	5700	0-6-0PT	1930
—	4566	GWR	4500	2-6-2T	1924
Bradley Manor	7802	GWR	'Manor'	4-6-0	1939
Erlestoke Manor	7812	GWR	'Manor'	4-6-0	1939
Hinton Manor*	7819	GWR	'Manor'	4-6-0	1939
Hagley Hall†	4930	GWR	'Hall'	4-6-0	1929
Taw Valley	34027	SR	WC	4-6-2	1946
—†	1501	GWR	1500	0-6-0PT	1949
—†	7325	GWR	4300	2-6-0	1932
—	75069	BR	4MT	4-6-0	1955
—†	80079	BR	4MT	2-6-4T	1954
Greyhound	D821	BR	42	B-B	1960
Western Ranger	D1013	BR	52	C-C	1962
Western Courier	D1062	BR	52	C-C	1963
—	D3022	BR	08	0-6-0DE	1952
—	08133	BR	08	0-6-0DE	1955
—	D3586	BR	08	0-6-0DE	1953
—	D3937	BR	08	0-6-0DE	1960
—	12099	LMS	11	0-6-0DE	1952
—	D5410	BR	27	Bo-Bo	1962
—	D7029	BR	35	B-B	1963
—	37906	BR	67	Co-Co	1963
Hood	D431	BR	50	Co-Co	1968
Ark Royal	50035	BR	50	Co-Co	1968
Exeter	D444	BR	50	Co-Co	1968
Defiance	D449	BR	50	Co-Co	1967
—§	E6005	BR	73	Bo-Bo	1962
—§	E6006	BR	73	Bo-Bo	1962
—	51933	BR	108	DMS	1960
—	51941	BR	108	DMBS	1960
—	52064	BR	108	DMC	1960
—	56208	BR	108	DTCL	1958
—	59250	BR	108	TBS	1958

+on loan to Barrow Hill Roundhouse Railway Centre
*on display at the McArthur Glen complex, Swindon
§on loan from the Dean Forest Diesel Association
†on display in the 'Engine House' at Highley (additional charge payable)

Industrial locomotives

Name	No	Builder	Type	Built
Warwickshire	—	M/Wardle (2047)	0-6-0ST	1926
The Lady Armaghdale	—	Hunslet (686)	0-6-0T	1898
—	—	Ruston (319290)	0-4-0DM	1953
—	—	R/Hornsby (414304)	0-4-0DM	1957
—	—	R/Hornsby (408297)	0-4-0DM	1957

England

Enlarged versions of all leaflets are available for the visually impaired from staffed booking offices
Special notes: A number of special enthusiasts' weekends and special events are held when extra trains are operated. In addition, supplementary trains with diesel haulage are run as advertised. 'Severn Valley Limited' and 'Severn Valley Venturer' Restaurant Car service operates on Sundays, some Wednesdays and as required on other occasions. Advance booking required. Charter trains with or without dining facilities can be arranged
Membership details: Mrs Kate Kirk, c/o above address
Membership journal: *Severn Valley Railway News* — quarterly
Share details: Mrs W. Broadhurst, c/o above address

Stock
27 ex-GWR coaches; 13 ex-LMS coaches; 24 ex-BR Mk 1 coaches; 9 ex-LNER coaches; numerous examples of ex-GWR, LMS and other freight vehicles and two 30-ton steam cranes

Owners
813 the GWR 813 Fund
1501 the 15xx Fund
2857 the 2857 Fund
42968 the Stanier Mogul Fund
4150 the 4150 Locomotive Fund
4566 the 4566 Fund
5164 the 51xx Fund
5764, 7714 the Pannier Tank Fund
34027 is privately owned
7325 the Great Western (SVR) Association
7802 and 7812 the Erlestoke Manor Fund
7819 the Severn Valley Rolling Stock Trust
43106 the Ivatt 4 Fund
46443 the SVR 46443 Fund
47383 the Manchester Rail Travel Society
48773 the Stanier 8F Locomotive Society
D431, 50035, D444 and D449 Class 50 Alliance Ltd
75069 the 75069 Fund
80079 the Passenger Tank Fund
D821 and D7029 the Diesel Traction Group
D1013 and D1062 the Western Locomotive Association
D3022 the Class 08 Society
D5410 Sandwell Metropolitan Council
4930 and 45110 the SVR(H) plc

Shillingstone Station Project

Railway Centre — **Dorset**

The station, dating from August 1863, was on the famous Somerset & Dorset Joint Railway. It remained open until closure of the line in 1966, the site being taken over by Dorset County Council and remained in use until December 2002. In November 2003 the North Dorset Railway Trust took over the custody of the station and commenced restoration

Location: Shillingstone Station, Shillingstone, Blandford Forum, Dorset DT11 0SF
SatNav postcode: DT11 0SF
Operating society/organisation: North Dorset Railway Society
Contact: David Mouser, Secretary, or Tony Ward
Telephone: (01258) 860078
Internet addresses:
e-mail: tonyward50@btinternet.com

Locomotive

Name	No	Origin	Class	Type	Built
Morning Star	92207	BR	9F	2-10-0	1959

Industrial locomotive

Name	No	Builder	Type	Built
—	—	R/Hornsby (466629)	4wDH	1962

Stock
Box van under restoration

Web site:
www.shillingstone.addr.com
On site facilities: Car park, light refreshments available, shop and museum
Access by public transport: Bus — Damory Coaches 309 from Blandford and Gillingham, approx 4 per day, no Sunday service
Length of line: Track being laid with extension from cattle dock to main platform to be completed in 2009
Public opening: Wednesday (March-November), Saturdays and Sundays 10.00-16.00. Also open some Wednesdays in winter, please check before travelling

The Silk Mill — Derby's Museum of Industry and History

Museum — **Derbyshire**

Member: TT
As would be expected of a railway town, the museum has an extensive collection of railway material including locomotives and rolling stock (on display at the Midland Railway Centre). The railway gallery tells the stories of railway industries in Derby, especially as they relate to the Midland Railway and its successors. Replica Midland Railway signalbox and model railway (under construction). The story is brought up to date by the Railway Research Gallery which looks at the role of the Railway Technical Centre and includes a replica of an InterCity 225 driving cab. The museum is now also home to the Midland Railway Study Centre. Appointments can be made through:
www.midlandrailwaystudycentre.org.uk
Location: Silk Mill Lane, off Full Street, Derby DE1 3AF
Operating society/organisation: Derby City Council
Telephone: (01332) 255308
Fax: (01332) 255108
Car park: Local car parks around city

Access by public transport: Temporary bus station nearby, railway station three-quarter mile
On site facilities: Shop, baby changing facilities
Opening times: Admission free. Mondays 11.00-17.00, Tuesdays to Saturdays 10.00-17.00, Bank Holidays 13.00-16.00 Sundays 13.00-16.00
Facilities for disabled: Parking by arrangement. Level access to building, lifts and ramps to all gallery areas, toilets

Sittingbourne & Kemsley Light Railway

Member: HRA

The Sittingbourne & Kemsley Light Railway is part of the 2ft 6in gauge railway built to convey paper and other materials between mills at Sittingbourne and Kemsley and the Dock at Ridham on the banks of the Swale. The first section of the line opened in 1877 with horse-drawn haulage, while steam haulage was introduced in 1906. Two of the engines then in use remain on the line today. The railway now operates on the old paper mills trackbed as a tourist attraction. Passenger trains are normally steam-hauled and are formed of a varied selection of open and covered coaches. For the first half mile of the journey the narrow gauge railway twists and turns through Milton Regis on a unique early reinforced concrete viaduct which was one of the first of its kind

Operations Director: Robert Newcombe

Registered charity: 1057079

Headquarters: Sittingbourne & Kemsley Light Railway Ltd, PO Box 300, Sittingbourne, Kent ME10 2DZ

Telephone: 0871 222 1568 (general enquiries & talking timetable) or 0871 222 1569 (advance bookings — evenings)

Internet address:
e-mail: info@sklr.net
Web site: www.sklr.net

Main station: Sittingbourne Viaduct

Other public stations: Milton Regis Halt, Kemsley Down

Car park: Sittingbourne Viaduct (opposite McDonalds and Homebase)

Party, credit card & advance bookings and Footplate Experience courses: Tony Nokes, 111 Hillary Road, Penenden Heath, Maidstone, Kent ME14 2JX. Tel: 01622 755313

Access by public transport:
Sittingbourne Viaduct — Sittingbourne (South Eastern) station;
Milton Regis Halt — Mill Way, Sittingbourne (access from ASDA car park); (Kemsley Down access by rail or on foot from Saxon Shore Way only)

Access by road: M2, A249 then A2 to Sittingbourne (follow brown tourist signs)

OS reference:
Sittingbourne TQ 905642
Milton Regis Halt TQ 909648
Kemsley Down TQ 920661

On site facilities at Kemsley Down: Refreshment facilities; Souvenir shop; Small Exhibits Museum; Museum Walk; Wildlife garden; children's play/picnic area; model and miniature railways

Depot: Kemsley Down (access by rail or on foot from Saxon Shore Way only)

Length of line: 2 miles, 2ft 6in gauge

Passenger trains: Hourly from 11.00, or 13.00 to 16.00 (refer to timetable: www.sklr.net or 0871 222 1568)

Journey time: 15min each way

Period of public operation: Easter to end September. Sundays and Bank Holidays. Wednesday during most school holidays during season

Locomotives

Name	No	Builder	Type	Built
Alpha	—	Bagnall (2472)	0-6-2T	1932
Triumph	—	Bagnall (2511)	0-6-2T	1934
Superb	—	Bagnall (2624)	0-6-2T	1940
Unique	—	Bagnall (2216)	2-4-0F	1924
Premier	—	K/Stuart (886)	0-4-2ST	1905
Leader	—	K/Stuart (926)	0-4-2ST	1905
Melior	—	K/Stuart (4219)	0-4-2ST	1924
Edward Lloyd	—	R/Hornsby (435403)	4wDM	1961
Victor	—	Hunslet (4182)	4wDM	1953
Barton Hall	—	Hunslet (6651)	4wDM	1965

Industrial standard gauge locomotives

Name	No	Builder	Type	Built
Bear	—	Peckett (614)	0-4-0ST	1896
—	1	Barclay (1876)	0-4-0F	1925

Locomotive notes: In service: *Melior, Victor, Edward Lloyd, Barton Hall*
Under repair: *Triumph, . Superb*, Leader ** (*expected back in service during 2009), *Premier* (major repair started 2007)
static display: *Alpha, Unique* and standard gauge exhibits

Stock

10 bogie coaches (including 4 ex-Chattenden & Upnor Railway); 2 open coaches; 37 various wagons

Special events: Extended openings and timetables for special events including: Easter — 11, 13 April; Diesel Mornings — 11 April, 26 July; Jack the Station Cat and Edward Bear — 3/4 May; Father's Day — 21 June; Junior Member's Day — 21 June; Steam and Beer Festival — 4/5 July (Festival fares apply); Model Railway Day — 9 August; Ivor the Engine — 29-31 August; Gala Weekend — 26/27 September; Santa Specials (advance booking required) — 5/6, 12/13, 19/20, 23, 26 December

Special notes: *The railway is under threat of closure — please check that the timetable for 2009 is running to avoid disappointment.* There is no public access to Kemsley Down other than by the railway or on foot from Saxon Shore Way on operating dates. When the line is closed all stock is stored in security compounds within the paper mill premises.
Normal fares apply except for the Steam & Beer Festival and Santa Specials. Family fares and senior citizens tickets available. Special

rates for parties. Dogs welcome and travel free
Disabled facilities: Limited access by prior arrangement until full facilities are available.

Tel: 01795 599511 for details
Special facilities: Footplate experience courses, special trains and children's parties available. Movie filmimg opportunities

Membership details:
John Sparrow, 20 Park Road, Sheerness, Kent ME12 1UY.
Marketing name: Sittingbourne's Steam Railway

| Museum | Snibston | Leicestershire |

Members: TT
Location: Snibston, Ashby Road, Coalville, Leicestershire LE67 3LN
Telephone: (01530) 278444
Fax: (01530) 813301
Operating group: Leicestershire County Council, Commercial & Support Services, Community Services Dept.
Tel: 01530 278444
Internet address: *e-mail:* snibston@leics.gov.uk
Web site: www.snibston.com
Museum contact: Mr N. Pell, Curator, Transport & Mining (museum collection enquiries). Tel: 0116 305 3452
Public opening: April-September — daily 10.00-17.00. October-March — Monday to Friday 10.00-15.00, weekends (10.00-17.00)
Car & coach parking: On site, free
Access by public transport: Arriva Fox from Loughborough and Nottingham (route 99); X1 and X2 from Leicester (217 and 218 on Sundays); Hinckley (route 159); routes 118 and 254 also run from Leicester. Connections at Ashby with Burton upon Trent. Further information, tel: 0870 608 2608
On site facilities: Shop, toilets, car park, café. Conference facilities. Family tickets, picnic areas, science play area. Special event days, nature reserve, golf driving range, colliery building tours
Disabled facilities: Fully available

Multiple-unit

Name	No	Origin	Class	Type	Built
—	70576	BR	4CEP/411	TBC	1956

Industrial locomotives (standard gauge)

Name	No	Builder	Type	Built
Mars II†	—	RSH (7493)	0-4-0ST	1948
—	2§	Barclay (1815)	0-4-0F	1924
—*	—§	Brush (314)	0-4-0ST	1906
Cadley Hill No 1†	—	Hunslet (3851)	0-6-0ST	1962
Pitt the Colliery Engine	16	Hunslet (6289)	0-6-0DM	1966
—	—	R/Hornsby (393304)	4wDM	1955

§on display in museum galleries

Industrial locomotives (2ft 6in gauge)

		Builder	Type	Built
—	—	E/Electric (2416)	4wBE	1957
—	—	H/Clarke (DM1812)	0-6-0DM	1960
—	63/000/449	Hunslet (8973)	4wDH	1979

Locomotive notes: 2009 locomotive for passenger trains will be Hunslet 6289 *Pitt the Colliery Engine*
†locomotive is stored, but may be brought out for display on special events
*originally Powlesland & Mason No 6 taken over by GWR in 1924 and numbered 921
Plus 2ft 6in gauge English Electric battery-operated electric manriding locomotives — ex-NCB

Rolling stock: 1920 Midland Railway brake van, other goods vehicles

on site apart from small section of colliery tour. Access to passenger trains
Railways on site: Approx two-thirds of a mile of standard gauge track with passenger trains on selected days. Please telephone for further information.

Narrow gauge railway about 80yd in length (non operational).
Volunteers to help maintain and run the railway are welcome to join our 'Friends of Coaltracks' support group; please contact Mr N. Pell at above address if interested

England

Museum — Somerset & Dorset Railway Trust — Somerset

Member: HRA

Situated at Washford on the West Somerset Railway, the Trust Museum houses Somerset & Dorset memorabilia and artefacts to stir memories of cross-country travel in the era of steam. The sidings and restoration shed give the visitor a chance to see locomotives, wagons and carriages close up. Midford signalbox display

Headquarters: Washford Station, Minehead Road, Washford, Somerset TA21 0PP

Telephone: 01984 640869

Internet address: *Web site:* http://www.sdrt.org

Car park: Small car park by main road

Access by public transport: West Somerset Railway trains on operating days, March to end October. Nearest main line station:

Taunton. First Bus service 28 (Taunton-Minehead) passes the station

On site facilities: Souvenir counter at the station. No refreshments on station but adjacent inn offers food and children are welcome

Public opening: 10.30-16.30 throughout June, July, August and September, plus Bank Holiday weekends and Gala Days

Membership details: Terry Dart, Membership Secretary, 17 Earl Edwin Mews, Whitchurch, Shropshire SY13 1DT

Membership journal: *Pines Express* (4 issues/year, plus 2 newsletters/year)

Locomotive

Name	No	Origin	Class	Type	Built
—	88	S&DJR	7F	2-8-0	1925

Industrial locomotive

Name	No	Builder		Type	Built
Kilmersdon	—	Peckett (1788)		0-4-0ST	1929

Stock

3 Somerset & Dorset 6-wheeled coaches undergoing restoration. Large wagon collection. Display of narrow gauge equipment from Sedgemoor peat railways

---

Timetable Service — South Devon Railway — Devon

Member: HRA, TT

A typical West Country branch line meandering up the Dart Valley to Buckfastleigh which is home to the railway's workshops, a butterfly and otter farm and several other attractions. The line is accessible from Totnes (main line) via a footbridge (4min walk)

General Manager: R. Elliott

Headquarters: South Devon Railway, Buckfastleigh Station, Buckfastleigh, Devon TQ11 0DZ

Telephone: 0845 345 1470

Internet addresses: *e-mail:* info@southdevonrailway.org

Web site: www.southdevonrailway.org

Main station: Buckfastleigh

Other public stations: Staverton, Totnes (Littlehempston)

OS reference:
Buckfastleigh SX 747663
Staverton SX 785638

Car park: Buckfastleigh (free), Staverton (free). Totnes — use main line pay & display or council car parks

Locomotives and multiple-units

Name	No	Origin	Class	Type	Built
—	1420	GWR	1400	0-4-2T	1933
—	1369	GWR	1366	0-6-0PT	1934
—	3205	GWR	2251	0-6-0	1946
—	3803	GWR	2884	2-8-0	1939
Dumbleton Hall	4920	GWR	'Hall'	4-6-0	1929
—	5526	GWR	4500	2-6-2T	1929
—	5786	GWR	5700	0-6-0PT	1930
—	D2246	BR	04	0-6-0DM	1956
—	D3666	BR	09	0-6-0DE	1959
—	D8110	BR	20	Bo-Bo	1962
—	20118	BR	20	Bo-Bo	1962
—	D7612	BR	25	Bo-Bo	1966
—	33002	BR	33	Bo-Bo	1960
Loch Trieg	D6737	BR	37	Co-Co	1962
Superb	50002	BR	50	Co-Co	1967
—	51592	BR	127	DMBS	1959
—	51604	BR	127	DMBS	1959
—	55000	BR	121	DMBS	1959
—	59659	BR	115	TS	1960
—	59719	BR	115	TCL	1960
—	59740	BR	115	TS	1960

Broad gauge — 7ft 0.25in

Name	No	Origin	Class	Type	Built
Tiny	—	SDR	—	0-4-0VBT	1868

Access by public transport: Bus, X38/9 Exeter-Plymouth; 88 Newton Abbot-Buckfastleigh; X80 Plymouth-Torquay. Main line trains to Totnes

Refreshment facilities: Buckfastleigh, Totnes (café at Totnes Rare Breeds Centre adjacent to and only accessible via SDR station)

Souvenir shop: On the train and Buckfastleigh station

Museum: Buckfastleigh

Depot: Buckfastleigh

Vintage bus: Operates to Buckfast Abbey and Buckfastleigh town most days (free service)

Miniature railway: Operates most Sundays and gala days at Buckfastleigh (7.25in gauge, half mile)

Model railway: Extensive 00 gauge model railway at Buckfastleigh. Admission included in train fare

Length of line: 7 miles

Passenger trains: Buckfastleigh-Totnes alongside the River Dart

Period of public operation: Daily April to October

Facilities for disabled: Good

Membership details: South Devon Railway Association, c/o above

Industrial locomotives

Name	No	Builder	Type	Built
Ashley	1	Peckett (2031)	0-4-0ST	1942
Lady Angela	1690	Peckett (1690)	0-4-0ST	1926
Sapper	WD132	Hunslet (3163)	0-6-0ST	1943
Glendower	—	Hunslet (3810)	0-6-0ST	1954
Carnarvon	47	Kitson (5474)	0-6-0ST	1935
—	—	Fowler (421014)	0-4-0DM	1958
Errol Lonsdale	68011	Hunslet (3796)	0-6-0ST	1953

4ft 6in gauge

Name	No	Builder	Type	Built
Lee Moor No 2	—	Peckett (784)	0-4-0ST	1899

Stock

13 ex-BR Mk 1 coaches; 12 ex-GWR coaches; 3 ex-GWR auto trailers; 25 wagons. Lee Moor Tramway china clay wagon (4ft 6in gauge)

Owners

Tiny, 7ft 0.25in gauge, part of the National Collection
Glendower is privately owned
5526 the 5526 Ltd
3205 the 2251 Fund
D2246 and 50002 the Devon Diesel Society
D8110, 20118, D7612 and 33002 the South Devon Diesel Traction Group
5786 the Worcester Locomotive Society
Errol Lonsdale, Sapper, 3803 and 4920 the South Devon Railway Trust
1369 and 1420 the South Devon Railway Association

address

Membership journal: *Bulliver* — quarterly

Timetable Service	South Tynedale Railway	Cumbria

Member: HRA

A narrow gauge line passing through the attractive scenery of the South Tyne valley, in the North Pennine area of outstanding natural beauty

Location: Approximately 0.75-mile north of Alston town centre, on A686 Hexham road

OS reference: NY 717467

Operating society: South Tynedale Railway Preservation Society, The Railway Station, Alston, Cumbria CA9 3JB

Telephone: Alston (01434) 382828 (timetable information); (01434) 381696 (other enquiries)

Internet address: *Web site:* www.strps.org.uk

Car park: Alston station

Access by public transport: Bus services vary seasonally. Routes include Haltwhistle-Alston and

Locomotives

Name	No	Builder	Type	Built
Barber	—	T/Green (441)	0-6-2ST	1908
Naworth	4	H/Clarke (DM819)	0-6-0DM	1952
Thomas Edmondson	6	Henschel (16047)	0-4-0T	1918
—	9	Hunslet (4109)	0-4-0DM	1952
Naklo	10	Chrzanow (3459)	0-6-0WTT	1957
Cumbria	11	Hunslet (6646)	0-4-0DM	1967
—	13	Hunslet (5222)	0-4-0DM	1958
Helen Kathryn	14	Henschel (28035)	0-4-0T	1948
—	—	Hunslet (4110)	0-4-0DM	1952
—	—	H/Clarke (DM1167)	0-6-0DM	1960
Carlisle	16	Hunslet (1859)	0-4-2T	1937
—	—	EE/Baguley (2519/3500)	4wBE	1958
—	17	B/Drewry (3704)	4wBE	1973
		rebuilt A/Barclay (6526)		1987
—	18	H/Clarke (DM1247)	0-6-0DM	1961
Permanent Way Trolley	DB965062	Wickham (7597)	4wDM	1957

Stock

5 bogie coaches; 1 brake van; 3 bogie open wagons; 8 4-wheel open

Carlisle-Alston. Please check with local Tourist Information Centres or, for public transport information in Cumbria, phone 0871 200 2223

On site facilities: Book and souvenir shop, picnic area, toilets (including disabled persons), parking, lineside footpath

Catering facilities: Most weekend trains serve coffee, tea, soft drinks and snacks. (Tea room at Alston is not operated by Society.) Confectionery, ice cream and soft drinks on sale in the railway shop at Alston

Length of line: 2.25 miles, 2ft gauge from Alston to Kirkhaugh

Public opening: Trains will run: 10-14, 16, 18/19, 25/26 April; 2-4, 9/10, 16/17, 23-26, 30/31 May; 2, 4, 6/7, 9, 11, 13/14, 16, 18, 20/21, 23, 25, 27/28, 30 June; 2, 4/5, 7, 9, 11/12, 14, 16, 18/19, 20-31 July; daily in August; 1, 3, 5/6, 8, 10, 12/13, 15, 17, 19/20, 22, 24, 26/27 September; 3/4, 10/11, 17/18, 24/25, 27-29, 31 October; 5/6,

wagons; 1 4-wheel box van; 3 4-wheel flat wagons; 1 4-wheel fuel tank wagon; 2 bogie well wagons, 4 4-wheel skip wagons; 5 bogie flat wagons; 6 bogie hopper wagons; 1 4-wheel hopper wagon; 1 4-wheel weedkiller wagon; 1 bogie compressor wagon; 2 4-wheel chassis

Owners
Barber is on loan from Leeds Industrial Museum
4, 6, 9, 10, 16, 17 and 2519/3500 the South Tynedale Railway Preservation Society
11, 13, 14, 18, DM4110, DM1167, DB965082 and Baguley/Drewry are privately owned

12/13, 19-21 December
Steam haulage scheduled for: 10-13 April; 2-4, 23-25 May; 6/7, 13/14, 20/21, 27/28 June; 4/5, 11/12, 18/19, 25/26 July, daily in August; 5/6, 12/13, 19/20, 26/27 September; 5/6, 12/13, 12-21 December

Special events: Santa Specials — 5/6, 12/13, 19-21 December. Other special events may take place during the year. Please telephone or check web site for information

Facilities for disabled: A carriage

with access for wheelchair users is available. Advance booking is recommended, tel: 01434 381696. Wheelchair accessible toilet at Alston

Special notes: The line has been constructed on the trackbed of the former BR Haltwhistle-Alston branch

Membership details: Membership Secretary, c/o above address

Membership journal: *Tynedalesman* — quarterly

Southall Railway Centre

Steam Centre — London

Due to circumstances the Great Western Railway Preservation Group were forced to end their activities within the former steam/DMU depot in 1997 and adopt new activities. With the vacation of part of the former depot by *Flying Scotsman* (now on display at the National Railway Museum) the Group were able to move into the former Wheel Drop Shop and ancillary building including open areas and sidings.

Whilst the Group caried out restoration and maintenance of the stock in the Wheel Drop Shed and adjacent sidings the situation is such that the GWRPG Ltd have to vacate the area by the end of January 2009 as the facilities are required by a main line operator.

This is causing a major disruption to the Group's plans. They have been fortunate to have been offered the lease of the three road sidings at the south side of the depot which will give a greater length of travel and variety of movement. Work is

Locomotives

Name	No	Origin	Class	Type	Built
—	2885*	GWR	2885	2-8-0	1938
—	4110†	GWR	4100	2-6-2T	1936
—	9682§	GWR	5700	0-6-0PT	1949

*cosmetically restored and on display at Moor Street station, Birmingham
†under restoration at Tyseley Locomotive Works
§on hire to Chinnor & Princes Risborough Railway

Industrial locomotives

Name	No	Builder	Type	Built
William Murdoch	—	Peckett (2100)	0-4-0ST	1949
Birkenhead	—	RSH (7386)	0-4-0ST	1948
—	1	AEC	0-4-0	1939
—	AD251	R/Hornsby (390772)	0-4-0DM	1956
—	AD911	B/Drewry	4wDM	—

Rolling stock
BR Mk 1 TSO, BR Mk 1 BSK, BR box van, LMS brake van, BP tank wagon, BR generator van, BR stores van, BR parcels van, LNER CCT, GWR Rectank, GWR Gane A, GWR 'Mink' tool van, GWR Toad brake van

Owner
William Murdoch the GWRPG are custodians for Portsmouth City Museum

already in hand for track clearance and maintenance with the facilities that are available
Operating society/organisation: GWR Preservation Group Ltd, 16 Grange Close, Heston, Middx TW5 0HW
Contact: Bob Gorringe, Chairman
Tel: 020 8574 1529
Fax: 020 8571 6538

Internet address: *Web site:* www.gwrpg.co.uk
Location: Southall, former steam/DMU depot
Car parking: Currently on site
Access by public transport: Southall station, access via Park Avenue or alternative Armstrong Way
On site facilities:

Light refreshments and shop
Period of public opening: 23/24 March, 19/20 April, 17/18 May, 14/15 June, 12/13 July, 24/25 August, 20/21 September, 6/7, 13/14 December
Membership details: Andrew Hunter c/o above address
Membership journal: *Southall Semaphore* — quarterly

Timetable Service — Spa Valley Railway — Kent

Member: HRA

This railway originally formed part of a system of cross-country lines in East Sussex running through the Wealden countryside

Location: The main station at Tunbridge Wells West is located in the western end of the town close to the A26 road and the popular 'Pantiles' area

OS reference: Tunbridge Wells West station TQ 577384

General Manager: Stephen Woolven

Operating society/organisation: Tunbridge Wells & Eridge RPS, Tunbridge Wells West Station, Nevill Terrace, Tunbridge Wells, Kent TN2 5QY

Telephone: 01892 537715

Internet address: *Web site:* www.spavalleyrailway.co.uk

Car parking: Tunbridge Wells West — several car parks nearby in town centre. Note: Sainsbury's car park, adjacent to station, is limited to 2¹/₂ hours for their customers only.

High Rocks — large free car park.

Groombridge — there is *no* parking here.

Eridge — large car park

SatNav postcodes:

Tunbridge Wells West — TN2 5QY

High Rocks — TN3 9JJ

Groombridge — TN3 9RD

Eridge — TN3 9LE

Access by public transport:

Tunbridge Wells West

National Rail services to Tunbridge Wells, then 15min walk, or short bus ride. Nearest bus stop served by many local bus services is at Sainsbury's, Tunbridge Wells, then

Locomotives and multiple-units

Name	No	Origin	Class	Type	Built
—	7715††	GWR	5700	0-6-0PT	1930
Sutton	32650*	LBSCR	A1X	0-6-0T	1876
—	47493	LMS	3F	0-6-0T	1927
—	68077*	LNER	J94	0-6-0ST	1947
—	09004	BR	09	0-6-0DE	1959
Colonel Tomline	D3489	BR	10	0-6-0DE	1958
—	15224	BR	12	0-6-0DE	1949
R J Mitchell	33063	BR	33/0	Bo-Bo	1962
Sealion	33065*	BR	33/0	Bo-Bo	1962
—	37254	BR	37	Co-Co	1965
—	E6047	BR	73	Bo-Bo	1966
—	51669†	BR	115	DMBS	1960
—	51849	BR	115	DMBS	1960
—	54408	BR	101	DTS(L)	1958
—	60142*	BR	207	DMBS	1962
—	60616*	BR	207	TC	1962
—	60916*	BR	207	DTS	1962

*undergoing overhaul
†converted to locomotive-hauled stock
††on loan from Buckinghamshire Railway Centre

Industrial locomotives

Name	No	Builder	Type	Built
Samson*	57	RSH (7668)	0-6-0T	1950
Ugly*	62	RSH (7673)	0-6-0ST	1950
North Downs*	13	RSH (7846)	0-6-0T	1955
Princess Margaret	—	Barclay (376)	0-4-0DM	1947
Lady Ingrid	—	Barclay (2315)	0-4-0ST	1951
Southerham	—	Drewry/Vulcan (2591)	0-4-0DM	1959
Topham*	—	Bagnall (2193)	0-6-0ST	1922
Fonmon	—	Peckett (1636)	0-6-0ST	1924
Spartan	—	Chrzanow (3135)	0-6-0T	1954
Hotspur*	—	Chrzanow (2944)	0-6-0T	1952

*undergoing overhaul

Stock

5 BR Mk 1 coaches; 1 BR Mk 2 coaches; buffet car from Class 420 EMU; 2 ex-London Transport T stock coaches; 1 LCDR coach body; 4 brake vans, 3 cranes; various freight wagons

Owners

Sutton by the London Borough of Sutton
33063 and 33065 the South East Locomotive Group

approx 100yd walk.

Eridge
Interchange with National Rail services on adjacent platform. Bus service No 29 Tunbridge Wells-Brighton stops on A26 road approx 100yd walk from station
Refreshment facilities: Static buffet car at Tunbridge Wells West. Also bar car *Kate* on some trains
Souvenir shop: Tunbridge Wells West (within engine shed)
Depot: Tunbridge Wells West shed is an original LBSCR design dating from 1891 and consists of four roads which house various items of rolling stock and motive power
Length of line: 5 miles Tunbridge Wells Test-Eridge
Passenger trains: Tunbridge Wells West-Eridge. The railway is expecting to extend services to Eridge during the 2009 season. Check web site or telephone for details
Period of public operation: Weekends and Bank Holidays from 21 March to 1 November plus some weekdays in June, July and August. Santa Specials in December.
Special events: Day out with Thomas — 21/22, 28/29 March; Easter Specials — 11-13 April; Country Affair — 23-25 May; Steaming Through the '40s — 27/28 June; Wings Wheels & Steam — 19 July; Diesel Gala — 7-9 August; Teddy Bears' Day Out — 22/23 August; Heritage Buildings Open Day — 10-13 September; Day out with Thomas — 43/4, 10/11 October; Diesel Days — 17/18 October; Santa Specials — 5-23 December; End of Season Sale — 27/28 December/ 1 January 2010
Facilities for disabled: Separate disabled persons' toilet at Tunbridge Wells West station. Ramps available for wheelchair access to trains. Note: at present Eridge has no step-free access for wheelchairs to the platforms
Special facilities: A private train can be hired for the day. Please contact address above for details
Membership details: c/o Tunbridge Wells West Station
Membership journal: *Spa Valley Starter*

```
 _____     STEAM —            _____
(  Museum    )  Museum of the Great ( Wiltshire )
 ‾‾‾‾‾‾‾‾‾‾‾     Western Railway      ‾‾‾‾‾‾‾‾‾‾‾
```

STEAM — Museum of the Great Western Railway

Member: HRA

STEAM — Museum of the Great Western Railway tells the remarkable story of the men and women who built, operated and travelled on the Great Western Railway. Situated on the old Swindon Railway Works site, the museum is housed in a 72,000sq ft Victorian machine shop. As well as locomotives, carriages and wagons the story is told by imaginative displays and plenty of 'hands-on' exhibits — build a bridge and shunt the wagons! Have a go at putting a locomotive together and take a ride on the train-driving simulator
Keeper: Felicity Jones
Location: Kemble Drive, Swindon, Wiltshire SN2 2TA
OS reference: tba
Operating society/organisation: Swindon Borough Council
Telephone: Swindon (01793) 466646
Internet address: *Web site:* www.swindon.gov.uk/steam
Car park: Swindon Designer Outlet

Locomotives

Name	No	Origin	Class	Type	Built
—	2516	GWR	2301	0-6-0	1897
—	4248	GWR	4200	2-8-0T	1916
Caerphilly Castle	4073	GWR	'Castle'	4-6-0	1923
—	9400	GWR	9400	0-6-0PT	1947
*North Star**	—	GWR	—	2-2-2	1837
—	4	GWR	Diesel railcar	Bo-Bo	1934
Hinton Manor†	7819	GWR	'Manor'	4-6-0	1939
Evening Star	92220	BR	9F	2-10-0	1960

*broad gauge (7ft 0.25in) replica
†on display in McArthur Glen's 'Designer Outlet' shopping centre located in the old works

Owners
7819 on loan from Severn Valley Railway
All other locomotives are part of the National Railway Museum Collection

Access by public transport: Swindon main line station 1 mile (20min walk)
On site facilities: SGift/souvenir shop
Facilities for disabled: Fully accessible
Period of public opening: Daily 10.00-17.00. Closed Christmas Day, Boxing Day and New Year's Day
Membership details: The Friends of Swindon Railway Museum, c/o STEAM
Membership journal: *North Star* — quarterly

143

Stephenson Railway Museum & North Tyneside Railway

Steam Centre | Tyne & Wear

Member: HRA
A display in buildings which began life as the Tyne & Wear Metro Test Centre now features locomotives and exhibitions which illustrate railway development from waggonways to the present day
Location: Middle Engine Lane, West Chirton
OS reference: NZ 396576
Internet address: *NTSRA web site:* ntsra.org.uk
Operating society/organisation: The Stephenson Railway Museum and the North Tyneside Railway are managed as a partnership between North Tyneside Council, Tyne & Wear Museums and the North Tyneside Railway Association (NTSRA). Each can be contacted c/o Stephenson Railway Museum, Middle Engine Lane, West Chirton, North Shields, Tyne & Wear NE29 8DX
Car park: On site, free
Length of line: North Tyneside Railway, 2 miles, Stephenson Railway Museum to Percy Main Village
Access by public transport: Bus services 300 from Newcastle (Haymarket bus station); 337 from Wallsend (Metro station interchange). Ring 0870 608 2608 for times and fares. Tyne & Wear Metro to Percy Main (then short walk to NTR station) when North Tyneside Railway is in operation
Public opening:
Museum — 11.00-16.00, every weekend from April to October,

Locomotive and multiple-unit

Name	No	Origin	Class	Type	Built
—	D2078	BR	03	0-6-0DM	1959
—	3267	NER	—	DMLV	1904

Industrial locomotives

Name	No	Builder	Type	Built
Billy	—	Killingworth or RS & Co (1)	0-4-0	c1826
—	A No 5	Kitson (2509)	0-6-0PT	1883
Ashington No 5 / Jackie Milburn	5	Peckett (1970)	0-6-0ST	1939
Ted Garrett, JP, DL, MP	1	RSH (7683)	0-6-0T	1951
—	E4	Siemens-Schuckert (457)	Bo-BoWE	1909
Thomas Burt MP 1837-1902	401	Bagnall (2994)	0-6-0ST	1950
—	10	Consett Iron Co	0-6-0DM	1958
—	801*	Alco	Bo-Bo	1950

*in store for restoration and future use on Aln Valley Railway

Stock
1 LNER Gresley BFK; 3 BR Mk 1 non-gangwayed coaches, 2 BR Mk 2 coaches, 1 LNER Gresley BGP

Owners
NER van National Railway Museum
801 the UK Alco Group

including all Bank Holidays. Every day during North Tyneside school holidays. Admission free. November to March closed.
Steam train rides — every Sunday and Bank Holiday Mondays, April to October. First train 12.15. Small charge applies, please contact the museum on 0191 200 7146 for details, or visit the web site www.twmuseums.org.uk/stephenson

Special notes: Stephenson Railway Museum and North Tyneside Railway share facilities in buildings. North Tyneside Steam Railway Association operates and maintains exhibits from the Museum Collection
Facilities for disabled: Access for wheelchairs to Museum building at Middle Engine Lane. Access to stations; also wheelchair ramp onto train

Swanage Railway — 'The Purbeck Line'

Timetable Service | Dorset

Member: HRA
Overlooked by the historic ruins of Corfe Castle, this railway is slowly extending towards Wareham and the connection to the main line network enables occasional stock and locomotive workings

Location: Swanage station
Operations Manager: Steve Dyer
Operating society/organisation: Swanage Railway Co Ltd, Station House, Swanage, Dorset BH19 1HB
Telephone: Swanage (01929)

425800. Talking Timetable — (01929) 425800
Fax: (01929) 426680
Internet addresses: *e-mail:* info@swanage-railway.co.uk
Web site: www.swanagerailway.co.uk

144

England

Other public stations: Herston Halt, Harmans Cross, Corfe Castle and Norden

OS reference: SZ 026789

Car park: Norden park & ride (charge payable) signposted off A351 Wareham-Swanage road on the approach to Corfe Castle. Limited parking available in Swanage town centre

Access by public transport: Regular bus services operated by Wilts & Dorset from Bournemouth, Poole and Wareham to Swanage and Norden park & ride

On site facilities: Souvenir shop at Swanage. Buffet car on most trains. Picnic areas at Swanage, Harmans Cross and Norden. Exhibition and cinema coach at Corfe. 5in gauge railway at Swanage on some weekends. Travel Agency at Swanage station

Length of line: 6 miles, Swanage-Herston Halt-Harmans Cross-Corfe Castle-Norden

Public opening: Swanage station open every day except Christmas Day. Trains operate weekends all year round from 14 February to 29 November. Daily from 7 April until 29 October. Also 26 December 2009 to 4 January 2010

Special events: Railway at Work Weekend — 21/22 March; Easter Specials — 10-13 April; Swanage Railway Beer Festival and Diesel Gala — 8-10 May; Swanage Regatta & Carnival — 25 July to 2 August; Steam Gala & Vintage Transport Rally — 11-13 September; Family Fun Week — 21-31 October; Santa Specials — 5/6, 12/13, 29/20, 22-24 December (advance booking essential); Mince Pie Specials — 26 December-4 January 2010. On special event days timetables and fares are liable to alteration. See web site for further details of these and other local events involving the Swanage Railway

Facilities for disabled: Access to shop and toilets; disabled facilities on most trains

Membership details: Liz Sellen, c/o above address

Membership journal: *Swanage Railway News* — 3 times/year

Marketing name: The Purbeck Line

Locomotives and multiple-units

Name	No	Origin	Class	Type	Built
—	6695	GWR	5600	0-6-2T	1928
—	30053	LSWR	M7	0-4-4T	1905
Sidmouth	34010	SR	WC	4-6-2	1945
Eddystone	34028	SR	WC	4-6-2	1946
Manston	34070	SR	BB	4-6-2	1947
257 Squadron	34072	SR	BB	4-6-2	1948
—	80078	BR	4MT	2-6-4T	1954
—	80104	BR	4MT	2-6-4T	1955
—	07007	BR	07	0-6-0DE	1962
—	08436	BR	08	0-6-0DE	1957
—	D3591	BR	08	0-6-0DE	1958
—	20188	BR	20	Bo-Bo	1967
Stan Symes	D6515	BR	33	Bo-Bo	1960
—	33034	BR	33	Bo-Bo	1960
—	33111	BR	33	Bo-Bo	1960
—	51341*	P/Steel	117	DMBS	1959
—	51346	P/Steel	117	DMBS	1959
—	51353*	P/Steel	117	DMBS	1959
—	51356§	P/Steel	117	DMBS	1959
—	51388	P/Steel	117	DMS	1959
—	51392§	P/Steel	117	DMS	1959
—	51395*	P/Steel	117	DMS	1959
—	51398*	P/Steel	117	DMS	1959
—	51933	P/Steel	108	DMBS	1960
—	54504	P/Steel	108	DTC	1960
—	59486	P/Steel	117	TCL	1960
—	59492§	P/Steel	117	TCL	1960
—	59516	P/Steel	117	TCL	1960
—	59521*	P/Steel	117	TCL	1960

*at Midland Railway — Butterley
§on loan to Weardale Railway

Industrial locomotives

Name	No	Builder	Type	Built
May	2	Fowler (4210132)	0-4-0DM	1957
Beryl	—	Planet (2054)	4wPM	1937
Progress	—	Peckett (1611)	0-4-0ST	1923
Secondus*	—	Bellis & Seekings	0-6-0WT	1874
Snapper†	—	R/Hornsby (283871)	4wDM	1950

*2ft 8in gauge, on display in Corfe Castle goods shed
†2ft gauge, stored nearby for use on Purbeck Mineral & Mining Museum project

Locomotive notes: 30053, 80078 and 80104 will be away periodically on short-term loan

Stock
3 ex-LSWR coach bodies; 4 ex-SR vans; 9 ex-SR coaches; 17 ex-BR Mk 1 coaches; 1 ex-BR Mk 1 Pullman; 15 various types of wagons; 1 ex-BR Mk 3 Sleeping coach; 1 ex-SR 15-ton diesel-electric crane; 1 ex-BR Corridor 2nd converted to disabled persons' coach. Brake vans from SR, LMS, LSWR including 3 'Queen Marys', Class 4-TC / 4xx unit 413 consiting vehicles Nos 70824 (TBSK), 70855 (TK), 76298 (DTSO), 76322 (DTSO).

Owners
6695 the 6695 Locomotive Group
34010, 34028, 34070, 34072, 80078 and 80104 the Southern Locomotives Ltd
30053 the Drummond Locomotive Society
D6515 and 33034 the 71A Locomotive Group
07007 the Eastleigh Railway Preservation Society

England

Member: HRA, TT
This is the only preserved section of the former Midland & South Western Junction Railway, the society having had to re-lay track and associated works. There is the station and the engine shed complex at Hayes Knoll
Location: Tadpole Lane, Blunsdon (approximately midway between Blunsdon St Andrew and Purton)
Chairman: J. Poor
Operating society/organisation: Swindon & Cricklade Railway, Blunsdon Station, Blunsdon, Swindon, Wiltshire SN25 2DA
Telephone: 01793 771615
Internet address: *Web site:* www.swindon-cricklade-railway.org
Station: Blunsdon
OS reference: SU 110897
Length of line: 1.5 miles
Car park: Tadpole Lane, Blunsdon
Refreshment facilities: Blunsdon station in former Norwegian State Railways coach. Buffet car at Hayes Knoll on open days. Picnic area
Toilet: Blunsdon station amenities building, Hayes Knoll
Souvenir shop: Blunsdon station. Various sales stands on Open Days around station area. Museum
Depot: Hayes Knoll
Public opening: Site open: 10.00-16.00 Saturdays, Sundays and Bank Holidays throughout the year and Wednesdays in local school holidays.
Passenger trains: A steam train planned to operate from 11.00-16.00 every Sunday from Easter to 26 October and on the dates listed below unless stated otherwise. A train service will also operate from 11.00-16.00 every Saturday and Sunday when special events are not planned and on Wednesdays during local school holidays
Special events: 11.00-16.00 unless otherwise noted
Easter Egg Specials (diesel) — 10 April; Easter Egg Specials (steam) — 11-13 April; Real Ale Weekend (11.00-17.00) — 2-4 May; Steam Gala — 23-25 May; Model Railway Weekend (10.00 start) — 5/6 July; Vintage Transport Weekend (10.30-17.00) — 8/9 August;

Locomotives and multiple-units

Name	No	Origin	Class	Type	Built
Foremarke Hall†	7903	GWR	'Hall'	4-6-0	1949
—*	5637	GWR	5600	0-6-2T	1924
—	2022	BR	03	0-6-0DM	1958
—	D2152	BR	03	0-6-0DM	1960
—	13261	BR	08	0-6-0DE	1956
Sir Herbert Walker	E6003	BR	73	Bo-Bo	1962
—	51074	GRCW	119	DMBC	1959
—	51104	GRCW	119	DMS	1958
—	59514	P/Steel	117	TCL	1959
—	60127	BR	207	DMBS	1962
—	60901	BR	207	DTS	1962

*on loan to East Somerset Railway
†on loan to Gloucestershire Warwickshire Railway

Industrial locomotives

Name	No	Builder	Type	Built
Swordfish	—	Barclay (2138)	0-6-0ST	1941
Salmon	—	Barclay (2139)	0-6-0ST	1942
—	—	Barclay (2352)	0-4-0ST	1954
Richard Trevithick	—	Barclay (2354)	0-4-0ST	1954
Woodbine	—	Fowler (21442)	0-4-0DM	1936
—	—	Fowler (4210137)	0-4-0DM	1958
—	—	Fowler (4220031)	0-4-0DH	1964
—*	70	H/Clarke (1464)	0-6-0T	1921
Slough Estates No 3	—	H/Clarke (1544)	0-6-0ST	1924
Gunby	—	Hunslet (2413)	0-6-0ST	1941

*on loan to Avon Valley Railway

Stock
10 BR Mk 1 coaches; 3 GWR coaches; Selection of goods rolling stock; Wickham railcar. Self-propelled Plasser & Theurer track machine (98504 of 1985)

Owners
7903 the Foremarke Hall Locomotive Group
5637 the 5637 Locomotive Group
Slough Estates the Slough & Windsor Railway Society
51074, 51104 and 59514 the Gloucester Railcar Trust
E6003 the Electro-Diesel Group

Children's Treasure Hunt — 30/31 August; Wartime Weekend (10.30-17.00) — 12/13 September; Diesel Gala, featuring the Class 73 — 3/4 October; Halloween — 30 October (18.30-20.45), 31 October (18.00-20.45);
Santa Specials — 28/29 November, 5/6, 12 (and 18.00-20.00), 13, 19/20 December.
Service operate:
School holidays (diesel):
Wednesdays 11.00-16.00 — 8, 15 April, 27 May, 5, 12, 19, 26 August, 28 October.

When special events are not planned the following service will operate:
Saturday service (diesel) from 10 April throughout the year (11.00-16.00);
Sunday service (steam), from 19 April to 25 October (11.00-16.00);
Sunday service (diesel) from 11 January to 5 April, 1-22 November (11.00-16.00)
Facilities for disabled: Access to trains, locomotive shed, shop, toilets and refreshments

Special facilities: Licensed for civil/wedding ceremonies. Suitable for up to 60 guests. Trains can be hired for special events
Membership details: Membership Secretary, c/o above address
Membership journal: S&CR magazine, quarterly

Timetable Service — Tanfield Railway — County Durham

Member: HRA
The oldest railway in the world, featuring 1725 route, 1725 Causey embankment, 1727 Causey arch, 1766 Gibraltar bridge and 1854 Marley Hill engine shed. Also collection of local engines, Victorian carriages and vintage workshop
Location: Off the A6076 Sunniside to Stanley road
OS reference: NZ 207573
Operating society/organisation: The Tanfield Railway, Marley Hill Engine Shed, Sunniside, Gateshead NE16 5ET
Telephone: General enquiries — 0845 463 4938.
Party and Santa bookings — 0845 463 4836
Internet address: *e-mail:* info@tanfield-railway.co.uk
Web site: www.tanfield-railway.co.uk
Main stations: Andrews House, Sunniside, Causey, East Tanfield
Car park: Marley Hill, Causey picnic area, East Tanfield
Access by public transport: X30/31 stop outside the railway evtrance on weekdays; 705, 706, 770 Sundays to Sunniside only, near to Sunniside station
Catering facilities: Light refreshments available on operating days
On site facilities: Shop and toilets
Length of line: 3 miles
Public opening: Trains run every Sunday and Bank Holiday Monday from January to November. Also Wednesdays and Thursdays in summer. Santa trains in December before Christmas. Marley Hill engine shed open daily for viewing
Special events: Easter Eggstravaganza — 10-12 April;

Locomotive

Name	No	Origin	Class	Type	Built
—	M2*	TGR	M	4-6-2	1951

*3ft 6in gauge, Tasmanian Government Railways (RSH 7630)

Industrial locomotives

Name	No	Builder	Type	Built
—	9	AEG (1565)	4w-4wE	1913
Gamma	—	Bagnall (2779)	0-6-0ST	1945
—	—	Baguley (3565)	2w-2DHR	1962
Horden	—	Barclay (1015)	0-6-0ST	1904
—	6	Barclay (1193)	0-4-2ST	1910
—	17	Barclay (1338)	0-6-0T	1913
—	32	Barclay (1659)	0-4-0ST	1920
Beryl	—	S/Crossley (7697)	0-6-0DM	1953
—	3	E. Borrows (37)	0-4-0WT	1898
—	6	Fowler (4240010)	0-6-0DH	1960
Enterprise	—	R&W Hawthorn (2009)	0-4-0ST	1884
Cyclops	112	H/Leslie (2711)	0-4-0ST	1907
—	2*	H/Leslie (2859)	0-4-0ST	1911
Stagshaw	—	H/Leslie (3513)	0-6-0ST	1923
—	3	H/Leslie (3575)	0-6-0ST	1923
—	13	H/Leslie (3732)	0-4-0ST	1928
—	3	H/Leslie (3746)	0-6-0F	1929
Renishaw Ironworks No 6	—	H/Clarke (1366)	0-6-0ST	1919
Irwell	—	H/Clarke (1672)	0-4-0ST	1937
—	38	H/Clarke (1823)	0-6-0T	1949
—	501	Hunslet (6612)	0-6-0DH	1965
—	—	Planet (3716)	0-4-0DM	1955
—	4	Sentinel (9559)	0-4-0T	1953
Twizell†	3	Stephenson (2730)	0-6-0T	1891
—	L2	R/Hornsby (312989)	0-4-0DE	1952
—	35	R/Hornsby (418600)	0-4-0DE	1958
—	158	RSH (6980)	0-4-0DM	1940
Hendon	—	RSH (7007)	0-4-0CT	1940
—	62	RSH (7035)	0-6-0ST	1940
—	3	RSH (7078)	4w-4wE	1940
—	49	RSH (7098)	0-6-0ST	1943
Progress	—	RSH (7298)	0-6-0ST	1946
Cochrane	—	RSH (7409)	0-4-0ST	1948
Bromborough No 2	—	RSH (7746)	0-6-0DM	1954
—	44	RSH (7760)	0-6-0ST	1953
—	38	RSH (7763)	0-6-0ST	1954
—	21	RSH (7796)	0-4-0ST	1954
—	47	RSH (7800)	0-6-0ST	1954
—	1	RSH (7901)	0-4-0DM	1958

England

Children's Day — 3/4 May; Miners Heritage Weekend — 16/17 May; Teddy Bear Day — 28 June; Steam and Canvas — 11/12 July; Children's Day — 9 August; 60s Bank Holiday — 30/31 August; Gala — 12/13 September; Coal Train Day — 8 November; Santa Specials — 28/29 November, 5/6, 12/13, 19/20, 23/24 December (pre-booking essential); Mince Pie Specials — 26/27 December
Family tickets: Available
Facilities for disabled: Access to East Tanfield and Andrews House stations and Marley Hill engine shed. Toilets at Causey car park and Andrews House station
Membership details: Miss E. Martin, 33 Stocksfield Avenue, Fenham, Newcastle upon Tyne NE5 2DX
Membership journal: *Tanfield Railway News* — 4 times/year
Special notes: Families can alight at Causey station for 2 miles of walks through the picturesque

Name	No	Builder	Type	Built
—	16	RSH (7944)	0-6-0ST	1957
FGF	—	Barclay (D592)	0-4-0DH	1969
—	2	A/Whitworth (D22)	0-4-0DE	1933

*on loan to Locomotion
†on long-term loan from Beamish

2ft gauge

Name	No	Builder	Type	Built
Escucha	11	B/Hawthorn (748)	0-4-0ST	1883
—	—	Clayton (133141)	4wBE	1984
—	—	Hunslet (7332)	4wDM	1973
—	—	L/Blackstone (53162)	4wDM	1962
—	—	L/Blackstone (54781)	4wDM	1962
—	—	R/Hornsby (323587)	4wDM	1952
—	—	R/Hornsby (244487)	4wDM	1946
—	25	RSH (8201)	4wBE	1960
—	—	W/Rogers	4wBE	—

Stock
19 4-wheel carriages; 3 6-wheel carriages; 1 6-wheel van; 14 hopper wagons; 9 contractors bogies; 3 brake vans; 3 steam cranes; 8 covered wagons; 4 open wagons; 4 black wagons; 3 flat wagons

Causey Woods; picnic facilities and toilet available in car park

---

Steam Centre	**Telford Horsehay Steam Trust**	Shropshire

Member: HRA
Telford Steam Railway is based at Horsehay & Dawley station and goods yard in Telford on the Great Western branch from Wellington to Craven Arms via Ironbridge. The site at Horsehay has a longer history, being at the site of one of the Coalbrookdale companies' first blast furnaces. The line saw its last passenger train in 1962 but the route from Lightmoor to Horsehay was kept open for freight traffic until 1979. The TSR acquired the former goods yard at Horsehay & Dawley in 1983. The railway is now extending northwards to Lawley Common, and southwards to Doseley. Excavation of Lawley Common cutting is continuing
Location: Horsehay, Telford, Shropshire
OS reference: SJ 675073
Operating society/organisation: Telford Horsehay Steam Trust, The Old Loco Shed, Horsehay, Telford, Shropshire TF4 2LT
Sales line: 07765 858348

Locomotives and diesel multiple-units

Name	No	Origin	Class	Type	Built
—	5619*	GWR	5600	0-6-2T	1925
—	50531	BRCW	104	DMC	1957
—	50479	BRCW	104	DMBS	1957
—	50556	BRCW	104	DMC	1957
—	59228	BRCW	104	TBSL	1958
—	RB004	Leyland		Railbus	1984

*on loan to Gloucestershire Warwickshire Railway

Industrial locomotives

Name	No	Builder	Type	Built
Ironbridge No 3	—	Peckett (1990)	0-4-0ST	1940
Beatty	—	H/Leslie (3240)	0-4-0ST	1917
—	MP1	Barclay (1944)	0-4-0F	1944
Tom	27414	N/British (27414)	0-4-0DH	1954
—	D2959	R/Hornsby (382824)	4wDM	1955
Folly	—	R/Hornsby (183062)	4wDM	1937
—	—	R/Hornsby (525947)	0-4-0DH	1968
Joanna	—	T/Hill (177C)	0-4-0DM	1967
		rebuild of Sentinel (9401) 0-4-0ST of 1950		
—	—	YEC (2630)	0-6-0DE	1956
—	—	YEC (2687)	0-4-0DE	1968
Thomas	—*	Kierstead	4wVBT	1979

*2ft gauge

England

Internet address: *Web site:* www.telfordsteamrailway.co.uk
On site facilities: Extensive model railway display, tea room, picnic area, children's play equipment, narrow gauge steam tramway, miniature railway operated by Phoenix Model Engineers (separate charge); ticket gives unlimited travel (except miniature railway)
Public opening: Every Sunday and Bank Holiday from Easter until last Sunday in September including Bank Holidays 11.00-16.30. Last Sunday in month steam-hauled and also steam on Bank Holidays and all Sundays in August, but steam tram every Sunday. Also pre-

Stock
2 ex-BR Mk 1 coaches; 1 ex-BR Mk 3 sleeper; 1 ex-GWR auto-trailer; 1 ex-GWR Toad brake van; 1 ex-GWR 3-ton hand crane; 1 Wickham trolley; Permaquip PW transporter vehicle No 68800; various wagons

Christmas weekends in December when Thomas the Tank pays a visit
Special events: Easter Bunnies — 11/12 April; 150th Anniversary Celebration — 2-4 May; Murder Mystery — 24/25 May; Model Gala — 19 July; Teddy Bears' Picnic — 30/31 August; Diesel Day — 13 September; Day out with Thomas Santa Specials — 4-6, 12/13, 19/20 December (subject to confirmation)
Facilities for disabled: Limited,

see below, or Accessibility on web site.
Mk 1 coaches are not really suitable for wheelchair access, DMUs when in service on diesel days have ramped brake van access. Small chairs can be accommodated in GWR brake van, platforms have easy access and shop, although steep ramp at Horsehay & Dawley. Tea room and model railway have level access

---

Museum — Tiverton Museum of Mid Devon Life — Devon

The Museum, dominated by No 1442, affectionately known as the 'Tivvy Bumper', houses a large collection of railway relics
Location: Tiverton, Devon
OS reference: SS 955124
Operating society/organisation: Tiverton & Mid Devon Museum Trust, Beck's Square, Tiverton, Devon EX16 6PJ
Telephone: (01884) 256295
Car park: Short term in Beck's Square, long term in multi-storey

Locomotive

Name	No	Origin	Class	Type	Built
(Tivvy Bumper)	1442	GWR	1400	0-4-2T	1935

Access by public transport: Rail to Tiverton Parkway, then by bus, or bus from Exeter
On site facilities: Museum, shop and toilets
Public opening:
February to Christmas:
Monday to Friday — 10.30-16.30;

Saturdays — 10.00-13.00; closed Sundays
Special notes: Disabled access to view locomotive. The transport gallery re-opened in April 2006 following re-display

---

Steam Centre — Tyseley Locomotive Works — Birmingham

Member: HRA
Location: 670 Warwick Road (A41), Tyseley, Birmingham B11 2HL
OS reference: SP 105841
Operating organisation: Tyseley Locomotive Works Ltd
Supporting society: Vintage Trains Society
Telephone: (0121) 708 4960
Fax: (0121) 708 4963
Internet address: *e-mail:* vintagetrains@btconnect.com
Web site: www.vintagetrains.co.uk/brm.htm
Car park: Site

Locomotives

Name	No	Origin	Class	Type	Built
Kinlet Hall	4936	GWR	'Hall'	4-6-0	1929
Pitchford Hall	4953	GWR	'Hall'	4-6-0	1929
Rood Ashton Hall	4965	GWR	'Hall'	4-6-0	1929
Nunney Castle	5029	GWR	'Castle	4-6-0	1934
Earl of Mount Edgcumbe	5043	GWR	'Castle	4-6-0	1936
Defiant†	5080	GWR	'Castle'	4-6-0	1939
Clun Castle	7029	GWR	'Castle'	4-6-0	1950
—	4110	GWR	5101	2-6-2T	1937
—	4121	GWR	5101	2-6-2T	1937
—	7752	GWR	5700	0-6-0PT	1930
—	7760	GWR	5700	0-6-0PT	1930
—	9600	GWR	5700	0-6-0PT	1945
Kolhapur§	5593	LMS	'Jubilee'	4-6-0	1934
Duchess of Hamilton	46229	LMS	'Duchess'	4-6-2	1939

Access by public transport:
Travel West Midlands route No 37 from city centre. Main line rail service to Tyseley station (Central Trains and Chiltern Railways)
On site facilities: The Museum is on the site of a former GWR/BR steam shed and has been equipped with specialised railway engineering machinery. It carries out many contract repairs to steam locomotives and rolling stock. Souvenir shop, passenger demonstration line and station
Refreshment facilities: Available in visitor centre
Length of line: Third of a mile
Public opening: Weekends only 10.00-16.00.
Special events: 'Shakespeare Express' runs from July to September 2009. Running from Birmingham Snow Hill to Stratford-upon-Avon twice daily
Special notes: Tyseley is a centre for 'Steam on the Main Line' railtours over a large area of the national rail network
Membership details: Membership is available to the public, providing free entry to site events and four copies of *Steam in Trust* magazine
Facilities for disabled: Disabled access to 'Shakespeare Express' available, but must be notified in advance
Note: All attractions and facilities are advertised subject to availability

Name	No	Origin	Class	Type	Built
—	670	LNWR*	Bloomer	2-2-2	1986
—	13029	BR	08	0-6-0DE	1953
—	20059	BR	20	Bo-Bo	1961
—	20177	BR	20	Bo-Bo	1966
—	37264	BR	37	Co-Co	1965
County of Essex	47732	BR	47	Co-Co	1964
Great Western	47770	BR	47	Co-Co	1964
The Queen Mother	47773	BR	47	Co-Co	1964
Royal Oak	50017	BR	55	Co-Co	1968
Rodney	50021	BR	55	Co-Co	1968
Glorious	50033	BR	55	Co-Co	1968
Les Ross	86259	BR	86	Bo-Bo	1965
Hal o' the Wind	87031	BR	87	Bo-Bo	1973
—	993	RR	7A	4-8-0	1896

*replica built at Tyseley Locomotive Works
†on loan to Buckinghamshire Railway Centre
§on loan to Barrow Hill Roundhouse

Industrial locomotives

Name	No	Builder	Type	Built
Cadbury No 1	—	Avonside (1977)	0-4-0T	1925
—	1	Peckett (2004)	0-4-0ST	1942
—	—	Baguley (800)	0-4-0PE	1920
Fred	—	RSH (7289)	0-6-0ST	1945

Note: Not all locomotives are on site, and some are undergoing restoration. Contract restoration work includes Nos (GWR) 5029, (LMS) 46229 (for streamlining), and GWR steam railmotor and industrial RSH 7289/1945; locomotives away on loan include 5593 and *Henry* (Barrow Hill), 5080 (Buckinghamshire)

Stock
22 BR Mk 2 coaches, 3 BR Mk 1 coaches, 3 BR Mk 1 Pullman Cars, goods and departmental vehicles, steam and diesel cranes

Owner
993 on loan from the National Railway Museum

Museum	# Vintage Carriages Trust # Museum of Rail Travel	West Yorkshire

Member: HRA, TT, AIM, ABTEM
A fascinating collection of elderly railway carriages and small locomotives, interestingly presented. Sit in a fully restored, prize winning 1876-built Manchester, Sheffield & Lincolnshire Railway carriage or relive the dark days of wartime travel in one of the three Metropolitan Railway carriages. Listen to the 'Travellers' Tales' and view the collection of railway posters and other items. Video presentation. The carriages and locomotives have appeared in over 60 cinema and television productions including:
Housewife, 49 (2006), *Booze Cruise 3* (2005), *North & South* (2004), *The Railway Children* (1970 and 1968 versions)
Location: Museum of Rail Travel, Ingrow Station Yard, Halifax Road, Keighley, West Yorkshire BD21 5EH.
On the A629 road
Operations Manager:
David N. Carr, Hon Secretary, VCT
Operating society/organisation:
Vintage Carriages Trust (a Registered Charity No 510776)
Telephone:
Keighley (01535) 680425
Fax: (01535) 610796
Internet address: *e-mail:* admin@vintagecarriagestrust.org
Web site:
www.vintagecarriagestrust.org
   Web site includes two databases: over 5,000 preserved carriages, with over 4,000 images.
over 1,000 preserved wagons, with over 400 images.
Car Park: On site. Also coach parking at Ingrow station
Access by public transport:

Northern Rail through trains from Carlisle, Settle, Morecambe, Lancaster to Keighley (one mile). Fast and frequent Metro Train services from Bradford Forster Square, Leeds, Shipley, and Skipton to Keighley. Then either KWVR train to Ingrow West (adjacent) or buses 500, 502, 663, 664, 665, 696, 697 and 720 from Keighley bus station.

Buses: Keighley & District 500 from Hebden Bridge (daily). First Calderline 502 from Halifax (Sundays only). Keighley & District buses 696 and 697 from Bradford via Thornton and Denholme. Tel: (0113) 245 7676 for bus and Metro Train information or log onto VCT web site for internet links to timetables and route map

On site facilities: Transport relics shop specialising in out of print magazines, secondhand railway books and models. Hot and cold drinks, ice cream and chocolate available. Toilets with full disabled access. A determined effort has been made to provide a museum which will interest the casual visitor who is not knowledgeable about railways

Public opening:
Daily 11.00-16.30, openings outside these times can be arranged for groups.
Closed 25 December
Facilities for disabled: The museum building is level with easy access for wheelchair users. A stairlift has been provided to allow wheelchair users to view carriage interiors, and enter guards' brake

Stock

Railway	BR or previous owner Number	Type	Date built	Seats	Weight	Length
MS&LR	176	4-wheel 1st/2nd/3rd/ luggage	1876	34	12T	28ft 0in
GNR	589	6-wheel 3rd brake	1888	40	14T	34ft 11in
MR	358	6-wheel 1st/3rd/ luggage	1886	32	15T	34ft 0in
Met	427	BS	1910	84	30T	54ft 0in
Met	465	S	1919	108	30T	54ft 0in
Met	509	F	1923	84	30T	54ft 0in
SR (SECR)	S3554S	BSK	1924	42	33T	65ft 3in
BR (SR)	S1469S	TSO	1951	64	32T	67ft 1in
GN	2856	Non vestibule composite, lav brake	1898	34	22T	45ft 0in

Industrial locomotives

Name	No	Builder	Type	Built
Bellerophon*	—	Haydock Foundry (C)	0-6-0WT	1874
Sir Berkeley†	—	M/Wardle (1210)	0-6-0ST	1891
Lord Mayor	—	H/Clarke (402)	0-4-0ST	1893

*on loan to the Foxfield Railway for 10 years
†on 10 year loan to Middleton Railway

areas, though naturally wheelchairs are too wide to enter individual passenger compartments. Toilets with full access for wheelchair users. Braille leaflet, guidebook and audio tape for loan during visit. Wheelchair available for loan.
  Winner of the 1998 Adapt Museum Award for best practice in access for disabled and older people. Runners up for the 1998 Yorkshire Electricity/Yorkshire &

Humberside Museums Council Access Awards. Highly commended in the 1999 White Rose Tourism For All Awards
Special notes: Free admission to holders of Worth Valley Railway 'Day Rover' tickets — otherwise small admission charge
Membership details: Membership Secretary, c/o above address
Marketing names: Vintage Carriages Trust or VCT

Timetable Service	Volks Electric Railway	East Sussex

Member: HRA
In 1883 Magnus Volk opened an electric powered railway along the seafront at Brighton. It was the first 'proper' electric railway in Britain. Today it holds the deserved position of being the oldest remaining operating electric railway in the world
Manager: Stuart Strong
Headquarters: Quality of Life & Green Spaces, Brighton & Hove

Motor cars

Nos	Type	Seats	Body	Built
3, 4	Semi-opens	40	—	1892
5	Winter car		—	1930
6, 7, 8	Semi-opens	40	—	1901
9	Open	40	—	1910
10	Open	40	—	1926

City Council, Kings House, Grand Avenue, Hove BN3 2LS
Office/Works: 285 Madeira Drive,

Brighton BN2 1EN
Telephone:
01273 292718 (railway)

Internet address: *Web site:* www.brighton-hove.gov.uk or the Volks Electric Railway Association web site: www.volkselectricrailway.co.uk
Main stations: Aquarium, Black Rock (5min walk from Marina)
Other public stations: Peter Pan's Playground
Car parks: Along the Promenade and town centre car parks

Access by public transport: By rail: main line services to Brighton
Bus services: No 7 from station to Marina (every 7min) then short walk to Black Rock station
Depot: Peter Pan's Playground
Length of line: Approx 1 mile, 2ft 8.5in gauge
Period of public operations: Easter to mid-September

Weekdays (10.00-17.00)
Weekends (10.00-18.00)
All days subject to weather conditions
Facilities for disabled: Disabled toilets in Black Rock station building and 50yd from Aquarium. Disabled access to stations and trains

---

| Heritage Site | Waltham Abbey Royal Gunpowder Mills | Essex |

Member: HRA
The Royal Gunpowder Mills at Waltham Abbey are set in 175 acres of natural and peaceful parkland with 21 buildings of major historical importance
Location: Royal Gunpowder Mills, Beaulieu Drive, Waltham Abbey, Essex EN9 1JY
Telephone: 01992 707370
Fax: 01992 707372
Internet address: *e-mail:* info@royalgunpowdermills.com
Web site: www.royalgunpowdermills.com
OS reference: TL 387011
Car parking: Free on site
Cycle parking: Cycle shed is available to secure bicycles
Access by car: Just off jct 26 on M25, follow A121 towards Waltham Abbey, cross traffic lights into Beaulieu Drive
Access by public transport:
By rail: trains from London Liverpool Street and Tottenham Hale Underground station to Waltham Cross, then 25min walk or short bus ride, routes 21, 212, 231, 240, 250, 505 and 517 (5min walk)
On site facilities: Toilets, cafe, baby changing. Bench style seats and picnic tables around the site
Depots: 2ft 6in gauge on western boundary, 1ft 6in gauge on eastern boundary (under construction)
Length of line: 2ft 6in gauge under construction, 1ft 6in gauge to follow
Period of public operation:

Industrial locomotives

Name	No	Builder	Type	Built
—	—*+	Clayton (B3482A)	0-4-0BE	1988
—	—*	Hunslet (8828)	0-4-0DH	1988
—	—*	Ruhrthaler (3920)	0-4-0DH	1969
—	—†	G/Batley (6099)	2w-2DE	1964
Budleigh	—§	R/Hornsby (235624)	4wDM	1945
Carnegie	—§	Hunslet (4524)	0-4-0+0-4-0DM	1954
Woolwich	—§	Avonside (1748)	0-4-0T	1916

*2ft 6in gauge
†3ft 0in gauge
§1ft 6 in gauge
+stored off-site

Rolling stock
Selection of wagons of the above gauges

Other exhibits
Boiler from *Mars* (Vulcan 1160 of 1885, 1ft 6in gauge) from Museum of Army Transport.
Cast iron tramway plates, c1880, from Woolwich Arsenal (1ft 6in gauge)

Weekends and Bank Holidays 25 April to 27 September. Wednesdays during school summer holidays.
11.00-17.00, last entry 15.30. It is suggested that 3-4 hours are allowed for the visit. Comfortable walking shoes recommended
Special events: Steam Fair — 16/17 May (please see web site). Demonstration freight trains run most weekends in season
Special facilities: Guided group visits available on Tuesdays and Wednesdays by appointment,

minimum group size applies. Lecture Theatre and Saltpetre House available for meetings
Facilities for disabled: A Land Train can accommodate wheelchairs (please check availability on arrival). Only guide and assistant dogs will be allowed on site, and must remain harnessed during visit
Membership details: Volunteers welcome, please ring Volunteer Manager on 01992 707340

152

Member: HRA

The line was originally built by the Stockton & Darlington Railway in 1847 to transport limestone to the ironworks of Teesside, and by 1895 had been extended to its final terminus of Wearhead. Although the passenger service was withdrawn in 1953, the line was retained for freight use transporting bulk cement from the Blue Circle works at Eastgate. This use also ceased in 1993, so the line was mothballed and threatened with lifting. 1993 saw the formation of the Weardale Railway with services re-commencing in 2004. Despite a financial setback in 2005/6, trains have been running regularly since August 2006 with many special events complementing the normal train service

General Manager: G. Lord

Headquarters: Weardale Railways CIC, Stanhope Station, Station Road, Stanhope, Bishop Auckland, Co Durham DL13 2YS

Telephone: 01388 526203

Internet addresses: *e-mail:* info@weardale-railway.org.uk

Web site: www.weardale-railway.org.uk

Main stations: Wolsingham and Stanhope

Other public stations: Frosterley

Car park: Limited parking at each station

Access by public transport: Buses from Bishop Auckland and Crook daily. Main line station at Bishop Auckland

Refreshment facilities: Stanhope (the Signal Box Café) in station building with light refreshments

Locomotives and multiple-units

Name	No	Origin	Class	Type	Built
—	20107	BR	20	Bo-Bo	1961
—	37414	BR	37	Co-Co	1965
—	56022	BR	56	Co-Co	1976
—	73103	BR	73	Bo-Bo	1966
—	73104	BR	73	Bo-Bo	1966
—	51356	P/Steel	117	DMBS	1959
—	51392	P/Steel	117	DMS	1959
—	59492	P/Steel	117	TCL	1960
—	55503	BR	141	DMS	1984
—	55510	BR	141	DMS	1984
—	55523	BR	141	DMSL	1984
—	55530	BR	141	DMSL	1984

Industrial locomotives

Name	No	Builder	Type	Built
—	3809	Hunslet (3809)	0-6-0ST	1953
—	7412	RSH	0-6-0ST	1948
—	7765	RSH (7765)	0-6-0T	1954
—	—	E/Electric (3870)	6wDH	1969
—	653*	E/Electric	6wDH	1956
—	—	R/Royce (10077)	4wDH	1961
—	—	R/Royce (10187)	6wDH	1964
—	—	R/Royce (10197)	4wDH	1965
—	—	R/Royce (10232)	4wDH	1965

*former Netherlands Railway locomotive

Owners

56022 ECT Mainline Trains

Souvenir shop: Stanhope (in station building)

Depot: Wolsingham (no public access)

Length of line: Present length in 5.5 miles, Wolsingham to Stanhope. 18.5 miles when fully opened, Bishop Auckland to Eastgate

Period of public operation: A mixture of weekends and daily operating throughout the year. For full details telephone or access web site as above

Special events: Mother's Day, Father's Day, Commercial Vehicle Rallies, Classic Car Rallies, and Santa Specials. See timetable/leaflet for full details

Membership details: Mr Frank Holmes, Membership Secretary, Weardale Railway Trust, at above address. Tel: 01388 526203

Membership journal: *Between the Lines* — quarterly

Member: HRA, TT

One man's railway, the life and love of retired naval commander, Roy Francis, this delightful line which is totally uncommercialised runs along the old Wells branch to Walsingham where the old station has been transformed into a Russian Orthodox Church by the addition of an onion-shaped dome to its roof. A must if you find yourself nearby

Location: On A149, Stiffkey Road,

England

Wells next the Sea, Norfolk
General Manager: Lt-Cdr R. W. Francis
Operating organisation: Wells & Walsingham Light Railway, Wells next the Sea, Norfolk NR23 1GB
Enquiries: 01328 711630
Internet address: *Web site:* www.wellswalsinghamrailway.co.uk
Car park: Yes
Access by public transport: Eastern Counties and Coast Hopper buses
On site facilities: Souvenir shop,

toilets and tea shop
Length of line: 4 miles, 10.25in gauge
Public opening: Daily Good Friday to the end of October
Special notes: Journey may be commenced at either end. Believed to be the world's longest 10.25in gauge line. Built on the old Wells & Fakenham Railway trackbed. Old Swainsthorpe signalbox on site at Wells. Motive power is provided by a Garratt and a tram locomotive.
Life passes in the form of a gilt

edged enamel medallion now available, please enquire for details
Facilities for disabled: Disabled can be seated in normal carriages and wheelchairs carried in luggage van. Occupied wheelchairs cannot be carried due to limitations of track gauge
Membership details: Membership Secretary, Wells & Walsingham Light Railway Support Group, c/o above address
Membership journal: Newsletter — quarterly

Timetable Service — Wensleydale Railway — North Yorkshire

Member: HRA

The Wensleydale Railway Association was formed in 1990 with a view to restoring the route from Northallerton to Garsdale. In 2000 agreement was reached to transfer the remaining 22 miles of line from Northallerton to Redmire to Wensleydale Railway plc. In 2003 services started between Leeming Bar and Redmire. Medium-term plans are to extend eastwards to Northallerton and in the west from Redmire and then on towards Aysgarth. The ultimate aim is to restore the entire route from Northallerton to Garsdale
Contact address:
Wensleydale Railway plc, Leeming Bar Station, Leases Road, Leeming Bar, Northallerton DL7 9AR
Ticketline: 08454 505474
Fax: 01677 427029
Internet addresses: *e-mail:* admin@wensleydalerailway.com
Web site: www.wensleydalerailway.com
Main stations: Leeming Bar and Leyburn
Other stations: Bedale, Finghall and Redmire
Car Parking: On site
Access by public transport: Yes
Refreshment facilities: Leeming Bar and Leyburn
Souvenir shops: Leeming Bar and Leyburn
Depots: Leeming Bar
Length of line: 22 miles (18 additional miles to rebuild)

Locomotives and multiple-units

Name	No	Origin	Class	Type	Built
Western Waggoner	D2114	BR	03	0-6-0DM	1961
—	47715	BR	47	Co-Co	1966
—	51210	BR	101	DMBS	1958
—	51247	BR	101	DMBS	1958
—	51400	BR	117	DMBS	1959
—	53746	BR	101	DMC	1957
—	59500	BR	117	TSL	1959
—	59509	BR	117	TSL	1959
—	51572	BR	108	DMC	1960
—	51813	BRCW	110	DMBC	1961
—	51842	BRCW	110	DMCL	1961
—	59701	BRCW	110	TSL	1961

Industrial locomotive

Name	No	Builder	Type	Built
Wensley	—	R/Hornsby (476141)	4wDM	1963

Owners

Class 101 and 117 by Wensleydale Railway plc
Class 110 by Allan Schofield
R/Hornsby by the Wensleydale Railway Association
D2144 the UK Government
Class 108 by Wallington Bros

Passenger trains: Normally DMU. Steam (provisional) in August and/or September
Period of public operation: Weekends and Bank Holidays after 1 March; daily June to September. Also Santa Specials. See web site or phone 08454 505474 for more information
Special events: Day out with Thomas (phone for details, or see web site)
Facilities for disabled: Ramp to facilitate access to trains.

All platforms are wheelchair friendly. Disabled toilets project ongoing
Membership details: Wensleydale Railway Association, c/o above address
Membership journal: *Relay* – 3 per year.
Special notes: Very helpful tourist information centre at Leyburn – tel 01969 623069 – will deal with a wide range of enquiries including Wensleydale Railway matters

West Lancashire Light Railway

Member: HRA

The WLLR is located in the village of Hesketh Bank, midway between Preston and Southport. Built by enthusiasts in 1967 in an endeavour to conserve some of the mainly industrial equipment that was fast disappearing. The railway serves as a working museum for a variety of historic locomotives and other railway equipment from industrial sites from Britain and overseas

Location: Alty's Brickworks, Station Road, Hesketh Bank, Nr Preston, Lancashire PR4 6SP

OS reference: SD 448229

Operating society/organisation: The West Lancashire Light Railway Trust, Secretary, 8 Croft Avenue, Orrell, Wigan, Lancs WN5 8TW

Telephone: (01772) 815881 Railway (24hr) or (01695) 622654 Secretary (evenings)

Internet address:
e-mail: secretary@westlancs.org
Web site: www.westlancs.org

Car parks: On site

Access by public transport: Main line rail to Preston or Southport. Bus route — service 2, between Preston and Southport

On site facilities: Gift shop, light refreshments, picnic tables, 2ft gauge line

Public opening: Steam trains operate Sundays 5 April to last Sunday in October inclusive. Opening times 12.30-17.30

Special events: Friendly Engines Day — 5 April; Teddy Bears' Outing — 10 May; Gala Weekend — 8/9 August; Autumn Steam Gala — 4 October; Children-in-Need — 15 November; Santa Specials — 13, 19/20 December.

Membership details: The Hon

Industrial locomotives

Name	No	Builder	Type	Built
Clwyd	1	R/Hornsby (264251)	4wDM	1951
Tawd	2	R/Hornsby (222074)	4wDM	1943
Irish Mail	3	Hunslet (823)	0-4-0ST	1903
Bradfield	4	Hibberd (1777)	4wPM	1931
—	5	R/Hornsby (200478)	4wDM	1940
—	7	M/Rail (8992)	4wDM	1946
Pathfinder	8	H/Hunslet (4480)	4wDM	1953
Joffre	9	K/Stuart (2405)	0-6-0T	1915
—	10	Hibberd (2555)	4wDM	1946
—	11	M/Rail (5906)	4wDM	1934
—	16	R/Hornsby (202036)	4wDM	1941
—	19	Lister (10805)	4wPM	1939
—	20	Baguley (3002)	4wPM	1937
—	21	H/Hunslet (1963)	4wDM	1939
—	25	R/Hornsby (297054)	4wDM	1950
Mill Reef	27	M/Rail (7371)	4wDM	1939
—	30	M/Rail (11258)	4wDM	1964
—	32	M/Rail (11246)	4wDM	1963
Montalban	34	O&K (6641)	0-4-0WT	1913
Utrillas	35	O&K (2378)	0-4-0WT	1907
—	36	R/Hornsby (339105)	4wDM	1953
—	38	Hudswell (D750)	0-4-0DM	1949
—	39	Hibberd (3916)	4wDM	1959
—	40	R/Hornsby (381705)	4wDM	1959
—	41	Lister (29890)	4wPM	1946
—	43	Greenbat (1840)	4wBE	1942
Welsh Pony	44	Wingrove (640)	4wWE	1926
—	45	Chrzanow (3506)	0-6-0T+WT	1957
Stanhope	46	K/Stuart (2395)	0-4-2ST	1917
—	47	Henschel (14676)	0-8-0T	1917
—	48	Fowler (15513)	0-4-2T	1920
—	49	Hibberd (1887)	4wDM	1934

Stock

Toastrack coach built 1986 by WLLR
Semi-open coach built 1993 by WLLR
Brake van built 1987 by WLLR
Large collection of goods rolling stock

Secretary, WLLR, Station Road, Hesketh Bank, Nr Preston, Lancashire PR4 6SP

West Somerset Railway

Member: HRA, TT

Running for 20 miles, the WSR is Britain's longest standard gauge heritage line and superbly captures

the secondary main line atmosphere of the great age of steam. There are many points of railway interest. Williton signalbox is the only

working example built by the Bristol & Exeter Railway and Blue Anchor box still controls a traditionally operated level crossing. Destinations served include the historic port of Watchet and medieval Dunster with its castle

General Manager: Paul Conibeare

Headquarters: West Somerset Railway, The Railway Station, Minehead, Somerset TA24 5BG

Telephone:
Minehead (01643) 704996

Internet address: *e-mail:*
info@west-somerset-railway.co.uk
Web site:
www.west-somerset-railway.co.uk
WAP-phone:
www.wapdrive.com/wsrwap/

Main station: Minehead

Other public stations: Dunster, Blue Anchor, Washford, Watchet, Williton, Doniford Halt, Stogumber, Crowcombe, Bishops Lydeard

OS reference: Minehead SS 975463, Williton ST 085416, Bishops Lydeard ST 164290

Car parks: Free parking at Bishops Lydeard, Crowcombe Heathfield, Stogumber, Williton and Dunster. Pay & display at Minehead and Watchet. No parking at Doniford Halt

Access by public transport: First service 28 runs from Taunton bus station and Taunton railway station to Bishops Lydeard. During galas free bus services operate from Taunton railway station, town centre and Silk Mills park and ride to Bishops Lydeard (see web sites for details)

Refreshment facilities: Minehead, Bishops Lydeard (limited opening). Dining Trains from Bishops Lydeard (01823 433856). Please contact for dates, reservations essential.

Buffet car on most steam trains

Souvenir shops: Large shops at Bishops Lydeard (01823 432125) and Minehead (01643 700387). Sales counters at other stations except Doniford Halt. 'Readers Halt' secondhand stall at Minehead

Museum: Somerset & Dorset Railway Museum Trust, Washford (contact 01984 640869 for opening times). GWR Museum at Blue Anchor (open Sundays and Bank Holidays during main WSR operating season plus Gala events). Gauge Museum at Bishops Lydeard (open daily). Diesel Heritage Visitor Centre open Saturdays May-September, plus during Gala

Locomotives and multiple-units

Name	No	Origin	Class	Type	Built
—	88	S&DJR	7F	2-8-0	1925
—	2874*	GWR	2800	2-8-0	1918
—	3850	GWR	2884	2-8-0	1942
—	4160	GWR	5101	2-6-2T	1948
—	4561	GWR	4500	2-6-2T	1924
—	9351	GWR	9351	2-6-0	2004
—	5542†	GWR	4575	2-6-2T	1928
—	6412	GWR	6400	0-6-0PT	1934
Dinmore Manor	7820	GWR	'Manor'	4-6-0	1950
Ditcheat Manor	7821	GWR	'Manor'	4-6-0	1950
Odney Manor	7828	GWR	'Manor'	4-6-0	1950
Braunton	34046	SR	WC	4-6-2	1946
—	D2119	BR	03	0-6-0DM	1959
—	D2133	BR	03	0-6-0DM	1959
—	D2271	BR	04	0-6-0DM	1952
—	D3462	BR	08	0-6-0DE	1957
—	D9526	BR	14	0-6-0DH	1964
—	25173	BR	25	Bo-Bo	1963
—	D6566	BR	33	Bo-Bo	1961
—	33057	BR	33	Bo-Bo	1961
—	D7017	BR	35	B-B	1962
—	D7018	BR	35	B-B	1962
North Star	D1661	BR	47	Co-Co	1965
Western Campaigner	D1010	BR	52	C-C	1962
—	50222	BR	101	DMBS	19??
—	50338	BR	101	DMC	19??
—	51663	BR	115	DMBS	1960
—	51852	BR	115	DMBS	1960
—	51859	BR	115	DMBS	1960
—	51880	BR	115	DMBS	1960
—	51887	BR	115	DMBS	1960
—	59506	BR	117	TC	1960
—	59678	BR	115	TC	1960

Note: 9351 rebuilt from '5151' class 2-6-2T No 5193
†on Gloucestershire Warwickshire Railway during 2009
*may not be on site for all of 2009

Industrial locomotives

Name	No	Builder	Type	Built
Kilmersdon	—	Peckett (1788)	0-4-0ST	1929
—	24	Ruston (210479)	4wDM	1941
—	—	Ruston (183062)	4wDM	1937
—	16	Sentinel (10175)	0-6-0DH	1964

Stock

23 ex-BR Mk 1 coaches; 2 ex-BR Restaurant cars; 1 ex-BR Sleeping car; 3 ex-S&DJR 6-wheel coaches, 7 ex-GWR camping coaches; 1 ex-GWR Sleeping coach; 1 ex-GWR 5-ton hand crane; more than 40 freight vehicles. *a return of some of these ex-GWR Toplight coaches to form a working vintage train is being planned by the west Somerset Steam Railway Trust. Details from Williton Station, Somerset TA4 4RQ

Owners

88, *Kilmersdon* the Somerset & Dorset Museum Trust
D1010, D7017, D7018 and D9526 the Diesel and Electric Preservation Group
D2119, D3462 and 25173 Dr John F. Kennedy
5542 the 5542 Ltd
3850 and 7820 the Dinmore Manor Locomotive Ltd
4160 the 4160 Ltd
2874, 7828, 9351 and D2271 the WSR plc

events
Depots: Bishops Lydeard, Williton, Washford, Minehead
Length of line: 20 miles
Passenger trains: Steam and diesel trains to Bishops Lydeard
Period of public operation: 7/8, 14/15, 21/22 26-29 March; 1/2, 4/5, 7-19, 21-23, 25/26, 28-30 April, daily 1 May to 4 October (except 8, 15 May), 6-8, 10/11, 13-15, 17/18, 20-22, 24-31 October, 1/2, 7/8 November, 4-6, 12-16, 19/20, 23/24 December, 27 December to 3 January 2010
Main special events: Spring Steam Gala — 21/22, 26-29 March (advance booking strongly recommended); Mixed Traffic Weekend — 12-14 June (advance booking recommended); Day out with Thomas — 4/5 July; Steam Fayre & Vintage Rally at Bishops Lydeard — 1/2 August; Toy and Collector's Fair— 3 August; Autumn Steam Gala — 1-4 October (advance booking strongly recommended); Somerset in Autumn — 24/25 October (advance booking recommended); Dunster by Candlelight — 4/5 December (advance booking essential); Santa Specials — 5/6, 12/13, 19/20, 23/24 December (advance booking essential); Carol Trains — 14-16 December (advance booking essential); Winter Steam Festival — 29/30 December
Other special events: Details on application
Facilities for disabled: Trains have limited accommodation for passengers in wheelchairs. There is level or ramped access to all stations except Doniford, and RADAR key access toilets at Bishops Lydeard and Minehead. Advance booking essential for groups
Special facilities: Conference room in Gauge Museum at Bishops Lydeard (details 01643 433856); Steam footplate experience courses (01643 700398)
Membership details: West Somerset Railway Association, The Railway Station, Bishops Lydeard, Taunton TA4 3BX.
Tel: 01823 433856
Membership journal: *WSR Journal* — quarterly
Other information: Vintage bus links run between Dunster station and the village on Bank Holiday Sundays and Mondays plus Saturday and Sunday of Spring and Autumn Steam Galas, Mixed Traffic Weekend and Somerset in Autumn

Whitwell & Reepham Station

Railway Centre — Norfolk

The station was opened at the end of February 2009, the 50th anniversary of the closure of the line to passenger services on the former Midland & Great Northern Joint Railway. At the time of writing normal opening times have yet to be confirmed but it is expected that at the very least the station will be open at weekends. Please check the web site for confirmation
Location: Whitwell Road, Reepham, Norfolk NR10 4RA
SatNav postcode: NR10 4RA
Operating society/organisation: Whitwell & Reepham Railway Society

Industrial locomotive

Name	No	Builder	Type	Built
—	7	B/Drewry (3733)	4wDH	1977

Stock
2 BR Mk 1 coaches, bogie brake and BR box van

Contact: Mike Urry
Telephone: (01603) 871694
Fax: (01603) 875101
Internet addresses:
e-mail: mike@whitwellstation.com
Web site: www.whitwellstation.com
On site facilities: Car park, shop and museum under development
Access by public transport: There is no access to the site by public transport
Length of line: A 1,500 ft running line is under construction
Public opening: Please visit web site to confirm
Membership details: Membership Secretary, c/o above address
Membership journal: Quarterly

Winchcombe Railway Museum

Museum — Glos

One mile from Winchcombe station on the Gloucestershire Warwickshire railway, the diverse collection includes signalling equipment, lineside fixtures, horse-drawn road vehicles, tickets, lamps, etc. Indoor and outdoor displays set in half an acre of traditional Victorian Cotswold garden. Visitors are encouraged to touch and operate exhibits
Location: 23 Gloucester Street, Winchcombe, Gloucestershire
OS reference: SP 023283
Operating society/organisation: Winchcombe Railway Museum Association, 23 Gloucester Street, Winchcombe, Gloucestershire
Telephone: Winchcombe (01242) 609305
Internet address: *e-mail:*

timpetchey@btconnect.com
Car park: On street at entrance
Access by public transport: Bus service from Cheltenham operated by Castleways Ltd
On site facilities: Relics and souvenir shop
Public opening: Easter to end October 2009.
Wednesdays, Thursdays, Fridays, weekends and Bank Holiday Mondays — 13.30-17.00; daily throughout August, 13.30-17.00
Facilities for disabled: Access to all parts except toilets
Special notes: Many visitor-operated exhibits, picnic area

Steam Centre — Windmill Farm Railway — Lancashire

The line was set up in 1997 by Austin Moss as a place to store and operate the historic engines and rolling stock he had collected. Of particular interest is the collection of ex-Fairbourne Railway locomotives and rolling stock; these include *Katie* and *Whippet Quick*.
Location: Situated within the grounds of Windmill Animal Farm
Headquarters: Windmill Animal Farm, Red Cat Lane, Burscough, L40 1UQ
Contact: Austin Moss
Telephone: Farm 01704 892282; Austin Moss 07971 221343;
Internet address: *Web site:* www.windmillfarmrailway.co.uk
Main station: At Farm
Other station: Lakeview, 1/2 mile away
Car parking: On site
Access by public transport: None
On site facilities: Farm café, shop
Depots: At farm site
Length of line: 1/2 mile each way (1 mile return) 15in gauge
Period of public operation: 14 February to Christmas 10.00-

Industrial locomotives

Name	No	Builder	Type	Built
Blue Pacific	4	Guinness	4-6-0VB	1935
Whippet Quick	–	Lister	4w-4DM	1935
Gwril	–	Lister	4wPM	1943
Princess Anne	—	Barlow	4-6w-2DE	1948
Duke of Edinburgh	—	Barlow	4-6-2	1950
Prince Charles	—	Barlow	4-6-2	1950
Katie	—	Guest	2-4-2	1953
Siân	—	Guest	2-4-2	1963
Connie	_	Severn-Lamb	2-8-0DH	1974
Neptune / (St Nicholas)	_	Severn-Lamb	2-8-0GH	1978
–	14	Walker	2w-2PM	1985
City Of London Jubilee	2870	Volante	4-6-0DH	1987
'The Bar Stool'	—	Moss	2w-2PM	1989
St Christopher	—	Exmoor	2-6-2T	2001

17.00. Weekends March to December. Daily Easter to end of September plus school holidays. Santa weekends in December, Daily June to September plus school holidays
Trains every 1/2 hour from 11.00 until 16.30
Special events: None planned but see web site

Facilities for disabled: Accessibility for wheelchairs around farm facilities etc, prior warning on railway
Membership details: No membership as such, just volunteer. Contact Austin Moss for details
Fare: £1.00 adults, 75p children plus farm entry fee.

Timetable Service — Wirral Transport Museum — Merseyside

The museum and tramway are owned by Wirral Borough Council and run by employees assisted by volunteers. The tramway licence is also held by the council as are two Hong Kong-built 4-wheel trams. The museum houses several locally rebuilt trams owned by the Merseyside Tramway Preservation Society which are used in turn with the Hong Kong trams. The museum also contains numerous local buses, cars, lorries, motorbikes etc, and a 1930s garage scene.
Location/Headquarters: Wirral Transport Museum, 1 Taylor Street, Birkenhead, Wirral CH45 8NX
Telephone: 0151 647 2128

Trams

No	Trucks	Builder	Date
69		Hong Kong	1992
70		Hong Kong	1992

Fax: As above, but must ring first
Internet address: *e-mail:* birkenheadtram@tiscali.co.uk
Web site: www.wirraltransportmuseum.org
Car parking: Pay & display at

Woodside Ferry, limited free parking in local roads
Access by public transport: Merseyrail stations at Hamilton Square (0.25 miles from Woodside Ferry) and Conway Park (0.5 miles from museum) with services from Liverpool Lime Street and Chester Bus stations at Woodside Ferry (25metres) and Birkenhead town centre (half mile)
On site facilities: Model shop (limited opening) in museum, along with Merseyside Tramway Preservation Society (open Sundays when trams are operating). Gift shop at Woodside Ferry Terminal

Depots: Wirral Transport Museum/depot across Old Colonial pub car park
Length of line: 0.7 mile (c1km) of standard gauge. Woodside Ferry Terminal via Pacific Road to Old Colonial tramstop
Refreshments: None on site, but several pubs and cafés around Chester Street and Hamilton Square.
Period of public operation: Most weekends, Wednesday to Sunday during school holidays, all Bank Holidays.
Half hour services operate from both ends — 13.00-17.00

Special events: Annual Bus & Tram Show — 1st Sunday in October; Merseyside Model Railway Show — last weekend in October
Special facilities: Tram rides and tours for school parties, midweek and weekends (ring Ernie Ruffler 0151 666 4000)
Facilities for disabled: Access to both levels in museum. Audio visual display for those unable to travel on the tramsNo toilet facilities in museum, but places with toilets close to tramway

Railway Centre — Yeovil Railway Centre — Somerset

Member: HRA

The Yeovil Railway Centre is operated by the South West Main Line Steam Co and is adjacent to the former London & South Western Railway main line at Yeovil Junction. It features the original British Railways turntable

Location: Adjacent to the main line at Yeovil Junction on the London (Waterloo)-Salisbury-Exeter line

Chaiman: Richard Abbott

Contact address: South West Main Line Steam Co (Yeovil Railway Centre), Yeovil Junction Station, Stoford, Nr Yeovil, Somerset BA22 9UU

Telephone: 01935 410420

Fax: 01935 478373

Internet address: *Web site:* www.yeovilrailway.free servers.com

Car park: On site. Follow signs to Yeovil Junction from Yeovil town centre or from A35 Dorchester-Yeovil road

Access by public transport: SouthWest Trains to Yeovil Junction or bus from Yeovil Bus station

On site facilities: Exhibition of relics and photographs in the newly acquired transfer shed (dating from

Locomotive

Name	No	Origin	Class	Type	Built
Fearless	50050	BR	50	Co-Co	1967

Industrial locomotives

Name	No	Builder	Type	Built
Pectin	—	Peckett (1579)	0-4-0ST	1921
—	—	Fowler (22900)	0-4-0DM	1941
Cockney Rebel	—	Fowler (4000007)	0-4-0DM	1947
Yeo	DS1174	R/Hornsby (458959)	4wDM	1961

Locomotive notes: Main line locomotives occasionally present for servicing during railtours

Rolling stock: Selection of freight wagons

1864) and shop. Light refreshments when brake van rides are operating
Length of line: 500 metres
Opening times: Shop open Sunday mornings throughout the year (except Christmas/New Year). Train Days run from March to October (see web site or telephone for dates and times). Brake van rides and turntable demonstrations feature. Also open on days when main line steam is being serviced (telephone or see web site for details) for Santa Specials in December and special events

Special facilities: Transfer shed available for wedding receptions, parties, shows etc (train hire can be arranged)
Disabled access: To site, but no wheelchair access (at present) to brake van rides
Membership details: Quentin McConnell, High Croft, Yeovil Junction, Stoford, Somerset BA22 9UU
Membership journal: *The Turntable*, three times a year

Left: The S&D Mendip Main Line Project is based at Midsomer Norton with plans to extend southwards to give a mile long section of track on the trackbed of the famous Somerset & Dorset Joint Railway. This view shows the rebuilt signalbox which is being re-equipped during 2009. *S&DMMLP*

Above: Further south another scheme is in hand to return track to the S&DJR route. This image shows the work in hand at Shillingstone.

Right: Two of the S&DJR'S heavy freight locomotives survive in preservation. Here No 88 arrives at Washford on the West Somerset Railway, home of the Somerset & Dorset Railway Trust. *ACB*

Left: No 778 was built by Baldwin in 1917 as part of the American World War 1 transportation system to take men and munitions to the trenches. It is seen here at one of the Leighton Buzzard Railways many road crossings. *LBR*

Above: Another wartime construction is this Kerr Stuart 0-6-0T, this time built for the British system. Works No 2451 dating from 1915, and now named *Axe*, has been restored to service on the Lynton & Barnstaple Railway. *L&BR*

Below: Another wartime-built Kerr Stuart (2395/1917), this time an 0-4-2, although it did not see military service. *Stanhope* is preserved by the Moseley Railway Trust and is generaly to be seen on the West Lancs Railway. Though seen here at Apedale Heritage Centre with a construction train. *MRT*

Three contrasting miniature railways are the Fairbourne, North Bay and Bure Valley lines, all use locomotives based on prototype designs.

Above: Based on the well known Darjeeling Railway this 12.25in 0-4-0STT *Sherpa* is seen heading towards Penrhyn Point, location of a ferry service to Barmouth *FR*

Below: The North Bay Railway LNER Pacific prototypes are diesel-powered and of 18in gauge. *Poseidon* was built in 1933 and is seen at Passing Loop station in August 2008. *Phil Barnes*

The 15in gauge Bure Valley Railway also use prototype-based locomotives. Here No 10 *Mark Timothy*, based on a Leek & Manifold Railway original powers a train through the Norfolk countryside. *BVR*

Left: A replica Richard Trevithick locomotive based on an 1802 prototype. Built by GKN Sankey it can sometimes be seen operating on a short stretch of line at Blists Hill Open Air Museum which is part of the Ironbridge complex. *Phil Barnes*

Below: Steam at Beamish in the shape of the Museum's 1873-built Head Wrightson 0-4-0VBT No 17. Seen here at Beamish station. *Phil Barnes*

Right: Agenoria was built for the Shutt End Colliery in 1829 by Foster/Raistrick and is now in the NRM at York. *Phil Barnes*

Below: Puffing Billy, built by Alan Keef in 2005 can usually be found in action at Beamish. Although seen here in company with *City of Truro* it was part of the attractions at Barrow Hill's Rail Power 2008 event. *Phil Barnes*

Above: Built by Arn Jung in 1908 and now on the Brecon Mountain Railway, *Graf Schwerin-Löwitz* is seen climbing towards Pontsticill. *David Barker*

Below: Palmerston shunts the stock of the Ffestiniog Railway's vintage train which will form a mid afternoon Porthmadog-Minffordd departure. *Phil Barnes*

The original Great Western Railway was built to a broad gauge of 7ft 0.25in.

Above: This replica of 4-2-2 *North Star* was built in 1985 as part of the GW150 celebrations. Based around an 'Austerity' type 0-6-0ST it is now in the NRM at York. *Phil Barnes*

Below: Firefly, a 2-2-2, was completed at the Didcot Railway Centre in 2005, and is based on an 1840 design. Seen here in action on the short broad gauge demonstration line. *Phil Barnes*

Left: 'Bubble car' No 55006 and Class 20 No 20001 await their next turns of duty at Wirksworth station on the Eclesbourne Valley Railway.
EVR

Below: In the 1950s BR had three locomotives on trial with Gas Turbine powerplants in an attempt to find an alternative to steam-powered locomotives.
The only survivor is No 18000, seen here at Barrow Hill following repainting.
Phil Barnes

Right: As part of its 2008 tour former BR Class 14 No D9521 visited the Mid-Norfolk Railway. It is seen here departing Dereham.
ACB

Below: Contrasting diesel power line up at Wansford depot on the Nene Valley Railway. Former BR locomotives Nos 47270 and 31271 share the limelight with a couple of centre cab industrial shunters. *Phil Barnes*

Owned by Museum of Scotland and on loan to the Bo'ness & Kinneil Railway, 1928-built LNER Class D49, No 246 *Morayshire* is seen departing from Bo'ness on a windy day. *B&KR*

Scotland

Alford Valley Railway

Steam Centre · **Aberdeenshire**

The Alford Valley Railway operates from the restored station yard which once marked the terminus of the branch line linking the villages of upper Donside with Kintore Junction, thence to Aberdeen
Location: On A944, 25 miles west of Aberdeen, adjacent to Grampian Transport Museum
Headquarters: Alford Valley Railway Co Ltd, Alford Station, Alford, Aberdeenshire
Internet adress: *Web site:* www.alford.org.uk/avr.htm
Main station: Alford
Car park: On site
Length of line: 3km, 2ft gauge
Museum: Grampian Transport Museum adjacent
Depot: Alford station
Period of public operation: Railway operates:
April, May and September — weekends only (13.00-17.00); June — Monday to Friday (10.30-14.30), Saturdays and Sundays (13.30-16.30); July and August — daily 13.00-17.00.
Trains run every half hour during these times.
Seasonal tickets available.
Alford Heritage Centre is open daily (10.00-17.00)

Special events: Easter Fayre, Santa Specials — please contact for details
Membership details: Membership Secretary, AVR Association, Creagmwor, Main Street, Alford, Aberdeenshire AB33 8AD

Industrial locomotives

Name	No	Builder	Type	Built
Hamewith	—	Lister (3198)	4wDM	c1930
—	—	A/Keef (63)	4wDM	2001
—	—	M/Rail (22129)	4wDM	1962
—	—	M/Rail (2221)	4wDM	1964
James Gordon	—	Keef (63)	0-4-0T (SO)	2001
Aberdeen Corporation Gas Works	3*	A/Barclay (1889)	0-4-0ST	1926

*standard gauge

Rolling stock

Two 24-seat coaches, 50-seat coach, 24-seat ex-Aberdeen tramcar, various wagons

Almond Valley Heritage Trust

Museum · **West Lothian**

Member: HRA
Part of a wide-ranging heritage centre containing a museum of Scotland's shale oil industry with award winning children's exhibits, working watermill, farmsteading with traditional livestock. indoor play areas, countryside walks and farmhouse kitchen tea room
Operating society/organisation: Almond Valley Heritage Centre, Millfield, Livingston Village, West Lothian EH54 7AR
OS reference: NT 034667
Telephone: 01506 414957
Fax: 01506 497771

Industrial locomotives

Name	No	Builder	Type	Built
05/576	—	Barclay (557)	4wDH	1970
Oil Company No 2	—	Baldwin (20587)	4wWE	1902
—	20	Brook Victor (612)	4wBE	1972
—	38	Brook Victor (698)	4wBE	1972
—	42	Brook Victor (700)	4wBE	1972
—	—	Brook Victor (1143)	4wBE	1972
3585	13	Greenwood (1698)	4wBE	1940
ND3059	Yard No B10	Hunslet (2270)	0-4-0DM	1940
—	7330	Hunslet (7330)	4wDM	1973
—	—	Simplex (40SPF522)	4wDM	1981
—	—	B/Drewry (3752)	4wDM	1980

Note

Barclay 557 and Hunslet 2270 operate passenger services

173

Internet address: *e-mail:* info@almondvalley.co.uk
Web site: www.almondvalley.co.uk
Access by public transport: Main line trains to Livingston North (1 mile)
On site facilities: Children's exhibits, indoor play areas, tea room

Public opening: Daily (except 25/26 December, 1/2 January) 10.00-17.00.
Trains operate weekends from March-September, daily July and August and certain public holidays
Length of line: 500m 2ft 6in gauge line from Livingston Mill to

Almondhaugh stations, with plans to extend
Facilities for disabled: Full disabled access to site, but not to coaches

Bo'ness & Kinneil Railway

Timetable Service

West Lothian

Member: HRA, TT, Registered Museum
Historic railway buildings, including the station and train shed, have been relocated from sites all over Scotland. In two purpose-built exhibition halls, the Scottish Railway Exhibition tells the story of the development of the railways in Scotland, and their impact on the people. The rich geology of the area, with its 300 million year old fossils, is explained during a conducted tour of the caverns of the former Birkhill Fireclay Mine
Operating society/location:
Scottish Railway Preservation Society, Bo'ness Station, Union Street, Bo'ness, West Lothian, EH51 9AQ
Access by public transport:
Nearest ScotRail station — Linlithgow. Bus services from Linlithgow, Falkirk, Stirling
OS reference: NT 003817
Telephone: Train services & Events 01506 825855
Talking timetable: 01506 822298
Fax: 01506 828766
Internet address: *e-mail:* enquiries@srps.org.uk
Web site: www.srps.org.uk
Main station: Bo'ness
Other station: Birkhill
Car parks: At Bo'ness and Birkhill (free)
Refreshment facilities: Extensive (unlicensed) buffet at Bo'ness. Picnic tables at both stations
Souvenir shop: Bo'ness
Depot: Bo'ness
Length of line: 3.5 miles
Period of public operation:
Weekends 4 April to 1 November, Tuesdays 26 May to 23 June. Daily 30 June to 23 August (EXCEPT

Locomotives

Name	No	Origin	Class	Type	Built
—	419	CR	439	0-4-4T	1908
Morayshire	246	LNER	D49	4-4-0	1928
Glen Douglas	256	NBR	D34	4-4-0	1913
—	42	NBR	Y9	0-4-0ST	1887
Maude	673	NBR	J36	0-6-0	1891
—	80105	BR	4MT	2-6-4T	1955
—	D2774	BR	—	0-4-0DH	1960
—	08443 (D3558)	BR	08	0-6-0DE	1958
—	D8020	BR	20	Bo-Bo	1959
—	25235 (D7585)	BR	25	Bo-Bo	1965
—	26004 (D5303)	BR	26	B0-Bo	1958
—	26024 (D5323)	BR	26	Bo-Bo	1959
—	27001 (D5347)	BR	27	Bo-Bo	1961
—	D5351	BR	27	Bo-Bo	1961
—	37025	BR	37	Co-Co	1961
—	37175	BR	37	Co-Co	1963
—	37403	BR	37	Co-Co	1965
—	37413	BR	37	Co-Co	1965
—	47643	BR	47	Co-Co	1968
—	51017	BR	126	DMS	1959
—	51043	BR	126	DMS	1959
—	59404	BR	126	TC	1959
—	79443	BR	126	TRBF	1956

26010 (D5310) on site for 2009

Industrial locomotives

Name	No	Builder	Type	Built
Clydesmill	3	Barclay (1937)	0-4-0ST	1928
Lord Ashfield	—	Barclay (1964)	0-4-0ST	1929
—	3	Barclay (2046)	0-4-0ST	1937
—	24	Barclay (2335)	0-6-0T	1953
Texaco	—†	Fowler (4210140)	0-4-0DM	1958
(Lord King)	—	H/Leslie (3640)	0-4-0ST	1926
—	19	Hunslet (3818)	0-6-0ST	1954
DS3	—	R/Hornsby (275883)	4wDM	1949
DS4	P6687	R/Hornsby (312984)	0-4-0DE	1951
(Ranald)	—	Sentinel (9627)	4wVBT	1957
—	970214	Wickham (6050)	2w-2PMR	c1951
—	—	Matisa (48626)	—	—
—	5	Hunslet (3837)	0-6-0ST	1955
—	(7)	Bagnall (2777)	0-6-0ST	1945
Borrowstounness	—*	Barclay (840)	0-4-0T	1899
—	—*	M/Rail (110U082)	4wDH	1970
—	—	Wickham (10482)	2w-2PMR	1970

174

Mondays in July)				

Special facilities: Private trains can be hired. Available for weddings

Facilities for disabled: Disabled access to platform and a specially adapted carriage for wheelchair users. Toilets at Bo'ness station. No facilities for wheelchairs at Birkhill Fireclay Mine

Special notes: Two large museum buildings: Fireclay Mine at Birkhill (both open same days as trains operate, except December)

Name	No	Builder	Type	Built
—	(17)	Hunslet (2880)	0-6-0ST	1943
—	970213	Wickham (6049)	2w-2PMR	c1951
—	17†	Barclay (2296)	0-4-0ST	1952
Lady Victoria	3	Barclay (1458)	0-6-0ST	1916
The Wemyss Coal Co Ltd	20	Barclay (2068)	0-6-0T	1939
—	(6)	Barclay (2127)	0-4-0CT	1942
No 1	—	Barclay (343)	0-6-0DM	1941
City of Aberdeen	—**	B/Hawthorn (912)	0-4-0ST	1887
F82 (Fairfield)	—	E/Electric (1131) (244)	4wBE	1940
Kelton Fell	13	Neilson (2203)	0-4-0ST	1876
Lord Roberts	1§	N/Reid (5710)	0-6-0T	1902
(Tiger)	—	N/British (27415)	0-4-0DH	1954
Kilbagie	DS2	R/Hornsby (262998)	4wDM	1949
—	—	R/Hornsby (321733)	4wDM	1952
DS6	(1)	R/Hornsby (421439)	0-4-0DE	1958
St Mirren	(3)	R/Hornsby (423658)	0-4-0DE	1958
—	D88/003	R/Hornsby (506500)	4wDM	1965
(Denis)	—	Sentinel (9631)	4wVBT	1958
—	—	Arrols (Glasgow)	2w-2DM	c1966

*3ft 0in gauge
**on loan to Tanfield Railway
†at present off site at Scottish Vintage Bus Museum, Lathalmond, Fife
§official licensed 'Thomas' replica locomotive

Stock

A large selection of coaching stock, many built by Scottish pre-Grouping companies, ex-BR Class 126 DMU, and an appropriate collection of early freight vehicles

Owners

80105 and (Denis) owned by Locomotive Owners Group (Scotland)
246 and 24 owned by Museum of Scotland
256 the Glasgow Museum of Transport
27001 the Class 27 Preservation Group
26004 and 26024 the 6LDA Group
37025 the Scottish Class 37 Group

Caledonian Railway (Brechin)

Timetable Service — **Angus**

Member: HRA

This Scottish country steam railway is a classic branch line starting at the Strathmore line junction station of Bridge of Dun, last stomping ground of the Gresley 'A4' Pacific locomotives, and climbs some steep gradients through scenic farmland with assorted wildlife and flora. The summit is reached at the Edzell & Forfar junction just short of Brechin station, itself one of the most impressive of Britain's preserved railways.

The National Trust for Scotland property House of Dun, built by

Locomotives

Name	No	Origin	Class	Type	Built
Brechin City	D3059	BR	08	0-6-0DE	1954
*—	12052	BR	11	0-6-0DE	1949
*—	12093	BR	11	0-6-0DE	1951
—	25072	BR	25	Bo-Bo	1963
—	25083	BR	25	Bo-Bo	1963
—	D5314	BR	26	Bo-Bo	1959
—	26035	BR	26	Bo-Bo	1959
—	27024	BR	27	Bo-Bo	1962
Old Fettercairn	37097	BR	37	Co-Co	1962

*on loan from Scottish Industrial Railway Centre

Industrial locomotives

Name	No	Builder	Type	Built
—†	—	Barclay (1863)	0-4-0ST	1926
Harlaxton	—	Barclay (2107)	0-6-0T	1941

William Adam in 1730, is approximately 1 mile from Bridge of Dun station, which is also close to the Montrose Basin, a tidal wildlife centre. Brechin itself has many attractions including the cathedral and round tower and the new Pictavia centre.

The railway is run entirely by volunteer members of the Brechin Railway Preservation Society
Headquarters: Caledonian Railway (Brechin) Ltd, The Station, 2 Park Road, Brechin, Angus DD9 7AF
Telephone: 01356 622992 (or 07740 363958)
Internet address: *e-mail:* calrail@engineer.com
Web site: www.caledonianrailway.co.uk
Main stations: Brechin and Bridge of Dun
OS reference: NO 603603
Car park: Brechin, Bridge of Dun
Access by car: Via A90 Dundee/Aberdeen to Brechin bypass. Brown tourist signs to stations. Free parking
Access by public transport: By ScotRail, GNER and Virgin services to Montrose (5 miles). By bus from Montrose, Strathtay Scottish — Dundee (01382) 228054/227201
Refreshment facilities: Light refreshments at Brechin on operating days
Picnic area: Bridge of Dun
Souvenir shop: Brechin
Museum: Brechin
Length of line: 4 miles 22 chains
Depots: Brechin (steam) Bridge of Dun (diesel)
Passenger trains: Industrial steam and heritage diesel-hauled trains between Brechin and Bridge of Dun
Period of public operation: Trains

Name	No	Builder	Type	Built
BAC No 1	—	Peckett (1376)	0-4-0ST	1915
Menelaus	—	Peckett (1889)	0-6-0ST	1935
—	5	Peckett (2153)	0-6-0ST	1954

†expected to be operational during 2009, others in store/under restoration

Coaching Stock
In service 6 x BR Mk 1, 3 x BR Mk 2s
Stored 4 x BR Mk 1s, plus 1 x BR Mk 1 in use as volunteer accommodation
BR Mk 3a restaurant car in use as a buffet

Engineer's Stock
c50 wagons including: 1 ex-BR diesel-electric 12-ton crane, 6 Dogfish, 1 Mermaid, 4 warflats, 3 rectanks, 1 Ferry van, 2 Lowmacs, 2 minfit, 1 21-ton minfit, 2 LNER vans, 2 LMS vans, 2 demountable tank wagons, 7 ex-BR vans, 1 ex-BR bolster

Departmental Stock
1 CR origin electrification coach, 1 ex-BR BCK, various vans

Owners
No 1 and *Menelaus* the Angus Railway Steam Engineers
D5314 the Class Twenty Six Preservation Group
D3059, 26035 and 27024 the Caledonian Diesel Group

run 11/12 April; 2-4, 31 May; 7, 14, 21, 28 June; 5, 11/12, 18/19, 26 July; 1/2, 8/9, 15/16, 22/23, 29/30 August; 6 September, 6, 12/13, 19/20 December.
Bridge of Dun station is open daily for static viewing Tuesday-Friday 11.00-16.00, Bridge of Dun site open daily all week
Special events: Day out with Thomas — 13/14 June, 11/12, 18/19 July, 29/30 August; Steam, Stories & Music Evenings — 25/26 July, 8/9 August; Santa Specials — 6, 12/13, 19/20 December
Facilities for disabled: Ramp access to both stations. Vehicular access to Brechin platforms by prior arrangement. Coach converted to take wheelchairs and attendants, prior notice required for access and

car parking
Family tickets: Available
Disclaimer: The Caledonian Railway (Brechin) Ltd reserves the right to amend, cancel or add to these events. And whilst every effort will be made to maintain the above services, the company does not guarantee that trains will depart or arrive at the time stated and reserves the right to suspend or alter any train without notice and will not accept any liability for loss, inconvenience or delay thereby caused
Membership details: D. Duncan, c/o above address
Membership journal: Quarterly
Marketing name: The Friendly Line

Glasgow Museum of Transport

Museum — Glasgow

Member: HRA, TT
A new Museum of Transport on the Clyde is under development by Glasgow Museums in collaboration with other Council departments and Glasgow Harbour Ltd. This landmark museum will create a more accessible and environmentally stable home for

Glasgow's significant Transport and Technology collections and for the first time allow proper interpretation of Glasgow's important maritime history through the museum site, the *Glenlee* tall ship and unique ship model collection

The railway collection represents

one of the best efforts by a municipal authority to preserve a representative collection of items appropriate to the 'locomotive builders of the Empire'
Access by public transport: Strathclyde PTE Underground. Kelvinhall: Strathclyde Buses 6, 6A, 8, 8A, 9, 9A, 16, 42, 42A, 57,

57A, 62, 62A, 62B, 64; Kelvin Scottish Buses 5, 5A; Clydeside Scottish Buses 17

Operating society/organisation: Glasgow City Council, Cultural & Sport Glasgow

Location: Museum of Transport, Kelvin Hall, 1 Bunhouse Road, Glasgow G3 8DP

Telephone: (0141) 287 2720

Fax: (0141) 287 2692

Internet address: *Web site:* www.glasgowmuseums.com

Car park: Opposite Museum entrance

On site facilities: Toilets, cafeteria, shop and public telephone, cloaking facility

Public opening: Monday-Thursday, and Saturday 10.00-17.00; Friday and Sunday 11.00-17.00. Closed 1/2 January and 25/26 December only. Please check before travelling

Locomotives

Name	No	Origin	Class	Type	Built
—	123	CR	123	4-2-2	1886
—	9	G&SWR	5	0-6-0T	1917
—	103	HR	—	4-6-0	1894
Gordon Highlander	49	GNSR	F	4-4-0	1920
—	3007	SAR*	15C	4-8-2	1944

*South African Railways, 3ft 6 in gauge, instore

Industrial locomotives

Name	No	Builder	Type	Built
—	1	Barclay (1571)	0-6-0F	1917
—	—	Chaplin (2368)	0-4-0TG	1888
—	—	BEV (583)	B	1927

Stock

Glasgow District Subway car 39T; Glasgow Corporation Underground cars 1 and 4; LMS King George VI's saloon 498 of 1941

Facilities for disabled: Both single-sex and uni-sex disabled facilities now available. A passenger lift to allow disabled access at the front entrance is now in operation

---

Timetable Service	Keith & Dufftown Railway	Banffshire

Member: HRA

The Keith & Dufftown Railway is an 11 mile line linking the World's Malt Whisky Capital, Dufftown, to the market town of Keith, towns famous round the world for names such as Glenfiddich and Chivas Regal. The line re-opened in 2001, and passes through some of Scotland's most picturesque scenery

Operating society/organisation: Keith & Dufftown Railway Association, Dufftown Station, Dufftown, Banffshire AB55 4BA

Contact: R. H. Furr (Publicity & Marketing)

Telephone: (01340) 821181 (operating days only) 01343 870429 (Monday to Thursday)

Internet address: *e-mail:* info@keith-dufftown-railway.co.uk *Web site:* www.keith-dufftown-railway.co.uk

Main station: Dufftown

SatNav postcodes:
Dufftown — AB55 4BA
Keith Town — AB55 3BR

Other public stations: Drummuir (access by rail only), Keith Town (not the ScotRail station)

Locomotives and multiple-units

Name	No	Origin	Class	Type	Built
—	51568	BR	108	DMC(L)	1959
—	52053	BR	108	DMC(L)	1960
—	53628	BR	108	DMBS	1958
—	56491	BR	108	DTC(L)	1959
—	55500*	BR	140	DMS	1981
—	55501*	BR	140	DMS	1981
—	Car 87§	M/Cam	5BEL	TPS	1932

*unit No 140001, in storage awaiting restoration
§ex-'Brighton Belle' Pullman Car, converted to locomotive-hauled

Industrial locomotives

Name	No	Builder	Type	Built
Spirit o' Fife	—	E/Electric (D1193)	0-6-0DH	1967
Wee Mac	—	Clayton	4wDH	1979

Rolling stock

3 Canadian 2- and 4-seat 'Speeder' vehicles
A selection of freight vehicles for maintenance purposes

Length of line: 11 miles, with 42 bridges and the twin span 60ft high Fiddich Viaduct

Car park: Dufftown and Keith stations

Access by public transport: Rail — ScotRail station at Keith (short walk to Keith Town)

Bus — Stagecoach service 10 (Inverness to Aberdeen) passes Keith Town station

Refreshments: Dufftown

Souvenir shop: Keith Town

On site facilities: Visitor centre and heritage display at Keith Town station. Information on local

accommodation providers, visitor attractions and souvenirs. Woodland walks from Drummuir station and access to the Walled Garden at Drummuir Castle
Period of public operation: Weekends — Easter until end of May and throughout September. Fridays, Saturdays and Sundays during June, July and August, and during festivals
Special events: Spring and autumn Whisky Festivals. Summer evening specials. Santa Specials in December. Dates and details on the web site
Facilities of disabled: Access to all stations, the refreshment rooms and to trains. Disabled toilet at Keith Town, limited facilities at Dufftown and on trains
Special facilities: Group booking welcome. Trains available for private charter on non-operating days. Keith Town station is licensed for weddings
Special note: The stations and stock are not available for viewing except on operating days
Membership details: Membership Secretary, c/o above address, or via web site
Membership journal: *The Keith & Dufftown Express* — half-yearly

Kerr's Miniature Railway

Miniature Railway — Angus

Location: Along the sea front to the west of town
Headquarters: West Links Park, Arbroath, Angus.
Contact: Jill Kerr (Proprietor)
Telephone: (01241) 874074/879249
Internet addresses:
e-mail: jillkerr@tiscali.co.uk
Web site: www.kerrsminiaturerailway.co.uk
Access by public transport: First ScotRail Arbroath station 1.5 miles; Strathtay Buses route A92
On site facilities: Small shop. The park has toilets, snack bar, etc
Length of line: 10.25 in gauge; 400yd (alongside main line)
Period of public operation: Easter-end of September — weekends (11.00-16.00). All of July and

Locomotives

Name	No	Builder	Type	Built
Ivor	—	Coleby-Simkins	0-6-0	1972
King George	2005	Bullock	4-6-0	1935
Auld Reekie	9872	Jennings	4-4-2	1936
—	25081	Eastwood	Bo-Bo	1981
Edie Ochiltree	D7594	Eastwood	Bo-Bo	1994
Firefly	3007	Bullock	0-6-0	1936

Note: All locomotives can be viewed when the railway is running

Rolling stock
3 open coaches

first half of August — daily 11.00-16.00. Sundays throughout the winter (end September-end March.
All times weather permitting
Special events: Easter and Halloween plus other occasional events
Facilities for disabled: One coach being modified for wheelchair access
Fare: £1

Leadhills & Wanlockhead Railway

Steam Centre — Lanarkshire

Member: HRA
Situated in the Lowther Hills between Abington and Sanquhar, the society was formed in 1983 to construct and operate a 2ft gauge tourist railway between the villages of Leadhills and Wanlockhead. The track now extends to the old county boundary between Lanarkshire and Dumfriesshire. The highest adhesion worked railway in Great Britain at 1,498ft above sea level. Signalbox built using terracotta bricks from the demolished viaduct at Risping Cleuch, with a variety of pre-Grouping signalling & telegraph equipment (eg North British Railway lever frame and Caledonian Railway lattice post signal)
Operating society/organisation: David Winpenny, Leadhills & Wanlockhead Railway, 31 Easter Drylaw Avenue, Edinburgh EH4 2QZ
Telephone: 0141 580 9133
Internet addresses: *e-mail: info@leadhillsrailway.co.uk*
Web site: www.leadhillsrailway.co.uk

Main station: Leadhills
Access by public transport: ScotRail trains stop at Sanquhar on Nith Valley Line (approx 10 miles) every 1hr 30min-2 hours. Bus service (Western Scottish Stagecoach) to Leadhills (please check for times). Nearest motorway — M74 — J14 from south/J15 from north. From A76 take B797 to Leadhills
Length of line: 1 mile
Journey time: Approx 30min round trip
On site facilities: Shop, ticket

office, toilets, small museum and picnic tables. Extensive country walks. Also on 'Southern Upland Way'. Scottish Lead Mining Museum at Wanlockhead (1 mile). Guided tour of signalbox and engine shed. Disabled access to shop and toilet

Period of public operation: Saturdays and Sundays 11.00-16.20 Easter weekend then May to September including Bank Holiday Mondays and special events (please see web site for details). Group of 10 or more discount 30%

Special events: Steam Fair weekend (usually late July)

Membership details: Simon Lowe, Flat 0/1, Holmlea Road, Glasgow G44 4BL

Society journal: Quarterly

Industrial locomotives

Name	No	Builder	Type	Built
Charlotte	—	O&K	0-4-0T	1913
Elvan	2	M/Rail (9792)	4wDM	1955
Luce	4	R/Hornsby (7002/0467/2)	4wDM	1966
Little Clyde	5	R/Hornsby (7002/0467/6)	4wDM	1966
Clyde	6	Hunslet (6347)	4wDH	1975
Nith	8	H/Clarke (DM1002)	0-4-0DMF	1956
Mennock	10	H/Barclay (LD 9348)	0-4-0DM	1994
—	—	Decauvill (917)	0-4-0T	1917
—	—	Clayton (18190)	4wDM	1978
—	—	Moyse	4wDM	1941

Rolling stock

2 air-braked passenger coaches and guard's van built at Leadhills. 1 air-braked coach chassis built by Talyllyn Railway, with the L&WR completing the bodywork. Assorted permanent way wagons and former industrial stock

---

Timetable Service   Mull Rail   Isle of Mull

Member: HRA, TT

Scotland's original island passenger railway. The terminal at Craignure is reached by ferry from Oban. The railway timetable links in with most ferry sailings. The journey is one of great beauty running alongside the Sound of Mull with extensive views of Ben Nevis, the Glencoe Hills, the island of Lismore and the mass of Ben Cruachan

Commercial Manager: Christopher James

Operations Managers: Nigel Smith, David Baxter

Operating society/organisation: Mull & West Highland (NG) Railway Co Ltd, Old Pier Station, Craignure, Isle of Mull PA65 6AY

Telephone/Fax: (01680) 812494/812567

Internet address: e-mail: info@mullrail.co.uk
Web site: www.mullrail.co.uk

OS reference: NM 725369

Car park: At Craignure, free

Access by public transport: Caledonian MacBrayne ferry from Oban (40min sail)

On site facilities: Gift shop, car park (free) at Craignure during operational hours

Family ticket: Available (2 adults & 2 children under 16)

Locomotives

Name	No	Builder	Type	Built
Lady of the Isles	—	Marsh	2-6-4T	1981
Waverley†	—	Curwen	4-4-2	1952
—	—	Alcock	4w-4PM	1973
Glen Auldyn	—	Davies	B0-B0 DH	1986
Victoria*	—	Vere	2-6-2T	1993
Frances	—	Vere	B0-B0 DH	1999

†currently at Rudyard Lake Railway
*largest tank engine built for 10.25in gauge

Rolling stock

9 coaches (two with wheelchair accommodation); 3 bogie wagons; 3 4-wheel wagons 1 crane on a 4-wheel underframe

Owners

Waverley — The Waverley Group
Victoria and Frances — Mull & West Highland NG Railway
Glen Auldyn and Lady of the Isles — both private

Length of line: 1.25 miles/10.25in gauge

Public opening: Daily 1 April to 25 October

Facilities for disabled: No steps on railway, two compartments for wheelchairs

Membership details: Friends of Mull Rail, David Crombie, 1 Mulberry Drive, Dunfermline, Fife KY11 8BZ. Tel: (01383) 728652

Membership journal:

Crankpin Journal — annual

Special facilities: Special trains can be chartered within and outside timetable hours

Special notes: First island passenger railway in Scotland, runs to Torosay Castle and 12 acres of gardens, superb panoramic views of mountains and sea. Group discount available for 20+ pre-booked passengers. Joint Torosay Castle/Mull Rail tickets available at Craignure station

Member: TT, Heritage Afloat
Paddle steamers: *Waverley* &
Kingswear Castle. Pleasure cruise
ship: *Balmoral*
The Paddle Steamer *Waverley*, the
last sea-going paddle steamer in the
world, was built for the London &
North Eastern Railway in 1946, and
replaced a vessel of the same name
which was sunk off Dunkirk during
May 1940. Sold to the PSPS — a
Registered Charity — in 1974,
Waverley sails on day trips and
afternoon cruises from ports and
piers in most coastal areas and river
estuaries of the United Kingdom,
from Easter until October each year.
Also in the 'fleet' is the traditional
motor cruiser *Balmoral*. The river
paddle steamer *Kingswear Castle*
sails from Chatham Historic

Dockyard on the River Medway
Commercial Director:
Kathleen O'Neil
Operations Director:
Ian McMillan
Headquarters:
Waverley and *Balmoral:*
Waverley Excursions Ltd, Waverley
Terminal, Anderston Quay,
Glasgow G3 8HA
Kingswear Castle:
The Historic Dockyard, Chatham,
Kent ME4 4TQ
On ship facilities: Self-service
restaurants, bars, toilets (disabled
toilets on *Waverley* and *Balmoral*),
souvenirs
Special facilities: *Waverley* and
Balmoral) are available for private
hire and party bookings
Membership details: Paddle

Steamer Preservation Society,
PO Box 365, Worcester WR3 7WH
Membership journal:
Paddlewheels — quarterly.
Details of the full programme of
cruises operated by and *Waverley*
and *Balmoral* can be obtained from
the National Booking Office,
Waverley Excursions Ltd, Waverley
Terminal, Anderston Quay,
Glasgow G3 8HA
Tel: 0845 130 4647.
Book online at:
www.waverleyexcursions.co.uk
Further info for *Kingswear Castle:*
Tel: 01634 827648
e-mail: kc@pskc.freeserve.co.uk
Online booking for *Kingswear
Castle:*
www.pskc.freeserve.co.uk

Location: On the B1348 between
Musselburgh and Prestonpans.
OS reference: NT 734737
Operating society/organisation:
East Lothian Museum Service,
Library & Museum Headquarters,
Dunbar Road, Haddington, East
Lothian EH41 3PJ
Telephone: (0131) 653 2904
(Prestongrange Visitor Centre),
(01620) 828200 (Museum Service)
Internet address:
e-mail: preston-
grange@btconnect.com
web site: www.prestongrange.org
Car park: On site
On site facilities: Once part of the
Scottish Mining Museum,
Prestongrange is being developed as
a museum which tells the story of
people and industries in East
Lothian — local coal deposits
encouraged the growth of numerous
other industries such as pottery,
pipe making, soap, glycerine and
brewing
Visitor centre: Changing exhibitions of local industries. Children's

Industrial locomotives

Name	No	Builder	Type	Built
—	6	A/Barclay (2043)	0-4-0ST	1937
—	17	A/Barclay (2219)	0-4-0ST	1946
Prestongrange	7	G/Ritchie (536)	0-4-2ST	1914
Tomatin	1	M/Rail (9925)	4wDM	1963
—	—*	Hunslet (4440)	4wDM	1952
—	32	R/Hornsby (458960)	4wDM	1962
George Edwards	33	R/Hornsby (221647)	4wDM	1943
—	—	E/Electric (D908)	4wDM	1964

*2ft gauge

Rolling stock
Steam crane, Whittaker No 30, c1890

Special note: The locomotives are stored under cover with no public
access at the time of writing. Visitors wishing to see the exhibits MUST
make arrangements before visiting

activity area. Cornish beam engine,
installed 1874 to pump water from
the mine. Colliery locomotives
restored by Prestongrange Railway
Society are housed in the Pit Head
Baths
Toilets: Visitor centre
Refreshment facilities: Available

at visitor centre
Public opening: Museum site open
daily throughout the year.
Visitor centre and exhibitions April
to October, 11.00-16.00.
Admission free
Length of line: 400m (standard
gauge). No public rides

Facilities for disabled: Access and toilet at visitor centre. Access to powerhouse exhibition, and footpaths along the site
Special events: Events held

throughout the season
Contact: For Prestongrange Railway Society — Colin Boyd, 3 Stuart Wynd, Craigmount View, Edinburgh EH2 8XU

Member: HRA

Major developments at Milton of Crathes during 2008 have seen the Deeside Railway progress considerably. A further section of track has been laid from milepost 15 at Woodbine along the Cashentroch straight to milepost 15.25 near Birkenbaud crossing. This section is being ballasted thanks to a donation by UK rail and bus operator First Group and will be opened for traffic during 2009. A donation of a futher 0.75 mile of track was made which will help push the railway closer to Banchory, 2.5 miles west of Milton. Also platform and station foundation works were completed, giving a more complete feel to the site.

The railway welcomed its first royal visitor since 1966 when King Siaosi Topou V of Tonga visited and had a trip along to Woodbine.

Trains now consist of the historic 'Sputnik' battery-electric unit in use as hauled stock behind recently acquired Barclay diesel No 415. The unit's own electrical restoration is ongoing; its 50th anniversary was quietly marked during the year.

Work is progressing to return two Mark 2 coaches on site to service; these will be in use in a push-pull basis with 112-year old *Bon Accord*. The off-site restoration was completed in November 2008 and it is now scheduled for delivery to Milton in spring 2009.

2009 will be a year of consolidation with the completion of trackwork at Milton and the transfer of the GNSR timber station building from Old Meldrum.

The railway is being rebuilt by volunteers of the Royal Deeside RPS in partnership with The Leys Estate

Locomotives and multiple-units

Name	No	Origin	Class	Type	Built
—	D2134†	BR	03	0-6-0DH	1960
—	D9551	BR	14	0-6-0DH	1965
—	79998*	BR	—	DMBS	1956
—	79999*	BR	—	DTCL	1956

†rebuilt with hydraulic drive
*battery-powered multiple-unit

Industrial locomotives

Name	No	Builder	Type	Built
Bon Accord	—	Barclay (807)	0-4-0ST	1897
—	1	Barclay (415)	0-4-0DH	1957

Rolling stock

2 BR Mk 2 coaches, GNSR full brake, GNSR 5-comp lav composite (body only), GNSR 5-comp lav Third (body only), GNSR 5-comp Third (body only), GNSR 4-comp First (body only), GNSR former steam railmotor (body only), LNWR Picnic Saloon (body only), LMS CCT, BR 20-ton brake van, BR Dogfish and Lomac wagons, ex-LMS wagon underframe, 75ton rail-mounted crane, (on loan from Strathspey Railway, their No 206)

Owner

Bon Accord — the Grampian Transport Museum, on long-term loan to Bon Accord Locomotive Society

Headquarters: Milton of Crathes Craft village
Operating society/organisation: Mr Frank Grant, Chairman, Royal Deeside Railway Preservation Society, The Station, Milton of Crathes, Banchory, Aberdeenshire AB31 5QH
Telephone: 01224 782479
Internet address: Web site: www.deeside-railway.co.uk
OS reference: NO 914962
Car parking: Free, on site
Access by public transport: By bus — Stagecoach Bluebird from Aberdeen rail/bus interchange (railway adjacent to A93).
Access by car — from south, A90 to Stonehaven, then A957 (historic Slug Road) to A93 at Crathes; from the west, A93 from Ballater, A980 from Donside to Banchory
On site facilities: Two static

display coaches with light refreshments available (seasonal weekend opening)
Length of line: 0.25 mile, 2.75 miles when complete
Public opening: Sundays April-September 13.00-17.00
Special events: Annual Deeside Steam & Vintage Club rally held at Milton of Crathes on third weekend in August
Disabled facilities: Access for wheelchair users on to the platform, guard's area on train and station shop. Multi-user footpath alongside railway allowing viewing of passing trains
Membership details: Mr W. Halliday, Membership Secretary, 32 Abbotshall Crescent, Cults, Aberdeen AB15 9JP
Membership journal: *The Queen's Messenger* (quarterly)

Note: Some locomotives and rolling stock undergoing restoration off-site with no public access, please contact for details

Affiliated society:
The Bon Accord Locomotive Society, c/o Mr Murray M. D. Duncan, 19 David Street,

Stonehaven, Kincardineshire
AB39 2AJ
Web site: www.bon-accord.org

Scottish Industrial Railway Centre

Steam Centre — Ayrshire

Member: HRA, TT, AIM

The Scottish Industrial Railway Centre is based on part of the former Dalmellington Iron Co railway system which was one of the best known industrial railway networks in Britain. Steam worked up until 1978 when the collieries it served in the scenic Doon Valley closed. It is the aim of the centre to preserve part of the railway.

The Centre is operated by the Ayrshire Railway Preservation Group, who also own the former Glasgow & South Western Railway station at Waterside, half a mile from the Centre.

During the winter of 2002/3 the ARPG moved its operations from the former colliery at Minnivey to the Dunaskin Ironworks site at Waterside, and is now based in the former NCB locomotive shed and wagon works there. As part of Doon Valley Heritage, an industrial heritage centre has now been established at the old Dunaskin Ironworks, based on the iron, coal and brickmaking industries

Location: 10 miles southeast of Ayr on the A713 to Castle Douglas

Contact address: Scottish Industrial Railway Centre, Dunaskin Ironworks, Waterside, Panta, Ayrshire KA6 7JF

OS reference: NS 438085

Operating society/organisation: Ayrshire Railway Preservation Group

Telephone: ARPG information line (01292) 269260. ARPG Secretary (01292) 313579 (evening & weekends)

Internet address: *e-mail:* agcthoms@aol.com
Web site: www.arpg.org.uk

Length of line: Approx 0.3 mile

Access by public transport: Nearest rail station, Ayr (10 miles). Half hourly Stagecoach bus service from Ayr. Tel: (01292) 613500

On site facilities: Steam-hauled

Locomotives

Name	No	Origin	Class	Type	Built
*—	MP228 (12052)	BR	11	0-6-0DE	1949
*—	MP229 (12093)	BR	11	0-6-0DE	1951

*on loan to Caledonian Railway

Industrial locomotives

Name	No	Builder	Type	Built
—	16	Barclay (1116)	0-4-0ST	1910
—	8	Barclay (1296)	0-6-0T	1912
—	19	Barclay (1614)	0-4-0ST	1918
—	8	Barclay (1952)	0-4-0F	1928
—	10	Barclay (2244)	0-4-0ST	1947
NCB No 23	—	Barclay (2260)	0-4-0ST	1949
—	25	Barclay (2358)	0-6-0ST	1954
—	1	Barclay (2368)	0-4-0ST	1955
—	—	Barclay (347)	0-4-0DM	1941
—	118	Barclay (366)	0-4-0DM	1943
—	7	Barclay (399)	0-4-0DM	1956
Lily of the Valley	—	Fowler (22888)	0-4-0DM	1943
—	—	Fowler (4200028)	0-4-0DM	1948
Tees Storage	—	N/British (27644)	0-4-0DH	1959
—	—	R/Hornsby (224352)	4wDM	1943
Blinkin Bess	—	R/Hornsby (284839)	4wDM	1950
Johnnie Walker	—	R/Hornsby (417890)	4wDM	1959
—	—	R/Hornsby (421697)	0-4-0DM	1959
—	107	Hunslet (3132)	0-4-0DM	1944
—	—	Sentinel (10012)	4wDM	1959
—	—	Donnelli (163)	4wDMR	1979

3ft gauge (stored off-site)

—	—	R/Hornsby (256273)	4wDM	1949
—	—	Hunslet (8816)	4wDH	1981

2ft 6in gauge (stored off-site)

—	2	R/Hornsby (183749)	4wDM	1937
—	3	R/Hornsby (210959)	4wDM	1941
—	1	R/Hornsby (211681)	4wDM	1942

Note: Not all standard gauge locomotives are on public display

Stock
1 BR Mk 1 TSO, 1 BR Mk 1 BSK, 2 Wickham trolleys; 1 steam crane; various other items

brake van rides (over third mile). Small museum of railway relics and photographs, and souvenir shop

Public opening: To be announced in spring 2009

Special events: Steam days (with an engine in steam) will be held on: Sundays 3, 24 May, 28 June; 5, 12, 19, 26 July; 2, 9, 16, 23, 30 August; 6, 27 September. Opening times 11.00-16.30

Membership details: Mr Charles

Robinson, 3 Links Crescent, Troon, Ayrshire KA10 6SS
Special notes: For further information and details of special events, please contact the

information line (01292) 269620, or the secretary Gordon Thomson (01292) 313579, or write to 9 Hillhouse Road, Troon, Ayrshire KA10 6SY

| Timetable Service | **Strathspey Railway** | Inverness-shire |

Member: HRA, TT

Scotland's steam railway in the Highlands connects the busy tourist resort at Aviemore to the more traditional highland village of Boat of Garten, famed as one of the few nesting places of the osprey (viewing site 3 miles from station). The golf course here was designed by James Braid, who also designed Gleneagles. Beyond Boat of Garten the scenery changes as the 'strath' opens out giving fine views of the Spey enroute to Broomhill. This station appears as 'Glenbogle' in the TV series 'Monarch of the Glen'. Broomhill is approximately 3.5 miles from Grantown on Spey, the railway's ultimate goal

Superintendent of the Line: Laurence Grant

Enquiries: Aviemore Station, Dalfaber Road, Aviemore, Inverness-shire PH22 1PY (SAE for copy of timetable brochure)

Telephone: 01479 810725.

Internet address: e-mail: strathtrains@strathspeyrailway.co.uk Web site: www.strathspeyrailway.co.uk

Main station: Aviemore. The railway occupies one platform at the main line Aviemore station

Other public stations: Boat of Garten and Broomhill

OS reference: Aviemore NH 898131, Boat of Garten NH 943789

Car parks: Aviemore (Strathspey Railway side of station (off Dalfaber Road) for railway customers only, Boat of Garten (access via A95 and minor roads 5 miles north of Aviemore and 10 miles south of Grantown-on-Spey) and Broomhill

Access by public transport: ScotRail services and express bus to Aviemore. Local service to Boat of Garten

Refreshment facilities: On-train

Locomotives and multiple-units

Name	No	Origin	Class	Type	Built
—†	5025	LMS	5MT	4-6-0	1934
E. V. Cooper, Engineer†	46512	LMS	2MT	2-6-0	1952
—†	828	CR	812	0-6-0	1899
—	D2774	BR	—	0-4-0DH	1960
—	08490	BR	08	0-6-0DE	1959
—†	D5302	BR	26	Bo-Bo	1958
—†	26025	BR	26	Bo-Bo	1958
—*	D5394	BR	27	Bo-Bo	1963
—	D5862	BR	31	A1A-A1A	1962
—	51367	BR	117	DMBS	1959
—	51402	BR	117	DMS	1959
—†	51990	BR	107	DMBS	1961
—	52008	BR	107	DMBS	1960
—	52030	BR	107	DMC	1960
—	54047	BR	114	DTC	1959
—	97651	BR	97	0-6-0DE	1959

Industrial locomotives

Name	No	Builder	Type	Built
—	48†	Hunslet (2864)	0-6-0ST	1943
Cairngorm	9	RSH (7097)	0-6-0ST	1943
Swiftsure	—†	Hunslet (2857)	0-6-0ST	1943
—	60†	Hunslet (3686)	0-6-0ST	1948
Niddrie	6	Barclay (1833)	0-6-0ST	1924
Forth	10*	Barclay (1890)	0-4-0ST	1926
Balmenach	2	Barclay (2020)	0-4-0ST	1936
Bruerency	17	Barclay (2017)	0-6-0T	1935
Inveresk	16	R/Hornsby (260756)	0-4-0DM	1950
—	—	T/Hill (277V)	4wDM	1977
—	14	North British (27549)	0-4-0DH	1956
Queen Anne	20†	R/Hornsby (265618)	4wDM	1948

*not on site
†stored and/or not on public display

Locomotive and multiple-unit notes: In service: 17, 51367, 51402, 52008 and 54047. Under restoration: 9, 828, 46512, D5394, 08490

Stock
20 ex-BR coaches; 4 ex-LMS coaches; 2 ex-LMS sleeping cars; 1 ex-LNER sleeping car; 1 ex-HR coach (stored at Bo'ness); 1 ex-NBR coach; numerous examples of rolling stock

Owners
6, 17 and 46512 the Highland Locomotive Co Ltd
828 the Scottish Locomotive Preservation Trust Fund
5025 the Watkinson Trust
D5302 and 26025 the Highland Diesel Locomotive Co Ltd
51367 and 51402 the Blue Square Heritage Group
51990, 52008, 52030 and 54047 My Little Sprinter Ltd

buffet car or facilities on many trains. Picnic tables at Boat of Garten (for use of ticket purchasers). No refreshment facilities on Saturday services

Souvenir shop: Boat of Garten and Aviemore

Depot: Aviemore (not open to public), sidings at Aviemore and Boat of Garten are not open to the public, those at Broomhill are visible from the road

Length of line: 10 miles

Journey time: Aviemore-Boat of Garten 15min; Aviemore-Broomhill 45min (outward) 35min, (inward). Round trip takes approximately 90min

Passenger trains: Steam-hauled services. Aviemore-Boat of Garten/ Broomhill. Most Saturdays, unless a special event is taking place,

services are run with a 'branch line' set

Period of public operation: 28, 29 March; 1-5, 8-13, 15/16, 18/19, 22/23, 25/26, 28/19 April; 2-4, 6/7, 9/10, 13/14, 16/17, 20/21, 23-27, 30/31 May; 3-7, 10-14, 17-21, 24-30 June; Daily July and August; 2-6, 9-13, 16-20, 23-27, 30 September; 1, 3/4, 7/8, 10/11, 14/15, 17/18, 21/22, 24/25, 28/29 October

Special events: Teddy Bears' Weekend — 23/24 May; Forties Weekend — 13/14 June; Steam Fair — 18/19 July; Santa Express — 12/13, 19/20, 24 December

Facilities for disabled: Access possible at Aviemore, Boat of Garten and Broomhill. Please contact in advance for directions and if a party involved

Special notes: First and third class travel available on most trains. Family fares available for third class travel. Special rates/arrangements for parties. Lunches on the train — Sundays 29 March to 25 October, also on Fridays 5 June until 26 September. Bicycles and dogs carried at a 'flat fee' of £1 — groups must give prior notice (bicycles must not be ridden on platforms or pedestrian pathways)

Membership details: Strathspey Railway Association, Spey Lodge, Aviemore Station.
Web site: www.strathspeyrailway association.org
Membership journal: *Strathspey Express* — quarterly

Museum — Summerlee Heritage Park — Lanarkshire

Due to major Heritage Lottery Fund support redevelopment, Summerlee's main exhibition hall and tramway was closed during 2006 and 2007 seasons. The redeveloped site has now been fully reopened

Manager: Neil Ballantyne

Operating society/organisation: Summerlee Heritage Park, Heritage Way, Coatbridge ML5 1QD (operated by North Lanarkshire Council)

Telephone: (01236) 638460

Fax: (01236) 440429

Public opening: Daily 10.00-17.00, except 25/26 December and 1/2 January.
Closes 16.00 Nov-March

Access by public transport: STP electric service from Glasgow Queen Street Low Level to Coatbridge Sunnyside (Airdrie/Drumgelloch line). Or from Glasgow Central via Motherwell to Coatbridge Central. Trains also run from Cumbernauld to Coatbridge Central, but not on Sundays

Car park: Opposite site

On site facilities: Tea room, gift shop. Working electric tramway

Locomotives

Name	No	Origin	Class	Type	Built
Springbok	4112	SAR	GMAM	4-8-2+2-8-4	1956

(3ft 6in gauge/built by North British Loco Co)

Unit 936103	977844	BR	303	DTS	1960
(303103)	977845	BR	303	DTS	1960
	977846	BR	303	MBS	1960

Industrial locomotives

Name	No	Builder	Type	Built
—	—	Barclay (472)	0-4-0DH	1966
—	—	H/Clarke (895)	0-6-0T	1909
—	—	G/Hogg	0-4-0T	1898
Robin	—	Sentinel (9628)	4wTG	1957

Stock

2 rail-mounted steam cranes.
Also on site are two former Glasgow trams: one, the Coplawhill Motor School training car, has just entered service at Summerlee; the second, a 'Coronation' class car, will shortly commence a full restoration to operational standards

with cars from Motherwell, and Düsseldorf; underground mine tour and miners' cottages

Special events: Organised events from April-October, details on request

Facilities for disabled: Toilets, wheelchair available

Wales

Bala Lake Railway (Rheilffordd Llyn Tegid)

Timetable Service — **Gwynedd**

Member: HRA, TT

This delightful narrow gauge railway follows the route of the former Bala-Dolgellau Railway, along the shore of Wales' largest natural lake. The railway's headquarters are to be found in the fine old station building at Llanuwchllyn at the south-western end of the line. Do not be deterred by the fact that the railway runs down the opposite shore of the lake to the main road — it is well worth the detour

General Manager: Roger Hine
Headquarters: Rheilffordd Llyn Tegid (Bala Lake Railway) Llanuwchllyn, Bala, Gwynedd LL23 7DD
Telephone: Llanuwchllyn (01678) 540666
Internet address: *Web site:* www.bala-lake-railway.co.uk
Main station: Llanuwchllyn
Other public stations: Llangower, Bala. Request halts at Pentrepiod and Bryn Hynod
OS reference: Llanuwchllyn SH 880300, Bala SH 929350
Car parks: Llanuwchllyn, Llangower and Bala town centre
Access by public transport: Arriva service No 94 to both Bala and

Industrial locomotives

Name	No	Builder	Type	Built
George B	—	Hunslet (680)	0-4-0ST	1898
Holy War	—	Hunslet (779)	0-4-0ST	1902
Alice	—	Hunslet (802)	0-4-0ST	1902
Maid Marian	5	Hunslet (822)	0-4-0ST	1903
Triassic	1270	Peckett (1270)	0-6-0ST	1911
Meirionnydd	11	Severn-Lamb (7322)	Bo-Bo	1973
Chilmark	12	R/Hornsby (194771)	4wDM	1939
Bob Davies	—	YEC (L125)	4wDM	1983
Cernyw	—	R/Hornsby (200748)	4wDM	1940
Lady Madcap	—	R/Hornsby (283512)	4wDM	1949

Locomotive notes: *Holy War* and *Maid Marian* are in regular use, remainder are on static display
Alice is being overhauled, *George B* is being re-assembled

Llanuwchllyn (from Wrexham or Barmouth)
Road access: Off the A494 Bala-Dolgellau road
Refreshment facilities: Llanuwchllyn. Large picnic site with toilet facilities by lake at Llangower
Souvenir shop: Llanuwchllyn
Depot: Llanuwchllyn
Length of line: 4.5 miles, 1ft 11.625in gauge
Passenger trains: Llanuwchllyn-Bala. Journey takes 25min in each direction

Period of public operation: Easter-end of September (except some Mondays and Fridays)
Facilities for disabled: Facilities available on most trains
Special notes: Small parties (10/12) may just turn up, but a day's notice required for larger groups
Family tickets: Available for all round trip journeys
Membership details: Membership Secretary, c/o Llanuwchllyn station
Membership journal: *Llanuwchllyn Express*

Barry Island Railway

Heritage Centre — **Vale of Glamorgan**

Member: HRA

At the end of 2008 the local council handed over the operation of the Barry Island Railway to a new operating company — Cambrian Transport Ltd. At the time of going to press no details were available of the 2009 operating dates.

Locomotives and multiple-units

Name	No	Origin	Class	Type	Built
—	28	TVR	O1	0-6-2T	1897
—	2861	GWR	2800	2-8-0	1918
—	4115	GWR	4101	2-6-2T	1936
—	5227	GWR	5205	2-8-0T	1924
—	6686	GWR	5600	0-6-2T	1928
—	44901	LMS	5MT	4-6-0	1945
—	80150	BR	4MT	2-6-4T	1956

Location: Barry Island Station, Barry Island, South Wales
General Manager: —
Operating society: Cambrian Transport Co
Car park: Large public car park near site
OS reference: ST 115667
Access by public transport: Frequent train services from Cardiff to Barry Island for cross platform interchange (Arriva Valley Lines)
On site facilities: Museum, shop, light refreshments
Public opening: Easter to mid-September (weekends and Bank Holidays), December (tel: 01466 748816 for more details)
Special events: PLease contact for details
Length of line: 3.5 miles
Facilities for disabled: Barry Island station is all on the level with no steps. Ramp access available for all trains. 100m level walk from ticket office to train. Parking by special arrangement to private car park
Further information: Vale of Glamorgan Railway Co, Barry Island Station, South Wales CF62 5TH
Membership details: Membership Secretary c/o above address
Note: As *Railways Restored 2009* went to press it was announced that the locomotives and rolling stock owned by the preservation society was expected to move to a site near Bridgend as part of the Garw Valley Regeneration scheme.

Name	No	Origin	Class	Type	Built
—	92245	BR	9F	2-10-0	1958
—	08481	BR	08	0-6-0DE	1958
—	08511	BR	08	0-6-0DE	1958
—	20228	BR	20	Bo-Bo	1966
—	D1725	BR	47	Co-Co	1964
—	73118	BR	73	Bo-Bo	1966
—	51339	P/Steel	117	DMBS	1959
—	51382	P/Steel	117	DMS	1959
—	51655	BR	115	DMBS	1959
—	51677	BR	115	DMBS	1959
—	51919	BR	108	DMBS	1956
—	52048	BR	108	DMCL	1960
—	54279	BR	108	DTC	1959
—	59664	BR	115	TC	1959

Locomotive notes:
Several of the locomotives listed above are expected to be used as a source of parts for 're-creation' projects. The 'Barry 7' are open to the public during the Transport Festival and Waterfront Festival

Industrial locomotives

Name	No	Builder	Type	Built
Pamela*	—	Hunslet (3840)	0-6-0ST	1956
—	7705	RSH (7705)	0-4-0ST	1952
Bill Caddick	—	H/Clarke (1168)	0-6-0DM	1959
—	—	Unilok (2183)		1964

*on hire to Lincolnshire Wolds Railway

Stock
BR Mk 1 and Mk 2 coaches, TVR coach No 153, operational steam crane, various freight vehicles

Owners
28 the National Railway Museum
08481, D1725 and DMU vehicles the Barry Railcar Project
08511 and 20228 Traditional Traction

Timetable Service	Brecon Mountain Railway	Merthyr Tydfil

A narrow gauge passenger-carrying railway close to Merthyr Tydfil built on part of the trackbed of the former Brecon & Merthyr Railway. Gradually being extended northwards, the railway has some interesting narrow gauge steam locomotives imported from East Germany and South Africa
General Manager: A. J. Hills
Headquarters: Brecon Mountain Railway, Pant Station, Dowlais, Merthyr Tydfil CF48 2UP
Telephone: Merthyr Tydfil (01685) 722988
Fax: (01685) 384854
Internet addresses: *e-mail:* enquiries@breconmountainrailway.co.uk
Web site: www.breconmountainrailway.co.uk
Main station: Pant
Car park: Pant station
OS reference: SO 063120
Access by public transport: Bus to Pant Cemetery — half hour frequency from Merthyr bus station. Main line rail service to Merthyr from Cardiff Central
Depot: Pant
Length of line: 5 miles (3.5 miles open for passenger traffic), 1ft 11.75in gauge
Journey time: Return trip approx 65min
Period of public operation: Daily

21 March-1 November 2009.
EXCEPT for: 23, 27, 30 March;
3, 6, 20, 24, 27 April;
1, 8, 11, 15, 18, 22 May;
21, 25, 28 September;
2, 5, 9, 12, 16, 19, 23 October
Refreshment facilities: Cafés at
Pant and Pontsticill
Special events: Santa Specials —
December
Facilities for disabled: Facilities
for disabled include ramps, toilets
and carriage designed to carry
wheelchairs
Special notes: There is no road
access to Pontsticill

Locomotives

Name	No	Builder	Type	Built
—	1	Baldwin (15511)	2-6-2	1898
—	2	Baldwin (61269)	4-6-2	1930
Sybil	—	Hunslet (827)	0-4-0ST	1903
Graf Schwerin-Löwitz	—	Arn Jung (1261)	0-6-2WT	1908
Pendyffryn	—	de Winton	0-4-0VBT	1894
Redstone	—	Redstone	0-4-0VBT	1905
—	146*	Henschel	2-8-2	1959
—	—	Brecon MR (001)	0-6-0DH	1987

*former South African Railways locomotive

Stock

Two balcony end 39-seat coaches; 2 balcony end 40-seat coaches; 1 19-seat
Caboose; 4 flat cars, crane and tamper, miscellaneous rail-carrying and
ballast wagons; Wickham petrol trolley

Museum — Conwy Valley Railway Museum — Betws-y-coed (Conwy CB)

Conveniently situated alongside
Betws-y-coed railway station, the
Museum presents some well-
displayed distractions to pass the
time including model train layouts
to delight both adult and child
Location: Adjacent to Betws-y-
coed station
OS reference: SH 796565
General Manager: Mr C. M.
Cartwright
Operating society/organisation:
Conwy Valley Railway Museum,
The Old Goods Yard, Betws-y-
coed, Conwy LL24 0AL
Telephone: 01690 710568
Fax: 01690 710132
Car park: On site
Access by public transport:
Betws-y-coed main line station
On site facilities: Refreshments in
buffet car. Bookshop and model/gift
shop in museum foyer, operating
train layouts, miniature railway
(1.25-miles, 7.25in gauge) steam-
hauled. Picnic area.
15in Tramway (operates daily) with
1989-built single-deck bogie tram.
A recent addition s a 60ft long 00
gauge model railway in a bogie
coach
Public opening:
Daily 10.00-17.00

Locomotives

Name	No	Builder	Type	Built
Britannia	70000	TMA Engineering (1ft 3in gauge)	4-6-2	1988
Old Rube*	—	Milner Eng	2-8-0	1983
Petunia*	—±	J. Stubbs	0-4-2T	1989
Shoshone*	—	Simkins/Milner	2-8-0	1975
Union Pacific*	—	R. Greatrex	Bo-Bo	1991
Douglas*	—†	P. Frank	2-4-0T	2004
Dragonfly*	—†	P. Frank	2-4-0T	2004
Gwyda Castle*	—	P. Zwicky-Ross/P. Frank	Bo-Bo	2004
—	—§	—	4-6-2	1935

*7.25in gauge
†based on Isle of Man Railway locomotives
§6in gauge Canadian Pacific locomotive, a prize winner at the Model
Engineer Exhibition
±on permanent loan

Stock

Standard gauge: 1 GWR fitter's van; 1 LMS 6-wheel van; 1 LNER CCT
van; 1 BR Mk 1 coach; 2 SR luggage vans; 1 Pullman coach; 15in bogie
tramcar
7.25in gauge: 5 articulated sit-in coaches; 2 twin-set articulated sit-in
covered coaches; 2 sets 3 articulated sit-in open coaches; 4 wagons plus
'self-drive' 0-4-0 'Toby Tram' and 2-4-0 *Billy*. 1 bogie ballast wagon and
2 three-plank wagons (P. Frank)
15in gauge: 1 wagon

Facilities for disabled: Access to
café, museum and toilets from car
park. Toilets are adapted for

Railway Centre/Museum — Corris Railway and Museum — Gwynedd

Member: HRA

In the heart of Wales' 'narrow gauge country', the Corris Railway provides a 50min round trip on the restored section of Mid Wales' first public narrow gauge railway. The Museum, situated in the remaining buildings of Corris station, displays relics, photographs and models of the railway

Location: In Corris village off A487 trunk road. Turn opposite Braichgoch Hotel, five miles north of Machynlleth and 11 miles south of Dolgellau

OS reference: SH 755078

Operating society: The Corris Railway Society, Corris Station Yard, Gwynedd (postal address: Corris, Machynlleth, Powys SY20 9SH)

Telephone: 01654 761303

Internet address:

e-mail: enquiries@corris.co.uk

Web site: www.corris.co.uk

Car park: Adjacent

Access by public transport: Arriva Trains services to Machynlleth. Bus Gwynedd services 2 (Aberystwyth-Dolgellau-Machynlleth), 30 (Machynlleth-Tywyn) and 34 (Machynlleth-Aberllefenni); Dyfi Valley service 530 (Tywyn-Machynlleth-Abergynolwyn)

Catering facilities: Snacks, teas and light refreshments

On site facilities: Souvenir shop, toilets and children's playground; close to Corris Craft Centre and King Arthur's Labyrinth; two miles from Centre for Alternative Technology

Passenger trains: Corris to Maespoeth

Length of line: Three-quarter-mile,

Locomotives

Name	No	Builder	Type	Built
Alan Meaden	5	M/Rail (22258)	4wDM	1965
—	6	R/Hornsby (51849)	4wDM	1966
—	7	Winson/Watkins	0-4-2ST	2005
—	8	Hunslet (7274)	4wDM	1973
Aberllefenni	9	Clayton (8045)	4wBE	1974

Locomotive notes: 5, 6 and 7 operational. 7 based on Corris No 4 now Talyllyn No 4 *Edward Thomas*. 8 and 9 undergoing restoration

In 2008 the Corris launched an appeal to build a new 'Falcon' 0-4-3ST locomotive to re-create the original CR Nos 1 to 3. The new locomotive will take No 10 in the fleet. Details from CRS 42 Bluebell Close, Taunton, Somerset TA1 3XQ

Stock

3 carriages (4th under construction) , 4 brake vans, 18 works wagons and 5 historic wagons

Owners

8 on loan from the National Mining Museum

9 donated by Winalate Ltd

2ft 3in gauge track. Planning permission for a further two miles of track has been granted

Public opening:

Museum and shop 10.30-17.00 open on train operating days (Full details on web site.)

Railway — passenger trains (usually steam-hauled) operate: 10-13, 19, 26 April; 2-4, 9/10, 16/17, 23-25, 30/31 May; 7, 14, 21, 28 June; 4/5, 11/12, 18/19, 25-28 July; 1-4, 8-11, 15-18, 22-25, 29-31 August; 5/6, 13, 20, 27 September; 24 October; 12/13 December. Trains leave Corris hourly 11.00-16.00.

Special trains and Museum openings can be booked by prior arrangement. Please check web site or write for further details

Special events: 2009 marks the 150th anniversary of the Corris. Gravity Goods Train — 1 April; Horse-worked freight trains — 11/12 April; Grand Opening of new carriage shed at Maespoeth — 9 May; Meet 'Kerr' from Christopher Awdry's book *Hugh Goes Sliding* — 17 May; Midsummer Modeller's Day — 21 June; Teddy Bears' sSpecial — 1/2 August; Poetry & Music Evening — 1 August; Model Railway & Toy Exhibition in Machynlleth — 29-31 August; Santa Specials — 12/13 December

Facilities for disabled: Disabled access carriage on all trains. Access to display area of Museum and shop

Membership details: Membership Secretary, c/o above address

Timetable Service — Fairbourne Railway — Gwynedd

Member: Britain's Great Little Railways

Since 1986 this railway has been regauged from 15in to 12.25in and has been transformed by the introduction of new locomotives and rolling stock, a tunnel through the sand dunes, new workshops and a café overlooking the Mawddach estuary. During the main season a two-train service is in operation. A free indoor attraction and small museum are open at Fairbourne terminus

Headquarters: Fairbourne Railway

Wales

Ltd, Beach Road, Fairbourne,
Gwynedd LL38 2EX
Telephone: (01341) 250362
Fax: (01341) 250240
Internet address: *e-mail:*
fairbourne.rail@btconnect.com
Web site:
http://www.fairbournerailway.com
Main station: Fairbourne
Other public stations: Golf Halt,
Barmouth Ferry Station
OS reference: SH 616128
Car parks: Fairbourne
Access by public transport:
Fairbourne railway station. Bus
Gwynedd service (No 28)
Refreshment facilities: Penrhyn
Point café, tea shop on platform at
Fairbourne
Souvenir shop: Fairbourne
Depot: Fairbourne
Length of line: 2 miles, 12.25in
gauge
Passenger trains: A 2-mile journey
connecting with ferry at Penrhyn
Point to Barmouth. 20min single
journey. Through tickets to
Barmouth (including ferry)
available
Period of public operation:
4-19, 25/26 April; April; daily 2

Locomotives

Name	No	Builder	Type	Built
Beddgelert	—	Curwen	0-6-4ST	1979
Yeo	—	Curwen	2-6-2T	1978
Sherpa	—	Milner	0-4-0STT	1978
Russell*	—	Milner	2-6-4T	1985
Lilian Walter†	—	FLW	A1-1AD	1985
Gwril	—	FLW	4wBE	1987
—§	—	Hunslet	4wDM	1994

FLW — Fairbourne Locomotive Works
*built as replica Leek & Manifold *Elaine*, rebuilt to present form 1985 at
FLW
†originally built by G&S Engineering in 1961 as 15in gauge *Sylvia*.
Rebuilt at Fairbourne in 1985
§to be regauged from 2ft to 12.25in

Stock
18 coaches; 14 freight

May to 20 September (closed low
season Fridays); 26/27 September;
3/4, 10/11, 17/18, 24-31 October;
1 November.
Santas operate 12/13 December
Special events: Friendly Fairbourne
Engines — 12/13 April; Little to
Large — Steam Engines in Action
— 24/25 May; Friendly Fairbourne
Engines — 27/28 July; Santa
Specials — 12/13 December

Membership details: Membership
Secretary, Fairbourne Railway
Supporters' Association, 8 Centre
One, Lysander Way, Old Sarum
Park, Salisbury SP4 6BU
Special notes: During inclement
weather the service may be
restricted or cancelled. Extra trains
and special parties by arrangement
with the manager

Timetable Service	**Ffestiniog Railway**	Gwynedd

Member: HRA
In many ways, evocative of the
early Swiss mountain railways as it
climbs high above Porthmadog
with some breathtaking views, the
railway still operates an interesting
variety of locomotives including
some unusual Victorian survivors.
Passengers have replaced slate as
the principal traffic over this
former quarry line
General Manager: Paul Lewin
Headquarters: Ffestiniog Railway
Co, Harbour Station, Porthmadog,
Gwynedd LL49 9NF
Telephone: Porthmadog (01766)
516000
Fax: 01766 516005
Internet address: *Web site:*
http://www.festrail.co.uk
Main stations: Porthmadog
Harbour, Blaenau Ffestiniog
Other public stations: Boston
Lodge, Minffordd, Penrhyn, Plas

Locomotives

Name	No	Builder	Type	Built
Princess+	1	G/England (199/200)	0-4-0STT	1863
Prince	2	G/England	0-4-0STT	1863
Palmerston	4	G/England	0-4-0STT	1863
Welsh Pony+	5	G/England (234)	0-4-0STT	1867
Earl of Merioneth	—	FR	0-4-4-0T	1979
Merddin Emrys	10	FR	0-4-4-0T	1879
David Lloyd George	12	FR	0-4-4-0T	1992
Taliesin	—	FR	0-4-4T	1999
Moelwyn	—	Baldwin (49604)	2-4-0DM	1918
Lilla	—	Hunslet (554)	0-4-0ST	1891
Blanche	—	Hunslet (589)	2-4-0STT	1893
Linda§	—	Hunslet (590)	2-4-0STT	1893
Britomart*	—	Hunslet (707)	0-4-0ST	1899
Mountaineer§	—	Alco (57156)	2-6-2T	1917
Livingston Thompson†+	3	FR	0-4-4-0T	1886
Harlech Castle	—	B/Drewry (3767)	0-6-0-DH	1983
Ashover	—	Hibberd (3307)	4wDM	1948
Moel Hebog	—	Hunslet (4113)	0-4-0DM	1955
Mary Ann	—	M/Rail (596)	4wDM	1917
Criccieth Castle	—	FR	0-6-0DH	1995
The Colonel	—	M/Rail (8788)	4wDM	1943
The Lady Diana	—	M/Rail (21579)	4wDM	1957

Wales

189

Halt, Tan-y-Bwlch, Dduallt,
Tanygrisiau

SatNav postcodes:
Porthmadog Harbour — LL49 9NF
Minffordd —LL48 6HF
Tan-y-Bwlch —LL41 3AC
Tanygrisiau —LL41 3TW
Blaenau Ffestiniog —LL41 3F
OS reference: SH 571384
Car parks: Porthmadog,
Minffordd, Tan-y-Bwlch,
Tanygrisiau, Blaenau Ffestiniog
Access by public transport:
Minffordd and Blaenau Ffestiniog
main line stations. Porthmadog,
Minffordd and Blaenau Ffestiniog
served by local buses
Refreshment facilities: Spooners
Café and Bar at Porthmadog, open
all day. Licensed café at
Tan-y-Bwlch, seasonal opening.
Refreshments available on most
trains
Souvenir shops: Porthmadog,
Tan-y-Bwlch, Blaenau Ffestiniog
Museum: Interesting artefacts in
Spooners Bar, Porthmadog
Depot: Boston Lodge
Length of line: 13.5 miles, 1ft
11.5in gauge

Name	No	Builder	Type	Built
Stefcomatic	—	Matisa (48589)	2-2-0DH	1956
Vale of Ffestiniog	—	Funkey	Bo-Bo	1968
Moel-y-Gest	—	Hunslet (6659)	0-4-0DM	1965
Harold	—	Hunslet (7195)	0-4-0DM	1974

*privately owned
†on loan to National Railway Museum
+museum condition, not operational
§out of service in 2009

Stock
37 bogie coaches; 8 4-wheel coaches; 4 brake vans, plus numerous service
vehicles

Passenger trains: Porthmadog-
Blaenau Ffestiniog
Period of public operation: Daily
mid March to end October. Limited
winter service
Special events: Halloween and
Santa Trains
Facilities for disabled:
Porthmadog and Blaenau Ffestiniog
easily accessible for wheelchairs.
Limited facilities on trains for
disabled in wheelchairs by prior
arrangement. Literature available in
large print and Braille

Special facilities:
Tan-y-Bwlch station is a registered
location for civil/wedding
ceremonies. Special Functions
department handles private train
bookings — phone for details:
01766 516024
Membership details: Ffestiniog
Railway Society (see above
address)
Membership journal: *Ffestiniog
Railway Magazine* — quarterly

Timetable Service	**Great Orme Tramway**	Conwy

Member: HRA
A cable-hauled street tramway to
the summit of the Great Orme is
operated as two sections involving a
change halfway. Opened to the
public in July 1903, it includes
gradients as steep as 1 in 3.9
Location: Great Orme Tramway,
Victoria Station, Church Walks,
Llandudno LL30 1AZ
OS reference: SH 7781
Operating society/organisation:
Conwy County Borough Council,
Property Services, Library
Buildings, Mostyn Street,
Llandudno LL30 1JP
Telephone: (01492) 879306
Internet address: *e-mail:*

tramwayenquiries@conwy.gov.uk
Web site:
www.greatormetramway.com
Car park: Approximately 100yd
from Lower Terminal or adjacent to
Summit Terminal
Access by public transport: Good
On site facilities: Shop
Exhibits for viewing: There are
exhibits displayed at the Halfway
station and a small exhibition (free)
Period of public operation: March
to end of October (daily) 10.00-
18.00 (17.00 March and October).
Trams run every 20min.
Can be subject to change
Special notes: The only remaining
cable-hauled street tramway in

Britain. 1 mile long rising to 650ft
(3ft 6in gauge)
Stock: 4 tramcars each seating 48,
built 1902/3
Family tickets: Available, along
with joint tickets for Great Orme
Mine — Bronze Age Heritage
Centre
Facilities for disabled: The
tramway has limited disabled access
and is unsuitable for the
wheelchair-bound, although
wheelchairs can be folded away in
the tramcars.

Access statement available upon
request/on our web site

Gwili Railway (Rheilffordd Gwili)

Member: HRA, TT

Runs alongside the River Gwili on part of the Carmarthen-Aberystwyth line. Attractions include a fully restored signalbox, historic station building, museum of signalling and other railway artefacts, and TPO. 2008 was the 30th anniversary of the first train to run on the railway. The line runs fron Bronwydd Arms to Danycoed Halt. There is a 7.25in gauge miniature railway and a riverside picnic site at Llwyfan Cerrig.

Headquarters: Gwili Railway Co Ltd, Bronwydd Arms Station, Bronwydd Arms, Carmarthen, SA33 6HT

Telephone: Carmarthen (01267) 230666

Internet address: *e-mail:* company@gwilirailway.co.uk
Web site: www.gwili-railway.co.uk

OS reference:
Bronwydd Arms —SN 417239
Llwyfan Cerrig —SN 405258

Main station: Bronwydd Arms

Other public station: Llwyfan Cerrig, Danycoed

Car park: Bronwydd Arms (free) (not 21-24 March, 13/14, 20/21 September when Park & Ride from United Counties Showground [AA signed] must be used)

Access by public transport: Carmarthen railway station, then First Cymru buses to Bronwydd (Traveline: 0871 200 2233)

Refreshment facilities: Bronwydd Arms

Souvenir shop: Bronwydd Arms

Depot: Bronwydd Arms, stock also kept at Llwyfan Cerrig

Length of line: 2.5 miles

Locomotive

Name	No	Origin	Class	Type	Built
—**	D2178	BR	03	0-6-0DM	1962

Industrial locomotives

Name	No	Builder	Type	Built
Trecatty	—	R/Hornsby (421702)	0-6-0DM	1959
Olwen	—	RSH (7058)	0-4-0ST	1942
Haulwen	—	V/Foundry (5272)	0-6-0ST	1945
Welsh Guardsman	71516	RSH (7170)	0-6-0ST	1944
Victory**	—	A/Barclay (2201)	0-4-0ST	1945
Sir John†	—	Avonside (1680)	0-6-0ST	1914

Stock

8 ex-BR Mk 1 coaches; 1 ex-BR griddle car; 1 ex-BR Mk 3 sleeper; 1 ex-TVR coach; 1 ex-GWR coach; 1 ex-GWR 'Mink' van; 2 ex-GWR Fruit D; 1 GWR Bloater; 1 ex-GWR Loriot D; 2 GWR brake vans; 2 GWR bogie bolsters; 1 SECR parcels van; 1 SR parcels van; 2 ex-Army vans; 1 ex-LNER open wagon; 3 open wagons; 2 ballast wagons; 1 Booth diesel-hydraulic crane

Owners
**Caerphilly Railway Society
†Vale of Neath Railway Society

Passenger trains: Bronwydd Arms-Llwyfan Cerrig-Danycoed (Llwyfan Cerrig only during special events)

Period of public operation: 10-13 April; 3/4, 24/25, 26-28 May; 3, 7, 10, 14, 17, 21, 24, 28 June; 1, 5, 8, 12, 15, 19, 22, 26-31 July; 2-7, 9-14, 16-21, 23-28, 30 August; 1, 2, 2, 13/14, 19/20, 27 September; 4, 11, 18, 25, 27-28, 31 October; 5/6, 12/13, 19/20, 22-24 December

Public opening: Trains leave Bronwydd Arms at 10.30, 11.50, 13.20, 14.50, 16.10 on Wednesdays in July, Bank Holiday Mondays and during weekdays of the main operating season. On all other dates 11.15, 12.45, 14.15, 15.45 (except special events when a more frequent service operates)

Facilities for disabled: Access to stations, TPO and trains

Special events: Day out with Thomas — 10-13 April, 13/14, 19/20 September; Halloween Evening Specials — 31 October (special timetable operates); Santa Specials — 5/6, 12/13, 19/20, 22-24 December

Special notes: Family tickets available

Special facilities: Trains may be hired for special events, tour parties, birthdays, etc

Llanberis Lake Railway (Rheilffordd Llyn Padarn)

Member: HRA

A narrow gauge passenger-carrying railway starting next to the historic Dinorwic Quarry workshops (now part of the National Museum of Wales) and running along the shores of the Llanberis lake using the trackbed of the former slate railway line to Port Dinorwic. Excellent views of Snowdonia and good picnic spots along the line

General Manager: David Jones

Headquarters: Llanberis Lake Railway, Gilfach Ddu, Llanberis, Gwynedd LL55 4TY

Telephone: Llanberis (01286) 870549

Internet address: *e-mail:*
info@lake-railway.co.uk
Web site:
www.lake-railway.co.uk
Main station: Padarn Park
station/Gilfach Ddu
Other public stations: Cei Llydan
and Llanberis (village)
OS reference: SH 586603
Car park: Padarn Park
station/Gilfach Ddu
Refreshment facilities: Padarn
Park station/Gilfach Ddu
Souvenir shop: Padarn Park
station/Gilfach Ddu, Llanberis
station
Length of line: 2.5 miles, 1ft 11.5in
gauge
Passenger trains: Gilfach Ddu-
Llanberis-Penllyn-Gilfach Ddu
The half mile extension from
Gilfach Ddu to Llanberis village is
now open
Journey time: Return trip approx
60min
Period of public operation:
Tuesdays and Wednesdays from
mid-February to mid-March, daily
February half-term week (15-22
February). Sundays,
Tuesdays/Wednesdays and

Industrial locomotives

Name	No	Builder	Type	Built
Elidir	1	Hunslet (493)	0-4-0ST	1889
Thomas Bach/Wild Aster	2	Hunslet (849)	0-4-0ST	1904
Dolbadarn	3	Hunslet (1430)	0-4-0ST	1922
Topsy	7	R/Hornsby (441427)	4wDM	1961
Twll Coed	8	R/Hornsby (268878)	4wDM	1956
—	—	R/Hornsby (425796)	4wDM	1958
Garrett	11	R/Hornsby (198286)	4wDM	1939
—	18	M/Rail (7927)	4wDM	1941
Llanelli	19	R/Hornsby (451901)	4wDM	1961
Una*	—	Hunslet (873)	0-4-0ST	1905

*not part of the railway's motive power stock. Housed at the adjacent slate museum and can sometimes be seen working demonstration freight trains

Stock
13 bogie coaches; 20 wagons

Thursdays from 15 March until Easter. Sundays to Fridays from Easter to September, daily 17 May to 4 September; Sundays to Thursdays in October. Wednesdays in November and until 19 December. Also Saturdays June, July and August.
Family tickets available, under 3s free
Special events: Easter Egg Hunt over Easter weekend; Teddy Bears'

Picnic — August Bank Holiday Weekend; Santa Trains in December
Facilities for disabled: Level approaches throughout shop, café and to train. Special toilet facilities provided. Specially adapted carriage for wheelchair users
Marketing names: Rheilffordd Llyn Padarn Cyfyngedig (Padarn Lake Railway Ltd); Llanberis Lake Railway

---

Timetable Service	**Llangollen Railway**	Denbighshire

Member: HRA, TT
The line, which is presently 7.5 miles long, is situated in the picturesque Dee Valley and follows the River Dee for much of its route affording good views of the dramatic Welsh countryside between Llangollen and Carrog. A notable event in 2002 was BBC 2's Timewatch programme re-enactment of the Rainhill Trials using the replica locomotives *Rocket, Sans Pareil* and *Novelty,* on the section of line between Glyndyfrdwy and Carrog. The extensive renovation of Berwyn Viaduct the following year won a national award. In 2006 the renovation of Llangollen station was completed with assistance from the Heritage Lottery Fund, and the renovation of Berwyn station commenced last year. Fortunately the railway took the

Locomotives and multiple-units

Name	No	Origin	Class	Type	Built
—	2859*	GWR	2800	2-8-0	1918
—	3802	GWR	2800	2-8-0	1938
—	5199	GWR	5101	2-6-2T	1934
—	5532*	GWR	4575	2-6-2T	1928
—	5539*	GWR	4575	2-6-2T	1928
—	6430	GWR	6400	0-6-0PT	1925
—	7754*	GWR	5700	0-6-0PT	1930
Foxcote Manor	7822	GWR	'Manor'	4-6-0	1950
—	47298	LMS	3F	0-6-0T	1924
Kenneth Aldcroft	44806	LMS	5MT	4-6-0	1944
—	80072*	BR	4MT	2-6-4T	1954
—	03162	BR	03	0-6-0DM	1960
—	13265	BR	08	0-6-0DE	1956
—	25313*	BR	25	Bo-Bo	1966
—	37240	BR	37	Co-Co	1964
Mirlees Pioneer	37901	BR	37	Co-Co	1963
—	46010*	BR	46	1Co-Co1	1961
Orion	D1566	BR	47	Co-Co	1962
—	50416	Wickham	109	MBS	1958
—	50447	BRCW	104	DMBS	1957
—	50454	BRCW	104	DMBS	1957
—	50528	BRCW	104	DMC	1957

Wales

opportunity to reinstate the platform extension cantilevered to the side of Berwyn Viaduct when that structure was restored, allowing the station to regain its original appearance. The platform extension had been removed by British Railways in 1962. Work is also continuing to allow the reinstatement of the railway between its current terminus at Carrog and the town of Corwen a distance of 2.5 miles, where a new station will have to be constructed. Clearance of the trackbed has been undertaken and materials are being obtained ready for the day when formal permission to commence the rebuilding is given

Location: Llangollen station is situated alongside the River Dee at the junction of Abbey Road (A542) with Castle Street/Mill Street (A539). Traffic from the A5 should turn off at the traffic lights into Castle Street (A539).

Chairman: Geoff Williams

Operating company: Llangollen Railway plc

Supporting organisation/ leaseholder: Llangollen Railway Trust Ltd

Headquarters/principal station: The Station, Abbey Road, Llangollen, Denbighshire LL20 8SN (both organisations)

Telephone:
General enquiries: 01978 860979 (office hours).
Talking Timetable: 01978 860951 (24hr).
Santa booking: 01978 860979 (1 October to 24 December)

Fax: 01978 869247

Internet address: *e-mail:* llangollen,railway@btinternet.com
Web site: http://www.llangollen-railway. co.uk

OS reference: SJ 214422

Car park:
Llangollen — Market Street and Mill Street public car parks; Carrog — station car park on B5437 off A5 west of Llangollen

Access by public transport:
By rail: Ruabon (5 miles) on Shrewsbury-Chester line, then by bus
By bus: Regular service runs Monday-Saturday and less frequently on Sundays.
Enquiries:
Traveline Cymru 0870 6082608

Name	No	Origin	Class	Type	Built
—	51618	BR	127	DMBS	1959
—	51907	BR	108	DMBS	1960
—	54490	BR	108	DTC	1960
—	56171	Wickham	109	DTC	1958
—	56456	Cravens	105	DMBS	1958

*locomotives either stored, under restoration or major overhaul currently not on public display. The frames and boiler of new-build 6880 *Bretton Grange* are located at Llangollen

Industrial locomotives

Name	No	Builder	Type	Built
Eliseg	—	Fowler (22753)	0-4-0DM	1939
Jennifer	—†	H/Clarke (1731)	0-6-0T	1942
Jessie	—†	Hunslet (1873)	0-6-0ST	1937
Darfield No 1	—†	Hunslet (3783)	0-6-0ST	1953
Austin No 1	—	Kitson (5459)	0-6-0ST	1932
—	68072	Vulcan (5309)	0-6-0ST	1945
—	391•	YEC (2630)	0-6-0DE	1959
—	398•	YEC (2769)	0-6-0DE	1959
—	D2892	YEC/BTH (2782)	0-4-0DE	1960
—	D2899	YEC (2854)	0-6-0DE	1961
Davy	—	E/Electric (1901)	0-6-0DE	1951

†expected to be away on hire for 2009
•on five year loan from Wilmott Bros, Ilkeston

Stock: *coaches, approx 45 in total including* — Service sets of Mk 1 stock, 4 BR suburban coaches; 1 LNER Thompson lounge car; 1 LNER Thompson brake coach; 3 GWR autocoaches; 1 GN brake, etc, some under restoration

Stock: *wagons, approx 50 including* — 2 Bolster wagons; 3 GWR Toad brake vans; 1 BR(E) brake van; 4 BR ballast wagons; 1 BR Presflow wagon; 1 GWR 'Fruit D'; 2 GWR Tube wagons; 1 Esso tank wagon; 1 Shell tank wagon plus various other items of freight stock

Stock: *maintenance* — Cowans 50-ton breakdown crane ARD96718 ex-Laira; DRG 12-ton diesel-hydraulic crane, Taylor & Hibberd 5-ton crane, Matisa track recording machine; Trackmaster light shunting vehicle; O&K road-railer

Owners
2859 and 5532 the Llangollen Railway GW Locomotive Group
3802 the GW 3802 Ltd
5199 the 5199 Project
7754, 13265, *Jennifer* and *Austin No 1* the Llangollen Railway Trust Ltd
7822 the Foxcote Manor Society
80072 the 80072 Steam Locomotive Co Ltd
03162 the Wirral Borough Council
All DMUs the Llangollen Railcar group
All main line diesel fleet (except 37901) plus *Davy* the Llangollen Diesel Group
Remainder are privately owned

(www.traveline.org.uk)
Bus enquiries: 08712 002233
National Rail enquiries: 08457 484950

Station information:
Llangollen — Toilets (inc disabled and baby changing, souvenir shop, café
Berwyn — Tea room only open on summer weekends
Deeside Halt — Trains call by request only, please inform guard or give a clear signal to driver to be picked up (please see timetable for specific services as not all trains stop)
Glyndyfrdwy — Toilets, tea room open on peak weekends

Carrog — Car and coach park (free), toilets with disabled access and tea room
Length of line: 7.5 miles
Passenger trains: Llangollen-Carrog
Period of public operation: 14/15, 21/22, 28/29 March; 6-26 April; daily 1 May to 18 October; 24-31 October; 1, 5 November; 5/6, 12/13, 19/20, 26-31 December; Daily 1-4 January 2010
Special events: Mothering Sunday — 22 March; Steam Gala — 17-26 April; Murder Mystery* — 2 May; Heritage Railcar (DMU) Gala — 16/17 May; Real Ale Train — 6 June;
Father's Day Real Ale Train — 21 June; Murder Mystery* — 4 July; Ivor the Engine — 18 July; Real Ale Train — 1 August; Day out with Thomas — 8-16 August;

Murder Mystery* — 5 September; Steam Gala — 11-13 September; Hope House Fundraiser — 3/4 October; Day out with Thomas — 24 October-1 November; Ride the Rocket — 5 November; Santa Specials* — 5/6, 12/13, 19/20 December; Mince Pie Specials — 26 December to 4 January 2010. *These events must be pre-booked
Driver experiences: The railway offers a varied programme of footplate and railway experience courses from early spring through to late autumn, ranging from the basic Summer Evening Ramble to the more advanced all-day railway experience. Corces are available on steam and diesel locomotives as well as diesel railcars for both individual and group bookings. A brochure is available from Llangollen station and early

booking is recommended
Special facilities: The Robertson Suite at Llangollen is licensed for civil/wedding ceremonies. Train hire available for receptions
Facilities for disabled: Special passenger coach for wheelchairs, toilet facilities at Llangollen and Carrog
Membership details: The Membership Secretary, Llangollen Railway Trust Ltd, c/o above address
Membership journal: *Steam at Llangollen*
Special note: For safety reasons visitors to the railway are not permitted access to the locomotive yard, engine shed or workshop unless accompanied by a qualified member of the Llangollen Railway

---

| Museum | Penrhyn Castle Industrial Railway Museum | Gwynedd |

Member: HRA
A collection of historic industrial steam locomotives, both standard and narrow gauge, displayed in Penrhyn Castle, a well-known National Trust property in the area regularly open to visitors
Location: Llandegai, near Bangor. One mile east of Bangor on the A5
OS reference: SH 603720
Operating society/organisation: National Trust, Penrhyn Castle, Industrial Railway Museum, Llandegai, Nr Bangor LL57 4HN
Telephone: Bangor (01248) 353084
Internet address: *Web site:* www.nationaltrust.org
Car park: Within castle grounds
Access by public transport:
By rail: Bangor (3 miles).
By bus: Arriva Cymru 5, 6, 7 and 67, 5X. Bus stop 1 mile walk through grounds
On site facilities: The castle is open to the public, and contains a gift shop. Light refreshments are available, hot meals are available between 12.00 and 14.30
Public opening: Daily (except Tuesdays) late March-end October 11.00-17.00. Last admission 30min

Industrial locomotives

Name	No	Builder	Type	Built
Kettering Furnaces No 3	—	B/Hawthorn (859)	0-4-0ST	1885*
Watkin	—	de Winton	0-4-0VBT	1893*
Fire Queen	—	Horlock	0-4-0	1848†
Hawarden	—	H/Clarke (526)	0-4-0ST	1899
Vesta	—	H/Clarke (1223)	0-6-0T	1916
Charles	—	Hunslet (283)	0-4-0ST	1882§
Hugh Napier	—	Hunslet (855)	0-4-0ST	1904§
—	1	Neilson (1561)	0-4-0WT	1870
Haydock	—	Stephenson (2309)	0-6-0T	1879
Acorn	—	R/Hornsby (327904)	0-4-0DM	1948

*3ft gauge
†4ft gauge
§1ft 10.75in gauge

Stock
10 narrow gauge rolling stock exhibits from the Padarn/Penrhyn system, most of which have been restored.
The small relics section includes a comprehensive display of railway signs and model locomotives in the upper stable block

The museum also has displays of tools used in the quarries and railway systems

Recent restorations now on display
One of the three coaches built at the quarry for the conveyance of visitors around the works. This one formed part of the train used by Princess Margaret and Lord Snowdon on their Royal visit to Wales in May 1962.
The Dinorwic Quarry Pedal Car is thought to have been built c1860 by the New Howe Co of Glasgow. It was used by the chief engineer of the quarry to inspect the track

194 **Wales**

before closing
Facilities for disabled: Access to castle and museum
Special notes: For those interested in stately homes the castle is well worth a visit. The entrance fee covers both the castle and the railway exhibits housed in the castle courtyard. Ruston Hornsby locomotive *Acorn* can be seen operating on some occasions during opening times. For exhibits not on display please ask a member of museum staff for assistance. Reduced entry fee for grounds and railway museum

Pontypool & Blaenavon Railway

Torfaen

Member: HRA

The historic Blaenavon site, complete with its railway installations and locomotives, can easily be included in a visit to Big Pit Mining Museum

Location: Just off the B4248 between Blaenavon and Brynmawr. Signposted as you approach Blaenavon

OS reference: SO 237093

Operating society/organisation: Pontypool & Blaenavon Railway Co (1983) Ltd, The Railway Shop, 13A Broad Street, Blaenavon, Torfaen NP4 9ND

Telephone/Fax: (01495) 792263

Internet address: *e-mail:* info@pbrly.co.uk

Web site: www.pontypool-and-blaenavon.co.uk

Car park: Adjacent to railway terminus

SatNav postcode: NP4 9SF

On site facilities: Light refreshments, souvenir shop and toilets available at Furnace Sidings. Light refreshments available on some services

Public opening:
10-13, 18/19, 25/26 April; 2-4, 9/10, 16/17, 23-25, 30/31 May; 6/7, 13/14, 20/21, 27/28 June; 4/5, 11/12, 18/19, 25/26 July; 1/2, 4-6, 8/9, 11-13, 15/16, 18-20, 22/23, 25-27, 29-31 August; 5/6, 12/13, 19/20, 26/27 September; 31 October; 5/6, 12/13, 19-22 December; 2/3 January 2010
Trains run every half hour from Furnace Sidings station from 11.30 16.30.
Return journey time about 17min
Note: All services will be either DMU or diesel-locomotive hauled except 9/10 August

Special events: Easter Bunnies — 12/13 April; Teddy Bears' Picnic — 3/4 May; Country & Western Weekend — 24/25 May; Little

Locomotives

Name	No	Origin	Class	Type	Built
—	4253	GWR	4200	2-8-0T	1917
—	5668	GWR	5600	0-6-2T	1926
—	9629	GWR	5700	0-6-0PT	1946
—	03141	BR	03	0-6-0DM	1960
Steve Orgam GM	D5627	BR	31	A1A-A1A	1960
—	37023§	BR	37	Co-Co	1961
—	37216	BR	37	Co-Co	1964
Silver Jubilee/ Jiwbili Arian	73128	BR	73	Bo-Bo	1966
—	51351	P/Steel	117	DMBS	1959
—	51397	P/Steel	117	DMS	1959
—	51942	BR	108	DMCL	1960
—	52044	BR	108	DMCL	1960
—	54270	BR	108	DTCL	1960
—	50632	BR	108	DMCL	1960
—	59520	P/Steel	117	TC	1959
—	60117	BR	205	DMBS	1957
—	60828	BR	205	DTC	1957
unit 1198	60573	BR	3CEP	TS	1958
unit 1198	61736	BR	3CEP	DMS	1958
unit 1198	61737	BR	3CEP	DMS	1958
unit 1399	62385	BR	3CIG	MBS	1971
unit 1399	76747	BR	3CIG	DTC	1971
unit 1399	76818	BR	3CIG	DTC	1971

§expected to arrive 2009 following restoration

Industrial locomotives

Name	No	Builder	Type	Built
Pontyberem	2	Avonside (????)	0-6-0ST	1900
Harry	—	Barclay (1823)	0-4-0ST	1926
Tom Parry	—	Barclay (2015)	0-4-0ST	1935
—	8	RSH (7139)	0-6-0ST	1944
Llanwern	104	E/Electric (D1249)	0-6-0DH	1968
—	106	E/Electric (D1226)	0-6-0DH	1971
—	RT1	Fowler (22497)	0-6-0DM	1938
Ebbw	17	Hunslet (7063)	0-8-0DH	1971
—	14	H/Clarke (D615)	0-6-0DH	1938
—	DL16	H/Clarke (D1387)	0-4-0DH	1968
Gower Princess	—	Ruston (200793)	4wDM	1940
Panteg No 1	—	Sentinel (10083)	0-6-0DH	1961
William Ellis	—	T/Hill (136C)	4wDM	1964
—	19*	Bagnall (2962)	0-4-0ST	1950

*on hire from Bodmin & Wenford Railway during 2009

Stock

10 ex-BR Mk 1 coaches, 4 ex-GWR coaches, 3 ex-LSWR coaches, 1 ex-LMS sleeper, 1 SR Post Office Tender, 35 other vans, china clay, coke and tank wagons

Wales

195

Engines Weekend — 6/7 June; Model Railway Show and Father's Day — 20/21 June; Gam Lakes Day — 28 June; 1960s Beer Festival — 11/12 July; Diesel Gala — 25/26 July; Ivor the Engine — 9/10 August; Transport Rally — 30/31 August; 140th Anniversary Gala — 12/13 September; Southern Region with Attitude — 26/27 September; Ghost Train — 31 October; Santa Specials (half-hourly 10.30-16.00) — 5/6, 12/13,

Owners
Class 108s the Gwent 108 Group
3CEP unit the EMU Preservation Society
3CIG unit the Save the CIGs Group

19-22 December; New Year DMU Specials — 2/3 January 2010 Please visit web site for up-to-date information.
Special notes: The railway is actively working on the southern extension to Blaenavon High Level

which it plans to open at Easter 2010
Membership details: c/o above address, or call at 'The Railway Shop', Broad Street, Blaenavon

---

Rheilffordd Eryri — Welsh Highland Railway (Caernarfon)

Member: HRA

Travel from the world famous Caernarfon Castle to the village of Rhyd Ddu, high in the foothills of Snowdonia, behind the most powerful 2ft gauge steam locomotives in the world. New extension opening 2009 to Beddgelert then Porthmadog later in the year

General Manager: Paul Lewin
Headquarters: Ffestiniog Railway Co, Harbour Station, Porthmadog LL49 9NF
Telephone: Porthmadog (01766) 516000
Fax: 01766 516005
Internet address: *Web site:* http://www.festrail.co.uk
Main station: Caernarfon
Other public stations: Bontnewydd, Dinas, Waunfawr, Plas y Nant, Snowdon Ranger, Rhyd Ddu, Beddgelert Forest, Beddgelert, Porthmadog
SatNav postcodes:
Caernarfon LL55 2YD
Dinas LL54 2UP
Waunfawr LL55 4AQ
Rhyd Ddu LL54 6TN
Porthmadog LL49 9NF
OS reference: SH 481625
Car parks: Caernarfon, Dinas and Porthmadog
Access by public transport: Caernarfon is served by local buses. The station at Bangor is served by Virgin and Arriva Trains (Wales). There is a regular bus service

Locomotives

Name	No	Builder	Type	Built
—	K1	B/Peacock (5292)	0-4-0+0-4-0	1909
—**	133	S. F. Belge (2683)	2-8-2	1953
—**	134	S. F. Belge (2684)	2-8-2	1953
*Millennium/ Mileniwm**	138	B/Peacock (7863)	2-6-2+2-6-2	1958
—*†	140	B/Peacock (7865)	2-6-2+2-6-2	1958
—*	143	B/Peacock (7868)	2-6-2+2-6-2	1958
—*	87	Cockerill (3267)	2-6-2+2-6-2	1936
Castell Caernarfon	—	Funkey	Bo-Bo	1968
Upnor Castle	—	Hibberd (3687)	4wDM	1954
Conway Castle	—	Hibberd (3831)	4wDM	1958

*former South African Railways NGG16 class locomotives
**former South African Railways NG15 class locomotives awaiting restoration
†undergoing restoration

Stock
16 bogie coaches, 1 brake van (goods), numerous service vehicles

between Bangor and Caernarfon
Depot: Dinas
Length of line: 12 miles, 1ft 11.5in gauge. Extending to 25 miles in 2009
Passenger trains: Caernarfon-Rhyd Ddu. Opening to Beddgelert and Porthmadog during the year. Please contact for details
Period of public operation: Easter to end of October. Limited winter service
Facilities for disabled: Limited facilities on trains for disabled in wheelchairs by prior arrangement. Literature available in large print and Braille

Refreshments: A refreshment trolley is available on most trains. Snowdonia Parc Hotel is situated at Waunfawr station serving a large selection of snacks, meals and real ale
Souvenir shop: There is a new enlarged gift shop at Caernarfon
Special event: 'Rail Ale' Beer Festival — May; Halloween and Santa Trains
Membership details: Welsh Highland Railway Society
Membership journal: *Snowdon Ranger* — quarterly

Rhyl Miniature Railway

Member: Britain's Great Little Railways

The miniature railway operating around the Marine Lake at Rhyl is among the oldest 15in gauge railways anywhere in the world. Its origins go back to 1911, and on peak days you can ride on the same train that visitors in 1920 would have found. The new building 'Central Station' opened in 1997 and has its own audio-visual touch screen

Operating society/organisation: Rhyl Steam Preservation Trust

Location: Marine Lake, Wellington Road, Rhyl, Denbighshire

Internet address: *Web site:* www.rhylminiaturerailway.co.uk

Trust secretary: Simon Townsend

Postal address: 10 Cilnant, Mold, Flintshire CH7 1GG

Telephone: 01352 759109

OS reference: SN 072124

SatNav postcode: LL18 1LN

Length: Approx 1 mile (1ft 3in gauge)

On site facilities: Car park

Locomotives

Name	No	Builder	Type	Built
Joan	101	Barnes	4-4-2	1920
Railway Queen	102	Barnes	4-4-2	1921
Michael	105	Barnes	4-4-2	c1925
Billy	106	Barnes	4-4-2	1934
—	44	Cagney	4-4-0	c1910
Clara	—	Guest & Saunders LE	0-4-2DM (SO)	1961
—	—	Lister	4wDM	1938
—	—	Hayne/Minirail	2w-2-4BER	1983

Rolling stock: 5 bogie 'cars de luxe' built in the 1910s and a similar vehicle built in 2001, 2 Cagney bogie coaches built c1904, ballast wagon

Owner
Billy Rhyl Town Council

Access by public transport: Approx 1 mile from Rhyl main line station, buses to Towyn and Abergele pass by

Period of public operation: Operation (steam) Bank Holiday Sundays and Mondays, every Sunday from Easter to September, every Thursday and Saturday during school holidays; from 12.00 or earlier. Also open with diesel or electric haulage, Saturdays from Easter to September, and all other days during summer school holidays

Special event: Gala — 23-25 May

Membership details: Friends of Rhyl Miniature Railway, details from 01745 339477, newsletters twice a year

---

Snowdon Mountain Railway

Member: HRA

The only public rack and pinion railway in the British Isles, opened in 1896, this bustling line climbs the slopes of Snowdon to the café at the top

General Manager: Alan Kendall

Engineering Manager: Dave Black

Commercial Manager: Vince Hughes

Marketing Manager: Jonathan Tyler

Headquarters: Snowdon Mountain Railway, Llanberis LL55 4TY

Telephone: 0871 720 0033 (advance bookings available via telephone)

Fax: (01286) 872518

Internet address: *e-mail:* info@snowdonrailway.co.uk

Web site:

Locomotives

Name	No	Builder	Type	Built
Enid	2	SLM (924)	0-4-2T	1895
Wyddfa	3	SLM (925)	0-4-2T	1895
Snowdon	4	SLM (988)	0-4-2T	1896
Moel Siabod	5†	SLM (989)	0-4-2T	1896
Padarn	6	SLM (2838)	0-4-2T	1922
Ralph	7*	SLM (2869)	0-4-2T	1923
Eryri	8*	SLM (2870)	0-4-2T	1923
Ninian	9	Hunslet (9249)	0-4-0DH	1986
Yeti	10	Hunslet (9250)	0-4-0DH	1986
Peris	11	Hunslet (9305)	0-4-0DH	1991
George	12	Hunslet (9312)	0-4-0DH	1992

All steam locomotives were built by Swiss Locomotive Works, Winterthur
All diesel locomotives were built by Hunslet Engine Co, Leeds
†currently out of service
*currently stored out of service (boilerless)

Stock
8 closed bogie coaches; 1 bogie works car; 1 4-wheel open wagon; a 3-car diesel-electric railcar set built 1995 by HPE Tredegar (fleet Nos 21, 22, 23 [Works Nos 1074/5/6])

Wales

www.snowdonrailway.co.uk
Main station: Llanberis
Other public stations: Summit, also Clogwyn/Rocky Valley when Summit is inaccessible
OS reference: SH 582597
Car park: Llanberis
Access by public transport: Bangor railway station then by bus, either direct, or alternatively via Caernarfon. Snowdon Sherpa Services to/from Beddgelert and Betws-y-coed stop outside the station
Refreshment facilities: Llanberis, Summit station
Souvenir shops: Llanberis, Summit station
Depot: Llanberis
Length of line: 7.5km, 800mm gauge

Passenger trains: *Early season:* Llanberis-Clogwyn. Journey time approx 45min. Round trip approx 1 hr 30min.
High season: Llanberis-Summit Journey time approx 1 hour. Round trip approx 2hr 30 min, including 30min stop at the Summit Departures from Llanberis at 30min intervals subject to passenger demand
Period of public operation: Daily late March to first week of November inclusive subject to winter maintenance. Please visit web site for up-to-date opening times
Group bookings: Bookings for groups of 15 or more can be taken in advance. Please call 0871 720 0033 for special rates

Facilities for disabled: Those requiring wheelchair access should please telephone in advance to discuss their particular requirements. Disabled parking is available and there are suitable toilet facilities in both Llanberis station and the Summit. Only officially registered support dogs can travel on the trains
Special notes: Trains depart subject to weather conditions and passenger demand. If weather conditions become severe on Snowdon, trains will terminate at Rocky Valley (5/8 distance up Snowdon)

Timetable Service — Talyllyn Railway — Gwynedd

Member: HRA, TT
The very first railway in the country to be rescued and operated by enthusiasts, the line climbs from Tywyn through the wooded Welsh hills past Dolgoch Falls to Nant Gwernol. The trains are hauled by a variety of veteran tank engines, all immaculately maintained by the railway's own workshops at Tywyn Pendre
General Manager: Larry Bridges
Headquarters: Talyllyn Railway Co, Wharf Station, Tywyn, Gwynedd LL36 9EY
Telephone: Tywyn (01654) 710472
Fax: (01654) 711755
Internet address: *Web sites:* www.talyllyn.co.uk www.ngrm.org.uk
Main station: Tywyn Wharf
Other public stations: Tywyn Pendre, Rhydyronen, Brynglas, Dolgoch Falls, Abergynolwyn, Nant Gwernol
OS reference:
Tywyn Wharf SH 586005
SatNav postcodes:
Tywyn Wharf car park LL36 0TF
Abergynolwyn LL36 9UR
Car parks: Tywyn Wharf, Dolgoch, Abergynolwyn
Access by public transport: Tywyn main line station. Bus

Locomotives

Name	No	Builder	Type	Built
Talyllyn	1	F/Jennings (42)	0-4-2ST	1864
Dolgoch	2	F/Jennings (63)	0-4-0WT	1866
Sir Haydn	3	Hughes (323)	0-4-2ST	1878
Edward Thomas	4	K/Stuart (4047)	0-4-2ST	1921
Midlander	5	R/Hornsby (200792)	4wDM	1940
Douglas/Duncan	6	Barclay (1431)	0-4-0WT	1918
Tom Rolt*	7	Barclay (2263)	0-4-2T	1949/1991
Merseysider	8	R/Hornsby (476108)	4wDH	1964
Alf	9	Hunslet (4136)	0-4-0DM	1950
Bryneglwys	10	Simplex (101T023)	0-4-0DM	c1985

Locomotive notes: In service — Nos 1, 2, 3, 4, 6 and 7
*virtually a new locomotive rebuilt from the original at Pendre Works.
Diesels as available

Stock
13 4-wheel coaches/vans; 10 bogie coaches; 45 wagons

Narrow Gauge Museum, Tywyn

Name	No	Builder	Type	Built
Dot	—	B/Peacock (2817)	0-4-0ST	1887
Rough Pup	—	Hunslet (541)	0-4-0ST	1891
—	2†	K/Stuart (721)	0-4-0WT	1902
Jubilee 1897	—	M/Wardle (1382)	0-4-0ST	1897
George Henry	—	de Winton	0-4-0T	1877
—	13	Spence	0-4-0T	1895
Nutty*	—	Sentinel (7701)	0-4-0VB	1929

Various wagons and miscellaneous equipment
*not currently on site, from Dundee Gas Works
§from Guinness

Gwynedd services to Tywyn
Refreshment facilities: Tywyn Wharf, Abergynolwyn hot and cold snacks available. Picnic areas at Dolgoch Falls and Abergynolwyn.

Railway adventure children's playground at Abergynolwyn station

Souvenir shops: Tywyn Wharf, Abergynolwyn

Museum: Tywyn Wharf

Depot: Tywyn Pendre

Length of line: 7.25 miles, 2ft 3in gauge

Passenger trains: Tywyn-Nant Gwernol

Period of public operation: Daily 4 April to 1 November, 26 December-3 January 2010

Journey times: Tywyn-Nant Gwernol — single 55min, return 2hr 15min

Special events: Mothering Sunday — 22 March; Founders Day (extra vintage trains)* — 14 May; Vintage Coach Get Together — 25 May; The Children's *Duncan* Day* — 28 May; Father's Day — 21 June; Have-a-go-Gala and Wharf Garden Railway Open Day — 4/5 July; Murder Mystery — Monday 27 July; Race the Train (limited service) — 15 August; The Children's *Duncan* Day* — 27 August; Series One Land Rover Gathering — 30 August; Halloween Special — 30 October; Carol Train — 19 December; Santa Specials — 19/20, 24 December.
*Thursdays

Talyllyn Vintage Train: The TR is probably alone in still being able to run its complete original passenger train dating from the 1860s, and invites you to enjoy this unique experience, travelling in original coaches behind an original locomotive. The train will depart at 11.00 on Thursdays in June, 2, 9, 16 July and 10, 17, 24 September, featuring photographic opportunities and guided tour. Advance booking is advised. Small supplement payable

Family tickets: Available

Facilities for disabled: No problem for casual visitors, advance notice preferred for groups. Access to shop, museum and cafeteria possible at Tywyn and Abergynolwyn. Disabled toilet facilities at Tywyn and Abergynolwyn. Limited capacity for wheelchairs on trains

Special notes: Parties, private charter trains, Talyllyn Treats and driver experience days by arrangement. Children under 5 years of age free. Great Little Trains of Wales discount card accepted

Membership details: L. & J. Garvey (TRPS), 2 Brynmair, Tywyn, Gwynedd LL36 9AG

Membership journal: *Talyllyn News* — quarterly

Marketing names: One of the Great Little Trains. The first preserved railway in the world

---

Timetable Service	Teifi Valley Railway	Ceredigion

Member: HRA

The line at Henllan was part of an extensive network of railways that spread through the valleys of west Wales in the mid-19th century. Originally laid in broad gauge, before being relaid to standard gauge. After the closure of commercial operations, the narrow gauge line was laid by enthusiasts

Operating society/organisation: Teifi Valley Railway, Henllan Station, Nr Newcastle Emlyn SA44 5TD

Telephone: (01559) 371077

Internet address: *Web site:* www.teifivalleyrailway.com

Main station: Henllan

Other public stations: Forest Halt, Pontprenshitw, Llandyfriog

Car park: Henllan (on B4334)

OS reference: SN 358407

Access by public transport: BR station — Carmarthen (14 miles). Bus service 461 to Henllan or 460

Refreshments: Henllan

Souvenirs: Henllan

Length of line: 2 miles (2ft gauge)

On site facilities: Children's play

Industrial locomotives (2ft gauge)

Name	No	Builder	Type	Built
Alan George	—	Hunslet (606)	0-4-0ST	1894
Sgt Murphy	—	K/Stuart (3117)	0-6-2T	1918
Sholto	—	Hunslet (2433)	4wDM	1941
Sammy	—	M/Rail (605)	4wDM	1959
Henry	—	Ruston (256314)	4wDMF	1959

Industrial locomotives (standard gauge)

Name	No	Builder	Type	Built
Rosyth	—	Barclay (1385)	0-4-0ST	1914
Swansea Vale No 1*	—	Sentinel (9622)	4wVBTG	1958

Owner
*The Railway Club of Wales

areas, woodland waterfall, nature trails, crazy golf and crazy quoits, picnic area, café and gift shop. Display of narrow gauge freight wagons

Depot: Henllan (not open to public)

Facilities for disabled: All facilities including portable steps and wide door for wheelchairs in two coaches

Period of public operation: Daily 10 April to 31 October (with the following exclusions: 20 April to 2 May; 5-9, 11-16, 18-23 May; Fridays and Saturdays in June; 3/4, 10/11 July; Fridays and Saturdays in September; 28 September to 25 October)

Special events: Bring a Teddy Bear Day — 4 May; Official opening of new platform — 18 July; Halloween Ghost Trains — 31

October; Santa Specials — 12/13, 19/20, 22-24 December. Please contact for further details
Special notes: Pay once only and ride all day. All trains will be steam-hauled provided crews are available, please ring to check
Membership details: Teifi Valley Railway Society, c/o Henllan station

Membership journal: *Right Away* — quarterly

Timetable Service — Vale of Rheidol Railway — Ceredigion

Member: GLTW
This narrow gauge railway offers a 23-mile round trip from Aberystwyth to Devil's Bridge providing spectacular views which cannot be enjoyed by road. At Devil's Bridge there are walks to the Mynach Falls and Devil's Punch Bowl. Many artists have been inspired by the magnificence of Devil's Bridge and the Rheidol Valley.
General Manager: N. Thompson
Headquarters: Vale of Rheidol Railway, The Locomotive Shed, Park Avenue, Aberystwyth SY23 1PG
Telephone: (01970) 625819
Fax: (01970) 623769
Internet address: *Web site:* www.rheidolrailway.co.uk
Main station: Aberystwyth (adjacent to main line station)
Other public stations: Devil's Bridge, Rhiwfron, Rheidol Falls, Aberffrwd, Nantyronen, Capel Bangor, Glanrafon, Llanbadarn
OS reference: SN 587812
Car parks: Aberystwyth, Devil's Bridge
Access by public transport: Aberystwyth main line station, and bus services to Aberystwyth
Refreshment facilities: Aberystwyth (not railway owned), Devil's Bridge (not railway

Locomotives

Name	No	Origin	Ex-BR Class	Type	Built
Owain Glyndwr	7	GWR	98	2-6-2T	1923
Llywelyn	8	GWR	98	2-6-2T	1923
Prince of Wales	9	GWR	98	2-6-2T	1924
—	10	Brecon MR (002)	98/1	0-6-0DH	1987

Stock
16 bogie coaches; 1 4-wheel guard's van; 14 wagons for maintenance use; 1 inspection trolley

The following locomotives are stored on the railway pending restoration and future display

Name	No	Builder	Type	Built
—	4	Decauville (1027)	0-4-0T	1926
Kathleen	—	de Winton	0-4-0VBT	1877
—	6	Fowler (10249)	0-6-0T+T	1905
—	21	Fowler (11938)	0-4-2T	1909
—	23	Fowler (15515)	0-6-2T	1920
Margaret	—	Hunslet (605)	0-4-0ST	1894
—	31	Mafei (4766)	0-8-0T	1916
—	—	H/Clarke (D564)	4wDM	1930
—	—*	R/Proctor (50823)	4wPM	1918
—	—	K/Stuart (3114)	0-4-0ST	1918

*metre gauge
Also Henschel bogie tender (11854/25 of 1917)

operated)
Souvenir shop: Aberystwyth
Depot: Aberystwyth (not open to the public)
Length of line: 11.75 miles, 1ft 11.75in gauge
Journey time: Single 1hr, return 3hr

Passenger trains: Aberystwyth-Devil's Bridge
Period of public operation: Daily 7 April to 29 October, with some exceptions end March, April, May, June, September and October

Timetable Service — Welsh Highland Heritage Railway — Gwynedd

Member: HRA, GLToW, Star-Attractions
The Welsh Highland Railway Ltd operates services at the south-western end of the old Welsh Highland line and has its base in the bustling holiday town of Porthmadog. The company is developing the combined WHR/FR museum, an interactive, 'hands-on' facility, at the Gelert's Farm site
Location: Tremadog Road, Porthmadog, immediately adjacent to main line railway station and opposite the Queen's Hotel
OS reference: SH 571393
Operating society/organisation: Welsh Highland Railway Ltd, Tremadog Road, Porthmadog, Gwynedd LL49 9DY
Telephone:

Porthmadog: 01766 513402

Out of hours phone: 01766 513402

Internet address: *e-mail:*
info@ .whr.co.uk

Web site: www.whr.co.uk

Car park: Free — overflow car park opposite the railway; this is council owned, with the usual charges, and includes accommodation for coaches

Catering facilities: 'Russell Tea Room' supplying a range of adult/children's meals and light refreshments

Access by public transport: Arriva Trains Wales to adjacent Porthmadog station. National Express Buses 200yd. Bus Gwynedd services 1, 2, 3, 97, 98, 99, 99a, S96, S97

On site facilities: Souvenir and railway book/video shop, disabled toilet facilities, information boards, footplate passes and extended shed tours. 7.25in gauge miniaaure railway operating around the works and through the woods on most days. Free of charge to WHR passengers. Steam Driver Experience courses available

Length of line: Porthmadog

Locomotives

Name	No	Builder	Type	Built
Gelert	—	Bagnall (3050)	0-4-2T	1953
—	590	Baldwin (44699)	4-6-0T	1917
Russell	—	Hunslet (901)	2-6-2T	1906
Karen	—	Peckett (2024)	0-4-2T	1942
Glaslyn	1	R/Hornsby (297030)	4wDM	1952
Kinnerley	2	R/Hornsby (354068)	4wDM	1953
Cnicht	36	M/Rail (8703)	4wDM	1941
Katherine	9	M/Rail (605363)	4wDM	1968
—	4	M/Rail (605333)	4wDM	1963
—	5	Hunslet (6285)	4wDM	1968
—	3	R/Hornsby (370555)	4wDM	1953
Jonathon	6	M/Rail (11102)	4wDM	1959
—	7	Hunslet (7535)	4wDM	1977
—	10	R/Hornsby (481552)	4wDM	1962
—	11	Hunslet (3510)	4wDM	1947
Beddgelert	NG120*	S. F. Belge	2-8-2	1950
Snowdonia/Eryri†	60	August 23 Works	0-6-0DM	1977
—†	69	August 23 Works	0-6-0DH	1980
—†	58	August 23 Works	0-6-0DH	1980
—	—	Barclay (554)	4wDH	1970
—	—	Barclay (555)	4wDH	1970
—	—	M/Rail (264)	4wPM	1916
—	—	M/Rail (22237)	4wDM	1965
Kathy	—	H/Barclay (LD 9350)	0-4-0DM	1994
Emma	—	H/Barclay (LD 9346)	0-4-0DM	1994

*ex-South African Railways Class NG15, for sale, may leave site during 2009

†ex-Polish State Railways class LYD2, August 23 Works is situated in Romania

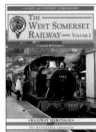

(WHR) to Pen-y-Mount Junction, just under 2 miles.
60cm gauge
Passenger trains: Porthmadog (WHR) to Pen-y-Mount Junction, return journey approx 50min incorporating guided tours of the engine sheds. Steam-hauled Bank Holidays, almost all weekends and daily from mid July to September during Easter week and May week and autumn half term
Family tickets: Available, 2 adults + 2 children
Tickets: Your ticket enables you to travel all day and includes the guided, interactive 'hands-on' shed tour in each journey
Period of public operation: Daily 28 March to 1 November; EXCEPT 2, 5, 9, 12, 16, 19, 23 October. Trains run 10.30, 11.30, 13.00, 14.00, 15.00, 16.00 (the 16.00 does not run in October or November)
Special events: Easter Bunnies — 12 April; Spirit of the Welsh Highland Gala —2-4 May; Teddy

Locomotive notes: No 590's chassis and cab is displayed in museum, but may leave site during 2009 for restoration.
Karen, Cnicht and LYd2 69 are in the museum with accessible footplates.
Russell is under restoration in the erecting shop, and can only be viewed by appointment.
Most works shunters only viewable by prior appointment (not kept in public areas).
Hunslet No 5 is on loan to the Hunslet Engine Co at Statfold Barn.
Gelert, Glaslyn and *Emma* will operate the 2009 service. There will be one or more visiting locomotives for the May Gala, and in July and August.

Stock
Passengers will have the opportunity to travel in the historic 'Gladstone' coach, the original WHR buffet car, WHR Hudson toastrack No 42 and replica Ashbury corridor No 25

Bears' Picnic — 30/31 May; Welsh Dragons — 18/19 July; Cambrian steam specials Thursday to Saturday late July and all August; Jack the Station Cat book signing — 30/31 August
Facilities for disabled: Toilet, ramp and provision on train, wheelchairs provided. Disabled passengers can be accommodated

without prior notice
Membership details: Membership Secretaries, R. & P. Hughes, 2 Clos Sulien, Llanbadarn, Aberystwyth, Ceredigion SY23 3GF. Instant membership available at the shop
Membership journal: *The Journal* — every four months

Welshpool & Llanfair Light Railway

Timetable Service · Mid Wales

Member: HRA
There is a decidedly foreign atmosphere to the trains over this line. The steam locomotive collection embraces examples from three continents, and the coaches are turn-of-the-century balcony saloons from Austria or 1950s bogies from Hungary. The line follows a steeply graded route (maximum 1 in 24) through very attractive rolling countryside, and is rather a gem in an area too often missed by the traveller heading for further shores
General Manager: Terry Turner
Headquarters: Welshpool & Llanfair Light Railway Preservation Co Ltd, The Station, Llanfair Caereinion SY21 0SF
Telephone: Llanfair Caereinion (01938) 810441
Fax: (01938) 810861
Internet address: *Web site:* www.wllr.org.uk
Main station: Welshpool (Raven Square)
Other public stations: Castle

Locomotives

Name	No	Builder	Type	Built
The Earl	1	B/Peacock (3496)	0-6-0T	1902
The Countess	2	B/Peacock (3497)	0-6-0T	1902
Monarch	6	Bagnall (3024)	0-4-4-0T	1953
Chattenden	7	Drewry (2263)	0-6-0DM	1949
Dougal	8	Barclay (2207)	0-4-0T	1946
Sir Drefaldwyn	10	S. F. Belge (2855)	0-8-0T	1944
Ferret	11	Hunslet (2251)	0-4-0DM	1940
Joan	12	K/Stuart (4404)	0-6-2T	1927
SLR No 85	14	Hunslet (3815)	2-6-2T	1954
Scooby	16	Hunslet (2400)	0-4-0DM	1941
TSC No 175	17	Diema	0-6-0DM	1978
CFI 764.423	18	Resita (1128)	0-8-0T	1954
CFI 764.425	19	Resita (???)	0-8-0T	1954
—	9150	Baguley (3746)	4wDM	1976

Locomotive notes: Locomotives expected in service 2009 — *The Earl, The Countess,* No 19 and SLR No 85. *Joan* is currently undergoing overhaul at Llanfair. Some locomotives may not be accessible by the public

Stock
2 replicas of original W&LLR Pickering carriages; 7 ex-Zillertalbahn-style coaches; 3 ex-Sierra Leone coaches, 2 Hungarian State Railway coaches, 6 W&LLR wagons; 8 ex-Admiralty wagons; 2 ex-Bowater wagons; 1Wickham trolley
Note: Not all of the vehicles are in service and some are stored in areas not accessible by the public

Wales

Caereinion, Sylfaen, Llanfair Caereinion
OS reference: SJ 107069
SatNav postcodes: Welshpool (Raven Square) — SY21 7LT
Llanfair Caereinion — SY21 0SF
Car parks: Llanfair Caereinion, Welshpool (both free)
Access by public transport: Main line station at Welshpool, one mile from Raven Square. Arriva buses from Shrewsbury, Oswestry and Newtown to Welshpool
Refreshment facilities: Light refreshments at Llanfair Caereinion. Picnic areas at Welshpool and Llanfair

Souvenir shops: Welshpool, Llanfair Caereinion
Depot: Llanfair Caereinion
Length of line: 8 miles, 2ft 6in gauge
Passenger trains: Welshpool-Llanfair Caereinion
Period of public operation: Weekends Easter to October. Daily in school holidays, plus some other days in June, July and September
Special events: Steam Gala — 5/6 September; Santa trains — 12/13, 19/20 December
Facilities for disabled: Specially adapted coaches for wheelchairs. Please phone in advance. Easy

access to shops. Disabled toilet facility at Welshpool and Llanfair
Membership details: David Barker, 458 Oxford Road, Gomersal, Cleckheaton, West Yorks BD19 4LB
Membership journal: *The Journal* — quarterly
Marketing name: Llanfair Railway
Special notes: Open balcony coaches — travel right next to the engine at the front of the train. Or see the line rolling away behind the back end!

Channel Islands & Isle of Man

Steam Centre | Alderney Railway | Channel Islands

In 1997 the Alderney Railway was 150 years old, having opened on 14 July 1847. Queen Victoria was the only passenger until 1980
Location: Alderney, Channel Islands
Operating society/organisation: Alderney Railway Society, PO Box 75, Alderney, Channel Islands
Telephone: (01481) 822978
Internet address: *Web site:* www.alderneyrailway.com
Car park: Yes
Access by public transport: Aurigny Air Services from Southampton
Location: Station at Braye Road (tickets & souvenirs)
Public opening: Weekends and Bank Holidays, Easter to end of September

Industrial locomotives

Name	No	Builder	Type	Built
Elizabeth	—	Vulcan (D2271)	0-4-0DM	1949
Molly 2	—	R/Hornsby	0-4-0DM	1958

Stock
4 Wickham cars
2 Goods wagons
2 ex-London Underground 1956 Stock tube cars (locomotive-hauled)
2 Wickham flats

Special events: Alderney Week August. Easter Egg Specials on Easter Sunday. Santa Specials, Saturday before Christmas
On site facilities: Miniature railway (7.25in gauge), quarter-mile circuit operates at Mannez in connection with standard gauge line
Length of line: 2 miles

Facilities for disabled: No, but train crew will always help wherever possible
President: Frank Eggleston
Chairman: Anthony le Blanc (tel: 01481 822978)
Notes: Engine shed at Quarry. Wickham 'train' operates in low season; *Elizabeth* and tube cars in

The railway was opened on 25 September 2004 and is a reconstruction of the surface section of the former Great Laxey Mine tramway which was used to haul wagon loads of ore from inside the mine and onto the former ore washing and dressing floors at Laxey. The railway runs beneath the main Laxey to Ramsey road — the longest railway tunnel on the Island

Contact: Andrew Scarffe

Operating company: Laxey & Lonan Heritage Trust, West Lynne, Mateland Drive, Laxey, Isle of Man IM4 7N4

Telephone: 01624 861706 (there is no direct telephone on the railway)

Car park: Available in nearby Laxey

Main station: Valley Gardens, Laxey

Locomotives

Name	No	Builder	Type	Built
Ant	—	GNS	0-4-0WT	2004
Bee	—	GNS	0-4-0WT	2004

GNS — Great Northern Steam Ltd, Darlington, based on original 1877 design by Stephen Lewin, Poole

Rolling stock

2004-built passenger vehicle, 2007-built passenger vehicle, both built by Alan Keefe. 6 replica ore wagons dating from 2000

Access by public transport: A few minutes' walk from Laxey station on the Manx Electric Railway and bus stop of the route 3 Douglas to Ramsey service

On site facilities: No refreshment facilities on site, but café and public house nearby

Length of line: 0.25-mile, 1ft 7in gauge

Public opening: Saturdays and Bank Holidays Easter until end of September, 11.00-16.30

Facilities for disabled: Unable to carry wheelchair-bound passengers, though Valley Gardens are accessible

Membership details: From above address

Following the successful development of the glen in the 1890s, and with the arrival of the Manx Electric Railway in 1893, the line was built using entirely local labour. The railway was an instant success, and dubbed as 'the smallest passenger railway in the world'. The line closed in 1962, with the locomotives and rolling stock being disposed. In 1982 a group of enthusiasts began the ambitious restoration project to reopen the line. *Sea Lion* and several passenger coaches survived to operate on the reopened line

Location: Groudle Glen Railway, Isle of Man

Officer in charge: Tony Beard

Operating company: Groudle Glen Railway Ltd (managed by the Isle of Man Steam Railway Supporters' Association) of 29 Hawarden Avenue, Douglas, Isle of Man IM1 4BP

Locomotives

Name	No	Builder	Type	Built
Dolphin	1	H/Hunslet (4394)	4wDM	1952
Walrus	2	H/Hunslet (4395)	4wDM	1952
Sea Lion	—	Bagnall (1484)	2-4-0T	1896
Annie	—	Booth/GGR	0-4-2T	1998
Polar Bear	—	BEV (556801)	2-B-2	2004
—	3232	Baguley (3232)	0-4-0DH SO	1947

Telephone: (01624) 622138 (evenings); (01624) 670453 (weekends)

Internet address: Web site: www.groudleglenrailway.com

Car park: Yes

Access by public transport: Manx Electric Railway (Groudle Hotel)

On site facilities: Sales shop and tea room visitor centre

Length of line: 0.75-mile, 2ft gauge

Public opening: Easter Sunday and Monday, Sundays May to September (11.00-16.30); Tuesday evening services August (19.00-21.00); Wednesday evening services July/August (19.00-21.00); Santa Trains — December (11.00-15.30)

Facilities for disabled: Due to the line's location, those who are disabled will have some difficulty. It is suggested that they telephone for advice

Further information and membership details: From above address

Membership journal: *Manx Steam Railway News* — quarterly

Isle of Man Railway — Isle of Man

Member: HRA

The 3ft gauge Isle of Man Railway is a survivor of a system which previously also operated from Douglas to Peel and Ramsey. Almost continuous operation since 1873 makes it one of the oldest operating railways in the British Isles. The majority of the track was completely renewed between 2002 and 2004 including the provision of platforms at intermediate stations and the installation of automatic level crossings along the line. It runs for over 15 miles between Douglas and Port Erin through the island's rolling southern countryside.

The line is owned and operated by the Isle of Man Government

Head of Railways: John Kannaugh

Chief Technical Officer: Peter Maddocks

Headquarters: Department of Tourism & Leisure, Heritage Railways, Service Delivery Directorate, Transport Headquarters, Banks Circus, Douglas, Isle of Man IM1 5PT

Telephone: Douglas (01624) 697400

Fax: (01624) 663637

Main station: Douglas

Other public stations: Port Soderick, Santon, Ballasalla, Castletown, Colby, Port St Mary and Port Erin

Locomotives

Name	No	Builder	Type	Built
Loch	4	B/Peacock (1416)	2-4-0T	1874
Fenella	8	B/Peacock (3610)	2-4-0T	1894
G. H. Wood	10	B/Peacock (4662)	2-4-0T	1905
Maitland	11	B/Peacock (4663)	2-4-0T	1905
Hutchinson	12	B/Peacock (5126)	2-4-0T	1908
Kissack	13	B/Peacock (5382)	2-4-0T	1908
Caledonia	15	Dubs & Co (2178)	0-6-0T	1885
Viking	17	Schottler (2175)	0-4-0DH	1958
Ailsa	18	Hunslet (22021)	4wDM	1994

Locomotive note: All operational, all other rolling stock stored off the line

On display in museum at Port Erin

Name	No	Builder	Type	Built
Peveril	6	B/Peacock (1524)	2-4-0T	1875
Mannin	16	B/Peacock (6296)	2-4-0T	1926

Rolling stock

16 coaches, 20 runners, 1 van, 2 open wagons, 1 well wagon, 1 track tamping machine

Car parks: Douglas, Ballasalla, Castletown, Port St Mary and Port Erin

Access by public transport: Isle of Man Transport bus to main centres

Refreshment facilities: Port Erin and Douglas

Souvenir shops: None

Museum: Port Erin

Depot: Douglas

Length of line: 15.5 miles, 3ft gauge

Passenger trains: Douglas-Port Erin

Period of public operation: Easter-October

Facilities for disabled: Level access throughout Douglas and Port Erin stations including refreshment area. Carriages able to carry wheelchairs, ramps provided. Advance notice helpful

Manx Electric Railway — Isle of Man

Member: HRA

The 3ft gauge Manx Electric Railway is a unique survivor of Victorian high technology. A mixture of railway and tramway practice, it was built in 1893 and was a pioneer in the use of electric traction. It illustrates an example of a true electric interurban line. Two of the original cars are still in service making them the oldest tramcars still in operation on their original route in the British Isles. After leaving Douglas, the railway passes the Groudle Glen Railway before reaching the charming village of Laxey, for the Snaefell Mountain Railway. The line continues over some of the most breathtaking coastal scenery in the island before reaching its terminus at Ramsey nearly 18 miles from Douglas.

The line is owned and operated by the Isle of Man Government

Head of Railways: John Kannaugh

Chief Technical Officer: Peter Maddocks

Headquarters: Department of Tourism & Leisure, Heritage Railways, Service Delivery Directorate, Transport Headquarters, Banks Circus, Douglas, Isle of Man IM1 5PT

Telephone: Douglas (01624) 697400

Fax: (01624) 663637

Main stations: Douglas (Derby Castle), Laxey and Ramsey

Other public stations: Groudle, Dhoon Glen, Ballaglass and numerous wayside stops

Channel Islands & Isle of Man

Car parks: Douglas, Laxey, Ramsey (nearby)
Access by public transport: Isle of Man Transport buses to main centres. Douglas Corporation Horse Tramway to Derby Castle in summer
Depots: Douglas and Ramsey
Refreshment facilities: Laxey in summer
Length of line: 17.5 miles, 3ft gauge
Passenger service: Douglas-Ramsey
Period of public operation: Easter- October
Special notes: Folded wheelchairs can be carried. Please notify in advance. One trailer with disabled access used on advance request

Motor cars

Nos	Type	Seats	Body	Built
1, 2	Unvestibuled saloon	34	Milnes	1893
5, 6, 7, 9	Vestibuled saloon	32	Milnes	1894
16	Cross-bench open	56	Milnes	1898
19-22*	Winter saloon	48	Milnes	1899
26	Cross-bench open	56	Milnes	1898
32, 33	Cross-bench open	56	UEC	1906
34	Engineer's Car	—	IoMT	2004

*22 rebodied 1991, McArd/MER

Trailers

Nos	Type	Seats	Body	Built
36, 37	Cross-bench open	44	Milnes	1894
40, 41, 44	Cross-bench open	44	EE Co	1930
42, 43	Cross-bench open	44	Milnes	1903
45-48	Cross-bench open	44	Milnes	1899
49-51, 53, 54	Cross-bench open	44	Milnes	1893
56*	Cross-bench open	44	ERTCW	1904
57, 58	Saloon	32	ERTCW	1904
59	Special Saloon	18	Milnes	1895
60	Cross-bench open	44	Milnes	1896
61, 62	Cross-bench open	44	UEC	1906

*rebuilt as disabled access trailer in 1993

Note: Other rolling stock stored off the line

Timetable Service — Snaefell Mountain Railway — Isle of Man

Member: HRA

The 3ft 6in gauge Snaefell Mountain Railway is unique. It is the only electric mountain railway in the British Isles. Almost all the rolling stock is original and dates back to 1895. The railway begins its journey at the picturesque village of Laxey where its station is shared with the Manx Electric Railway. The climb to the summit of Snaefell (2,036ft) is a steep one and the cars travel unassisted up gradients as severe as 1 in 12. From the summit, the views on a clear day extend to Wales, Scotland, England and Ireland.

The line is owned and operated by the Isle of Man Government
Head of Railways: John Kannaugh
Chief Technical Officer: Peter Maddocks
Headquarters: Department of Tourism & Leisure, Heritage Railways, Service Delivery Directorate, Transport Headquarters, Banks Circus, Douglas, Isle of Man IM1 5PT
Telephone: Douglas (01624) 697400
Fax: (01624) 663637
Main station: Laxey
Other public stations: Bungalow, Summit
Car parks: Laxey, Bungalow (nearby)
Access by public transport: Manx Electric Railway or Isle of Man Transport bus to Laxey

Trams

Nos	Type	Seats	Body	Built
1-4, 6	Vestibuled saloon	48	Milnes	1895
5 (rebuild)	Vestibuled saloon	48	MER/ Kinnin	1971

Depot: Laxey
Refreshment facilities: Laxey, Summit
Souvenirs shops: None
Length of line: 4.5 miles, 3ft 6in gauge
Passenger service: Laxey-Snaefell summit
Period of public operation: Easter to end of September
Special notes: Elderly and/or disabled passengers may find the access and egress steps narrow and steep

Northern Ireland

Downpatrick & County Down Railway

Member: HRA

The railway museum is the only preserved Irish standard gauge (5ft 3in) railway operating in Ireland. It is a representative of the former Belfast & County Down railway terminus in Downpatrick, which closed in 1950, two years after being taken into state ownership

Location: The Railway Station, Market Street, Downpatrick, Co Down BT30 6LZ

OS reference: J483444

Operating society/organisation: Downpatrick & County Down Railway Society

Telephone: 028 4461 5779

Internet address: *Web site:* www.downrail.co.uk

Car park: Free parking adjacent to station

Access by public transport: A regular service is operated by Ulsterbus from Belfast Europa bus centre (next to Great Victoria Street railway station). Tel: (028) 9032 0011

Refreshment facilities: Buffet carriage open on operating days

On site facilities: Souvenir shop, toilets

Length of line: 4 miles open to public traffic. Current terminus: King Magnus's Halt. Track was extended southwards to Ballydugan and north to a new station at Inch Abbey

Public opening: Special events (see web site for detail) and weekends 13 June-6 September

Journey time: 45min return journey from Downpatrick town to Downpatrick Loop Platform and King Magnus's Halt and Inch Abbey

Diesel locomotives and multiple-unit

Name	No	Origin	Class	Type	Built
W. F. Gillespie OBE	E421	CIE	421	C	1962
—	E432	CIE	421	C	1962
—	G611	CIE	611	B	1962
—	G613	CIE	611	B	1962
—	G617	CIE	611	B	1962
—	RB3	BRE-Leyland	—	4wDM	1981

Name	No	Origin	Class	Manufacturer	Type	Built
—	712	CIE	–	Wickham (8919)	4wDH	1962

Steam locomotives

Name	No	Builder	Type	Built
—	1*	O&K (12475)	0-4-0T	1934
—	3	O&K (12662)	0-4-0T	1935

*at Railway Preservation Society at Whitehead for overhaul

Rolling stock

2 CIE Brake open standards (Nos 1918 & 1944); CIE Travelling Post Office (No 2978); 1 CIE Brake open standard generating steam van (No 3223); CIE Buffet open standard (No 2419); NIR '70' class railcar brake open standard intermediate (No 728); B&CDR 'Royal Saloon' (No 153); B&CDR 1st/2nd composite (No 152); B&CDR 3rd open (ex-railmotor); B&CDR 6-wheeled 2nd (No 154); B&CDR 6-wheeled brake 3rd (No 39); GS&WR 3rd open (No 836); GSWR 6-wheeled brake first (No 69); Ulster Railway Family Saloon (No 33); GNR 6-wheeled third; 4 LMS (NCC) parcels vans; 2 LMS (NCC) open wagon; LMS (NCC) brake van; CIE closed van; 2 GNR closed vans; GNR brake van; GSWR ballast hopper; GSWR ballast plough; LMS (NCC) steam crane; 2 private oil company tankers, CIE track inspection vehicle No 712; selection of carriage and wagon underframes for internal use

Owners

712, G611 and G617 the Irish Traction Group
G613 and M&GW full brake privately owned
RB3 is owned by Translink
E421 and E432 the Downpatrick & County Down Railway Society

Facilities for disabled: Toilets, shop, platform and trains accessible for disabled

Membership details: The Membership Secretary, Downpatrick & County Down Railway Society, The Railway Station, Downpatrick, Co Down BT30 6LZ

Giant's Causeway & Bushmills Railway

The GC&BR was opened in 2002 using the stock of the former Shane's Castle Railway on the last two miles of the site of the Portrush to Giant's Causeway electric tramway closed in 1949. The line runs between Bushmills and the Giant's Causeway with its charming views along the River Bush, and spectacular vistas across the sea to Donegal

Location: The railway links the distillery (open to visitors) in the village of Bushmills to the entrance of the Giant's Causeway. Follow the signs to either Bushmills or the Giant's Causeway and the railway is clearly signposted. Car parking is dedicated to railway passengers at both Bushmills and the Giant's Causeway

Operating organisation: Giant's Causeway & Bushmills Railway, Giant's Causeway Station, Runkerry Road, Bushmills, Co Antrim, Northern Ireland BT57 8SZ

Bushmills Platform: Ballaghmore

Industrial locomotives

Name	No	Builder	Type	Built
Tyrone	1	Peckett (2264)	0-4-0T	1904
Rory	2	Simplex (102T016)	4wDH	1976
Shane	3	Barclay (2281)	0-4-0T	1949

Road, Bushmills BT57 8YS
Telephone/Fax: (028) 2073 2844
Internet address: *e-mail:* infogcbr@btconnect.com
Web site: www.freewebs.com/giantscauseway railway
OS reference: 943437 (Irish Grid)
Access by public transport: Nearest Translink railway stations are Portrush (5 miles), Coleraine (7 miles). Various bus routes (including an open topped vehicle on fine days in the summer) operate from either or both, depending on the route. For timetables either contact Translink enquiries on (028) 9066 6630 or www.translink.co.uk
Length of line: 2 miles, 3ft gauge
On site facilities: Souvenir shop,

toilets and picnic tables at Giant's Causeway station. Free parking at both stations for railway passengers
Passenger trains: Bushmills-Giant's Causeway
Public opening: St Patrick's weekend; daily at Easter; weekends from Easter until end of June; daily July and August; weekends September and October
Note: Trains will operate at other times for advance party bookings in excess of 20 persons
Facilities for disabled: Access avaiable at Giant's Causeway station and Bushmills platform. One coach has been adapted for wheelchair use

---

Railway Preservation Society of Ireland

Members: HRA, TT
The RPSI was formed in 1964, making it one of the older preservation societies in these islands. It has always specialised in main line steam operations, and runs an intensive summer programme of trips out of both Belfast and Dublin. The main maintenance base is situated at Whitehead, 15 miles north of Belfast on the NIR route to Larne Harbour. Here not only are the traffic locomotives shedded but the locomotive shed is also used for heavy maintenance; currently the society is completing the full rebuilding of its sixth boiler 'in-house'. A large engineering workshop has just been constructed for the Locomotive Department, with the 100-year-old overhead crane which was originally in the

Belfast & County Down Railway Locomotive Erecting Shop at Queen's Quay in Belfast. This workshop which will undertake all heavy engineering for the Society is currently being fitted out. A large carriage shed is also on site where traffic vehicles are maintained and coaches are fully rebuilt. There are also heavy lifting facilities on site, and access may occasionally be limited for safety reasons when these are in use. Annual operations commence with 'Easter Bunny' trains out of Belfast, usually on Easter Monday. In May the 'International Railtour' is the main event, a three day steam extravaganza. During June there are main line trips out of Belfast and Dublin (steam and jazz). July and August see the 'Portrush Flyers' from Belfast to Portrush and

back, around 180 miles of main line steam, as well as the 'Sea Breeze' excursions from Dublin to Rosslare and back, covering 205 miles. During June, July and August there are steam train rides on site at Whitehead on Sunday afternoons, and at the end of July there will be an Open Day in conjunction with the Whitehead Community Association when there will be access to the workshop areas. The season usually ends with Halloween and Christmas trains in Belfast and Dublin
Location: Whitehead Excursion Station, Co Antrim, Northern Ireland
Operating society: Railway Preservation Society of Ireland, Castleview Road, Whitehead, Carrickfergus, Co Antrim BT38 9NA

Telephone/fax:
From UK (028) 2826 0803.
From Eire (01) 280 9147
Internet address: *e-mail:*
rpsitrains@hotmail.com
Web site:
www.steamtrainsireland.com
Car park: Public car parking is
readily available adjacent to the
Society premises, with a further
large car park less than 5min walk
away on the sea front. Both car
parks are normally free
Access by public transport:
Northern Ireland Railways or
Ulsterbus to Whitehead
On site facilities: Souvenir shop
(operating days only)
Public opening: Visitors welcome
most weekends. Site not open
during the week (except public
holidays) or when main line trains
are operating from Whitehead or
Belfast. Special opening for parties,
or in the evening, may be arranged
by telephoning in advance
Special notes: The RPSI is noted
for its main line excursions and
traditional rolling stock. For details:
www.steamtrainsireland.com
Facilities for disabled: Please note
that wheelchair facilities can be
provided on trains, with advance
notice if possible. A dedicated
coach for carrying wheelchairs
operates on Dublin-based trains.
Wheelchair access around the
workshops at Whitehead is
possible, but difficult, and advance
warning is requested of any visitors
who may need special facilities
Membership details: Membership
Secretary, 148 Church Road,
Newtownabbey, Co Antrim
BT36 6HJ

Locomotives

Name	No	Origin	Class	Type	Built
Merlin	85*	GNR(I)	V	4-4-0	1932
—	131**	GNR(I)	Q	4-4-0	1901
Slieve Gullion	171†	GNR(I)	S	4-4-0	1913
—	4	LMS (NCC)	WT	2-6-4T	1947
—	184†	GS&WR	J15	0-6-0	1880
—	186§	GS&WR	J15	0-6-0	1879
—	461††	D&SER	K2	2-6-0	1922
Lough Erne	27	SL&NCR	Z	0-6-4T	1949
Eagle	101	NIR	DL	Bo-Bo	1969
Falcon	102	NIR	DL	Bo-Bo	1969

Industrial locomotives

Name	No	Builder	Type	Built
Guinness	3	H/Clarke (1152)	0-4-0ST	1919
R. H. Smyth	3	Avonside (2021)	0-6-0ST	1928
—	23	Planet (3509)	0-4-0DM	1951
—	1	R/Hornsby	0-4-0DM	1954

*on loan from Ulster Folk & Transport Museum
**frames and boiler only
†awaiting restoration
††undergoing restoration
§returned to traffic in 2004

Stock
The Society also owns some 20 operational coaches, normally divided
between Whitehead and Dublin. Further coaches are awaiting restoration
and a small number of freight wagons are also preserved, as well as a
steam crane. A serious fire due to vandalism a couple of years ago
destroyed several vehicles, and any rebuilding is likely to be some years in
the future at best. The Society has purchased a variety of Mk 2 coaches
which are undergoing major overhaul and six of which returned to traffic in
2004 with a diner/bar coming into service in 2008. The Society's secondary
maintenance base is at Mullingar, Co Westmeath, but there is **no** access to
the public

Future developments: Completion
of a new museum facility is
planned, as well as a projected
extension to the Carriage Shed and
additional stores and maintenance
areas, and there are further
developments in the pipeline which
will hopefully improve access.
Additional locomotive and coach
restoration is proposed

Museum	Ulster Folk & Transport Museum	County Down

Member: HRA
Forty-five acres are devoted to the
Transport Galleries. Permanent
exhibitions include the earliest
forms of transport, horse-drawn
vehicles, bicycles, motor cars and
the Museum's *Titanic* exhibition.
  The Irish Railway Collection is
displayed in an award-winning
purpose-built gallery — the largest

Locomotives (5ft 3in)

Name	No	Origin	Class	Type	Built
—	93	GNR(I)	JT	2-4-2T	1895
—	30	BCDR	I	4-4-2T	1901
Dunluce Castle	74	LMS(NCC)	U2	4-4-0	1924
Maedb	800	GSR	B1A	4-6-0	1939
—	1	R/Stephenson (2738)	—	0-6-0ST	1891
*Merlin**	85	GNR(I)	V	4-4-0	1932
—	1	GNR(I)	—	Railbus	1932

Transport Museum gallery in Ireland.

The collection features *Maedb* — the largest locomotive run in Ireland. The display includes narrow gauge and standard gauge rolling stock, locomotives, carriages, goods wagons, railcars and railbuses along with memorabilia

Location: Ulster Folk & Transport Museum, Cultra, Holywood
Operating organisation: Ulster Folk & Transport Museum, Cultra, Holywood BT18 0EU
Telephone: (028) 9042 8428
Fax: (028) 9042 8728
Internet address: *Web site:* www.magni.org.uk
Access: By car or bus the museum is about 7 miles from Belfast city centre on the A2 Belfast-Bangor road. You can also reach the museum by train
Car park: Extensive free parking
On site facilities: Shops, toilets, tea room
Opening times: All year round; opening times vary with season, check with the Museum for details

*on loan to Railway Preservation Society of Ireland at Whitehead

Locomotives (narrow gauge)

Name	No	Origin	Class	Type	Built
Blanche	2	CDRJC	5A	2-6-4T	1912
Kathleen	2	CLR	—	4-4-0T	1887
Phoenix	11	CVR	—	4wD	1928
—	20	Industrial	—	0-4-0	1905
—	2	Industrial	—	0-4-0	1907

Stock

1 Dublin, Wicklow & Wexford Railway coach; 1 Dundalk, Newry & Greenore Railway coach; 1 Midland & Great Western Railway director's saloon (ex-private vehicle); 1 Electric tramcar of Bessbrook-Newry Tramway; 2 trams from Giant's Causeway Tramway, Great Northern Railway Ireland Fintona tram, Great Northern Railway Ireland Hill of Howth electric tramcar, 1 Cavan-Leitrim Railway coach; 2 County Donegal Railway railcars; 1 County Donegal Railway director's coach; 1 County Donegal Railway trailer coach (bodywork ex-Dublin & Lucan Railway coach); 1 Giant's Causeway (P&BVR) saloon trailer; 1 Castlederg & Victoria Bridge Tramway 1st/3rd coach; 1 County Donegal Railway 7-ton open wagon, 3 Belfast trams, 1 Belfast trolleybus, 1 Belfast double-deck bus. Extensive collection of cars, motorcycles, bicycles, commercial vehicles, horse-drawn vehicles, fire-fighting equipment and industrial railway vehicles

Republic of Ireland

Steam Centre	Cavan & Leitrim Railway	County Leitrim

Restoration work commenced in June 1993 and to date some half-mile of line has been rebuilt, water tower and engine shed refurbished and new workshops and carriage shed constructed. The ultimate objective is to rebuild a further 5.75 miles of line to Mohill
Location/headquarters: The Narrow Gauge Station, Dromod, Co Leitrim, adjacent to the Irish Rail station

General Manager: Michael Kennedy
Telephone/Fax: 071-9638599
Internet address: *e-mail:* info@irish-railway.com *Web site:* www.irish-railway.com
Main station: Dromod
Car park: Dromod terminus
Access by public transport: Rail service to Dromod (Irish Rail) on the Dublin-Sligo line. Bus Eireann

and Ulsterbus routes also call at Dromod
Refreshment facilities: Tea room open by arrangement. Full meals available at nearby bars
Souvenir shop: Dromod
Length of line: Half-mile (3ft gauge)
Museum: Large collection of locomotives, rolling stock, road vehicles and aircraft, many still awaiting restoration

Period of public operation:
Closed 23 December to 2 January, otherwise every Saturday, Sunday and Monday. Diesel trains run on demand
Special events: Halloween Ghost Train — 31 October; Santa Trains — 6, 13, 20 December
Contact address: The Cavan & Leitrim Railway Co Ltd, Station Road, Dromod, Co Leitrim, Republic of Ireland

Locomotives

3ft gauge

Name	No	Builder	Type	Built
Dromod	1	K/Stuart (3024)	0-4-2ST	1916
*Nancy**	1	Avonside (3024)	0-6-0T	1908
Dinmor	F511	Fowler (3900011)	4wDM	1947
—	LM11	Ruhrthaler (1082)	4wDM	1936
—	9	M/Rail (115U093)	4wDH	1970
—	LM350	Simplex (60SL748)	4wDM	1980
—	LM91	R/Hornsby (371962)	4wDM	1952
—	LM131	R/Hornsby (379086)	4wDM	1955
—	LM87	R/Hornsby (329696)	4wDM	1952
—	LM131	R/Hornsby (382809)	4wDM	1955
—	LM260	Deutz (57841)	0-4-0DM	1965
—	LM180	Deutz (57122)	0-4-0DM	1960
—	LM186	Deutz (57132)	0-4-0DM	1960
—	—	Hunslet (6075)	4wDM	1961

*Nancy under restoration at Alan Keef Ltd, Ross on Wye

5ft 3in gauge

Name	No	Builder	Type	Built
—	SZA 979	Scammel lorry	2-2wDM	1959

2ft gauge

Name	No	Builder	Type	Built
—	D5	H/Hunslet (2659)	4wDM	1942
—	1	H/Hunslet (7340)	4wDM	1940
—	2	H/Hunslet (7341)	4wDM	1940
—	3	H/Hunslet (7341)	4wDM	1943
—	LM198	R/Hornsby (398076)	4wDM	1954

1ft 10in gauge (Ex Guinness locomotives)

Name	No	Builder	Type	Built
—	22	Spence	0-4-0T	1912
—	31	Planet (3446)	4wDM	1950
—	36	Planet (3447)	4wDM	1950
—	26	Planet (3255)	4wDM	1948

Railcars

Name	No	Builder	Type	Built
—	*5	Drewry Car (1945)	4wDMR	1927
—	C11	Bord na Móna	4wDMR	–

Railcars

Name	No	Builder	Type	Built
—	C42	Wickham (7129)	4wPMR	1955
—	C47	Bord na Móna	4wPMR	1958
—	C56	Wickham (7681)	4wPMR	1957
—	W6/11-4	Wickham (9673)	2-2-0PM	1964

*built as 5ft 3in gauge inspection car for Great Southern Railway, regauged in 1994
C42 used as unpowered p-way trolley

Rolling stock
Tralee & Dingle coaches 47C (6T), 45C (7T), 48C (8T) and 44C (10T) all built 1890 ; Great Northern Railway (Ireland) AU345 built 1955 as motor bus. Alan Keef-built No 13, (built 1997)
GNR Gardiner Bus No 389, built Dundalk 1951

County Donegal Railway Restoration Society

Museum | **County Donegal**

Member: HRA

Old Station House opened as a permanent Railway Museum & Heritage Centre from Easter 1995. There are numerous outside exhibits ranging from *Drumboe* to a garden railway. Inside attractions include a video-viewing room, railway pictures and railway memorabilia

Location/Headquarters: Old Station House, Tírconaill Street, Donegal Town, Co Donegal, Ireland

Telephone: (00353-7497 [from UK]) (07497 [from Ireland]) 22655

Fax: (00353-7497 [from UK]) (07497 [from Ireland]) 23843

Internet address: *e-mail:* rrailway@gofree.indigo.ie

Web site: http://cdrrs.future.easyspace.com/

Contacts: Anna Temple

Locomotive

Name	No	Origin	Class	Type	Built
Drumboe*	5	CDR	5	2-6-4T	1907

*undergoing restoration at RPSI, Whitehead

Stock

1 CDR brake/third coach No 28
1 CDR railcar No 14
1 CDR trailer No 5
1 CDR combined goods/cattle and horse van (247 of 1893)
1 goods van

Viewing of all rolling stock is by arrangement only

Public opening: October-May Monday-Friday 09.00-16.00 (closed weekends). June-September Monday-Friday 09.00-17.00, Saturday and Sunday 14.00-17.00

Membership details: From above address

Membership journal: *The Phoenix*

Fintown Railway An Mhuc Dhubh

Steam Centre | **County Donegal**

This stretch of track has been laid on the formation of the Fintown-Glenties line. The railway runs along the shore of Lough Finn and it is planned to have a dual ride, out by rail and return by boat. The rolling stock presently used consists of an ex-mining Simplex locomotive with three turn of the century (19th/20th) passenger tramcars from Charleroi (Belgium)

Location/headquarters: Fintown Railway Station, Fintown, Co Donegal, Eire

Tel: 00353-(0)74 9546280

Internet addrersses: *e-mail:* info@antrean.com

Web site: www.antrean.com

Manager: Anne-Marie Bonner

Main station: Fintown Station

Car park: Located at station area

Access by public transport: Local buses

Refreshment facilities: Local café at top of station lane

Souvenir shop: Located at station area

Locomotives

Name	No	Builder	Type	Built
—	LM77	R/Hornsby (329680)	4wDM	1952
—	—	M/Rail (102T007)	4wDM	1974

Railcar

Name	No	Origin	Class	Type	Built
—	18	CDRJC	—	Diesel railcar	1940

Rolling stock

3 Belgian tramcars

Length of line: 3 miles (3ft gauge)

Museum: Not in operation but a collection of antiquated farm machinery is being restored

Period of public operation: June to early September *Monday-Saturday* 11.00-16.00, *Sunday* 13.00-17.00, Departures from Fintown on the hour. Return journey time 34-40 minutes

Special events: Halloween Ghost Train, Santa Specials in December

On site facilities: Toilet, it is also hoped to have a playground in operation

Membership details: Bernadette McGee, (Membership Secretary), c/o above address

Membership journal: *An Mhuc Dhubh* — annually

Irish Steam Preservation Society

Steam Centre — **County Laois**

Member: HRA, NTET
Location: Stradbally Hall, eight miles from Athy, six miles from Portlaoise (on N80 road).
Telephone: 00353 502 25151 (from UK)
Internet address: *Web site:* www.irishsteam.ie
Access by public transport: Irish Rail train to Athy or Portlaoise. Kavanagh's Bus Portlaoise-Stradbally-Carlow (Monday-Saturday), also Bus Eireann Waterford-Kilkenny-Stradbally-Portlaoise-Athlone (one daily service including Sunday)
On site facilities: 3ft gauge railway
Catering facilities: None on site but town centre quarter-mile away
Length of line: 1km
Public opening: Easter Sunday and Monday — 12/13 April; May Bank Holiday weekend Sunday & Monday — 3/4 May; June Bank

Industrial locomotives

Name	No	Builder	Type	Built
—	2	Barclay (2264)	0-4-0WT	1949
Nippy	—	Planet (2014)	4wDM	1936
—	4	R/Hornsby (326052)	4wDM	1952

Stock
1 passenger coach; 2 ballast wagons; 1 brake van

Holiday weekend Sunday & Monday — 31 May/1 June; Vintage Club Rally* — 21 June;National Steam Rally* — 2/3 August; October Bank Holiday weekend Sunday & Monday — 25/26 October.
Trains run as required 14.30-16.45 on all dates except 2/3 August when 12.00-17.30
*On these dates admission charge in addition to train fare.
Any additional operating dates which may be arranged will be

shown on the web site
Special notes: This is the longest established heritage railway in Ireland, now in its 46th year. It is hoped to reopen the Steam Museum in Stradbally in 2004. Please contact Rally Secretary, for further details or telephone above number or visit web site. All trains will be operated by a veteran diesel locomotive, pending repairs to the steam locomotive due for completion in 2009

Irish Traction Group

Museum — **County Tipperary**

Member: HRA
The Irish Traction Group was formed in 1989 with the objective of preserving at least one of each class of diesel locomotive to have operated on the Irish railway system. The ultimate aim of the Group is to restore its collection of locomotives to full main line standard
Location: The former goods store adjacent to Carrick-on-Suir railway station
Operating society/organisation: Irish Traction Group, 31 Hayfield Road, Bredbury, Stockport, Cheshire SK6 1DE, England
Telephone: 07713 159869 (Mon-Sat 09.00-18.00 only)
Internet addresses: *e-mail:* info@irishtractiongroup.com
Web site: www.irishtractiongroup.com
Car park: Available in station goods yard
Access by public transport: Infrequent train service. Services

Locomotives/Railcar

Name	No	Origin	Class	Manufacturer	Type	Built
—	1	NIR	DH	E/Electric (D1266)	6wDH	1969
—	A3R	CIE	001/A	M/Vickers (889)	Co-Co	1955
—	A39	CIE	001/A	M/Vickers (925)	Co-Co	1956
—	B103	CIE	101/B	BRCW (DEL22)	A1A-A1A	1956
—	226	CIE	201/C	M/Vickers (972)	Bo-Bo	1957
—	C231	CIE	201/C	M/Vickers (977)	Bo-Bo	1957
—	G601	CIE	601/G	Deutz (56119)	4wDH	1956
—	G611	CIE	611/G	Deutz (57225)	4wDH	1962
—	G616	CIE	611/G	Deutz (57227)	4wDH	1962
—	G617	CIE	611/G	Deutz (57229)	4wDH	1962
—	712	CIE	–	Wickham (8919)	4wDH	1962

Notes:
A3R and A39 are stored at IE Inchicore Works
G611 and G617 currently on loan to Downpatrick & Co Down Railway
C231 is stored at IE Inchicore Works
712 is currently on loan to Downpatrick & Co Down Railway
1 is currently stored at the premises of Beaver Power Ltd, Merthyr Tydfil.South Wales

operated by Bus Eireann from Dublin, Limerick and Waterford
Facilities: Toilets on IE station. Site is located quarter-mile from town centre

Special events: Operation of rail-tours over IE/NIR systems
Opening times: Premises not open to the public, locomotives B103 and G601 are both stabled outside

Republic of Ireland

Tralee & Blennerville Steam Railway

The Tralee & Blennerville Steam Railway is Europe's most westerly line and as part of the former Tralee & Dingle Light Railway (1891-1953) it has folklore and tradition stretching back over 100 years. The railway links the town of Tralee with Blennerville on the coast
Location: Tralee (Ballyard) station is situated near the Aqua Dome, Blennerville station is adjacent to the windmill, 1 mile to the west of town on the main road to Dingle (N86)
Headquarters: Tralee & Blennerville Steam Railway, Tralee, Co Kerry, Republic of Ireland
General Manager: Nora Teahon
Telephone: 066 7121288 (Tralee Tourist Office)
Internet address: *e-mail:* blen-mill@eircom.net
Car park:

Locomotives
3ft gauge

Name	No	Builder	Type	Built
—	5*	Hunslet (555)	2-6-2T	1892
—	LM92L	R/Hornsby (371967)	4wDM	1954

*an original Tralee & Dingle Railway locomotive

Rolling stock
A selection of passenger coaches and works wagons

At Tralee (Ballyard) station. Blennerville Windmill car park
Access by public transport:
By rail service to Tralee (Irish Rail).
By air to Kerry airport (10 miles) (car hire available).
By Bus Eireann to Tralee
Refreshment facilities: Restaurant at Blennerville in windmill complex
Length of line: 3km (3ft gauge)
Period of public operation: Daily

June to September (subject to confirmation)
Passenger service: Trains operate from Blennerville 10.30-16.30 (17.30 in July and August); from Tralee at 11.00-17.00
Facilities for disabled: Toilets and wheelchair access, museum and catering facilities available at Blennerville windmill

---

Waterford & Suir Valley Railway

This heritage narrow gauge railway follows over 6km of the route of the abandoned Waterford-Dungarvan line. The line runs mostly along the picturesque banks of the River Suir between Kilmeadan and Waterford City. It offers views of the Mount Congreve Gardens and the recently discovered site of a Viking settlement at Woodstown. This is an area rich in history and only accessible by train
Location: Kilmeadan station, Kilmeadan, Co Waterford on the R680
Contact: Maria Kyte, Business Development Manager, Waterford & Suir Valley Railway Co, Kilmeadan Station, Kilmeadan, Co Waterford
Telephone: 00353 (0) 51 384058
Internet address: *e-mail:* info@wsvrailway.ie

Industrial locomotives

Name	No	Builder	Type	Built
—	LM179	Deutz (57121)	0-4-0DM	1960
—	LM183	Deutz (57127)	0-4-0DM	1960
—	—	M/Rail (60SP382)	4wDM	1969

Stock
Two carriages built specially for the railway. The steel coaches have approximately two thirds of the accommodation in open toastrack seating, the remainder being an enclosed saloon, accessed from an end veranda

Web site: www.wsvrailway.ie
Charity number: CHY 13857
Access by public transport:
Suirway bus service to Kilmeadan (schedule can vary)
Access by road: Kilmeadan is 10km outside Waterford City on the Cork Road, N25. From the Waterford/Cork road take the R680 towards Portlaw/Carrick-on-Suir for 1.3km. The entrance to Kilmeadan

station is on the left
Length of line:
6km, 3ft gauge railway.
Round trip approximately 40min
Catering facilities: Coffee shop at station
Souvenir shop: Kilmeadan
Car parking: On site
Length of track: 6km of track laid from Kilmeadan to Carriganore. The summer schedule will provide

for a 12km round trip on the 6km of track

Public opening:
April and September — Monday to Saturday 11.00-15.00, Sundays 12.00-16.00.
May to August — Monday to Saturday 11.00-16.00, Sundays 12.00-17.00.

February and October — Midterm break 12.00-14.00.
December — Santa Express
Special events: Halloween Ghost Trips — October; Santa Trips — December. Please contact for dates
Special facilities: Children's birthday parties (ride and refreshments).

Gift vouchers available for tickets, special events, Friends membership
Facilities for disabled: Train carriages accessible to wheelchairs, ticket office, shop and toilets

Steam Centre — West Clare Railway (The Percy French Line) — County Clare

Operating over 1.5 miles of 3ft track gauge from its base at Moyasta Junction, the West Clare Railway is now extending its line and plans to link Kilrush to Kilkee (10 miles) in the next couple of years. The existing track has been relaid in preparation for the return of its 1892 steam locomotive No 5 *Slieve Callan,* which will be running on its original trackbed from March. A new museum display is being built at the station house reflecting the railway's impact on the area and an engine shed with inspection pit will soon be completed. Resulting from Percy French's song 'Are ye right there, Michael', this railway is Ireland's most famous line and, it hopes, its most friendly
Location/headquarters: West Clare Railway, Moyasta Junction, Kilrush, Co Clare, Republic of Ireland

Locomotives

Name	No	Builder	Type	Built
Slieve Callan	5*	Dübs (2890)	0-6-2T	1892
—	101L	RFS	4wDH	1989

*an original West Clare Railway locomotive

Rolling stock
2 carriages, with extra vehicles currently under construction

Telephone: 00353 (0) 65 905 1284
Internet address: *Web site:* www.westclarerailway.ie
Chief Executive: Jackie Whelan
Access by public transport: On National Route N67 between Kilrush and Kilkee
Main station: Moyasta Junction
Car park: Located beside station
Length of line: 1.5 miles (3ft gauge), currently being extended
On site facilities: Refreshment coach beside station. Museum in Station House. Engine shed and facilities beside car park

Period of public operation: Daily all year round. Steam days at weekends and by special arrangement
Facilities for disabled: Fully fitted including wheelchair access to all areas
Membership details: Membership Secretary, c/o above address

Heritage Railway Association

www.heritagerailways.com

Company Limited by Guarantee and not having a share capital.
Registered in England No 2226245
(Registered Office: 2 Littlestone Road, New Romney, Kent TN28 8PL)
President: Dame Margaret Weston DBE
Vice Presidents: Ian Allan OBE, Allan Garraway MBE, Brian Simpson MEP

Friends of HRA Membership Secretary:
Dr Alan Saunders, 31 Cedar Avenue, Malvern Link, Malvern, Worcs WR14 2SF
E-mail: alanhra@waitrose.com

Corporate Membership Secretary:
Steve Wood, 15 Croftlands Drive, Ravenglass, Cumbria CA18 1SJ
Tel: 01229 717080 (weekends)
E-mail: woodsysteve@hotmail.com

Members of the Heritage Railway Association

UK Affiliate Members (not in the main part of the book)

Association of Community Rail Partnerships:
Dr P. Salvenson, The Rail and River Centre, Canalside, Slaithwaite Civic Hall, Huddersfield HD7 5AB

Brookes No 1 Locomotive Co: Mr D. R. C. Moncton, 10 Blenheim Terrace, Woodhouse Lane, Leeds LS2 9HX

Edmondson Ticket Printing Co: The Pightie, Dervaig, Isle of Mull, Argyll PA75 6QN

English Welsh & Scottish Railways: Mr P. Johnson, Locomotive Engineer, Toton TNMD, Toton Sidings, Long Eaton, Nottingham NG10 1HA

R. E. V. Gomm Ltd: Mr M. J. Tyler, Jayesco Works, 31 Commercial Street, Birmingham B1 1RJ

Guild of Railway Artists: Mr F. Hodges, Chief Executive Officer, 45 Dickins Road, Warwick CV34 5NS

Helston Railway Society: Mr Stuart Walker, Chairman, 149 Polwithen Drive, Carbis Bay, St Ives, Cornwall TR26 2SW

HIT Entertainment: Maple House, 149 Tottenham Court Road, London W1T 7NF

Lloyd's Railway Society: Mr Douglas Cooper, 24 Yew Tree Road, Southborough, Tunbridge Wells, Kent TN4 0BA

Locomotive Club of Great Britain: Mr R. L. Patrick, 8 Wolviston Ave, Bishopgate, York YO1 3DD

Marsh (UK) Ltd: Mr A. J. C. Brown, No 1, The Marsh Centre, London EC1 8DX

Rannoch Station Visitor Centre: Normanhurst Enterprises Ltd, 9 Burscough Street, Ormskirk, Lancs L39 2EG

Transport Trust: 202 Lambeth Road, London SE1 7JW

Westinghouse Signals Ltd: Helen Webb, PO Box 79, Pew Hill, Chippenham, Wiltshire SN15 1ND

Overseas Affiliate Members

Australian Railway Historical Society: Mr R. Jowett, New South Wales Division, 67 Renwick St, Redfern, NSW 2016, Australia

Puffing Billy Railway: Mr Mel Elliot, PO Box 451, Belgrave, Victoria 3160, Australia

Stoomscentrum Maldegem: Rik Degruyter, De Streep 19, B-8340 Damme-Sysele, Belgium

Additional Corporate Members not listed in the main part of the book

Aln Valley Railway Society:
Mr S. Manley, Alnwick Station, Alnwick, Northumberland NE66 2NP

Altrincham Electric Railway Preservation Society:
Mr A. D. Macfarlane, 25 Prestbury Avenue,
Timperley, Altrincham, Cheshire WA15 8HY

Battle of Britain Locomotive Preservation Society:
Les Mitchell, 30 Hilton Way, Sible Hedingham, Essex
CO9 3JW

Bridgend Valleys Railway:
Mr J. Leach, 10 Y-Wern, Bettws, Bridgend,
Mid Glamorgan CF32 8RR

Britain's Great Little Railways: Mr M. B. Beevers,
64 Bullar Road, Southampton SO18 1GS

Britannia Locomotive Society:
Mr A. Sixsmith, 6 Vermont Grove, Peterborough
PE3 6BN

Bulleid Society Ltd:
Mr A. J. Fry, 28 Houndean Rise, Lewes, Sussex
BN7 1EQ

Burry Port & Gwendraeth Railway Co Ltd:
Mr Stuart Thomas, Wellfield, Yrecor Lane, Ferryside
Carms SA17 5UT

Caerphilly Railway Society Ltd: Mr A. Smith,
51 Worcester Crescent, Newport NP9 7NX

Camelot Locomotive Society: Mr P. W. Gibbs,
13 Clarendon Road, High Wycombe, Bucks
HP13 7AW

Class 40 Preservation Society: Martin Walker, c/o
Beaver Sports (YOMO) Ltd, Flint Street, Fartown,
Huddersfield HD1 6LG

Class 45/1 Preservation Society: Mr N. Burden,
97 Richmond Park Crescent, Handsworth, Sheffield
S13 8HF

Class 56 Group: Tim Dawe, 1 Stanley Avenue,
Sutton Coldfield B75 7EQ

Clwyd & District Railway Heritage Trust: Arfryn,
13 Pen-y-maes Avenue, Rhyl LL18 4ED

Cornish Steam Locomotive Preservation Society Ltd:
Mr M. Orme, 3 Jubilee Terrace, Goonhavern, Truro,
Cornwall TR4 9JY

Cravens Heritage Trains:
James Deacon, 43 Ashpole Furlong, Loughton,
Milton Keynes MK5 8ED

Darjeeling Himalayan Railway Society:
Mr P. D. Whittle, 8 Broadwater Close, Woking, Surrey
GU21 5TW

Darlington Railway Preservation Society:
Mr M. Bentley, 64 Dimsdale View East, Porthill,
Newcastle under Lyme ST5 8HL

Dean Forest Locomotive Group:
Mr J. S. Metherall, 15 Sudbrook Way, Gloucester
GL4 4AP

Deltic Preservation Society: Nigel Paine,
49 Woodgate Road, Wootton Fields, Wootton,
Northants NN4 6ET

Devon Diesel Society Ltd: Steve Squires,
15 Springfield, Acle, Norfolk NR13 3JW

Diesel and Electric Group:
Mr J. E. Cronin, The Old Goods Shed, Williton
Station, Williton, Somerset TA4 4RQ

Diesel Unit Preservation Associates Ltd:
Mr M. Cornell, 24 Ashbury Drive, Marks Tey,
Colchester, Essex CO6 1XW

Dolgarrog Railway Society:
Mr P. Smith, 84 Gorlan, Conwy LL32 8RR

East Essex Locomotive Preservation Society:
Mr R. Moore 7 Woodbine Grove, Enfield, Middx
EN2 0EA

Eastleigh Railway Preservation Society Ltd:
Neil Kearns, 38 Arundel Road, Boyatt Wood,
Eastleigh, Hants SO50 4PQ

Eden Valley Railway Trust:
Ms G. Boyd, 1 Victoria Road, Barnard Castle,
Co Durham DL12 8HW

EPB Preservation Group: Mr R. Baines, 73
Woodhurst Avenue, Petts Wood, Orpington, Kent
BR5 1AT

Firefly Trust: Mr S. Bee, 9 Shenstone, Lindfield,
West Sussex RH16 2PU

The Flour Mill: Mr W. A. Parker, Stowe Grange,
St Briavels, Lydney, Glos GL15 6QH

Foxcote Manor Society:
Mr G. Heddon, 31 Lordsmill Road, Shavington,
Crewe, Cheshire CW2 5HB

Furness Railway Trust:
Tim Owen Meadowside, 105 Station Road, Cark in
Cartmel, Grange over Sands, Cumbria LA11 7NY

Garw Valley Railway Co Ltd:
Adrian R Thomas, General Manager,
c/o 56 Dinam Park, Ton Pendre, Pentre, Rhondda
Cynon Taf, South Wales CF41 7DY

Gloucester Railcars Trust Ltd:
John Bull, 61 Walsingham Gardens, Stoneleigh,
Epsom, Surrey KT19 0LT

Glyn Valley Tramway Group:
David Norman, 4 Yew Tree Court, Gresford,
Wrexham LL12 8ET

GWR 813 Preservation Fund:
Mr P. Goss, 23 Hatchmere, Thornbury, Bristol
BS35 2EU

Haig Colliery Mining Museum: John Greasley,
Haig Colliery Mining Museum, Solway Road, Kells,
Whitehaven, Cumbria CA28 9BG

Hampshire & Sussex Units Preservation Society:
Mr C. Dann, 48 Hollybrook Park, Bordon, Hants
GU35 0DL

Hastings Diesels Ltd:
Mr J. White, The Rail Engineering Centre, Bridgeway,
St Leonards on Sea, East Sussex TN38 8AP

Heaton Park Electric Tramway: Roger Morris,
38 Wolsey Road, Sale, Cheshire M33 7AU

Holden F5 Steam Locomotive Trust: Steve Cooper, 49 Beech Avenue, Halstead, Essex CO9 2TT

Hull & Barnsley Railway Stock Fund:
Mr A. E. Hallman, 6 Chequerfield Court, Pontefract, West Yorkshire WF8 2TQ

Kingdom of Fife Railway Association (The):
Jim Rankine, 'Lairg', Haughmill Lane, Windygates, Fife KY8 5DH

Lambton No 29 Syndicate:
Mr J. M. Richardson, 509 Westgate Apartments, York YO26 4ZF

Lancashire & Yorkshire Railway Preservation Society:
Mr E. Ring, PO Box 3593, Newport Pagnell MK16 9ZJ

Lincolnshire Coast Light Railway Historical Vehicles Trust:
Mr Frederick Ellis, Chairman, c/o Ellis Bros (Contractors), 7 Lansdowne Road, Skegness, Lincolnshire PE25 2DJ

Llanelli & Mynydd Mawr Railway: Martin Doe, 16 Melrose Avenue, Penylan, Cardiff CF23 9AR

LMS Carriage Association: David Winter, 42 Tandlewood Park, Royton, Oldham OL2 5UZ

Locomotive Owners Group (Scotland) Ltd:
Mr H. Stevenson, 28 Hazeldean Avenue, Bo'ness, West Lothian EH51 0NJ

London & North Western Society: Mr R. J. Williams, 3 Chieveley Court, Emerson Valley, Milton Keynes MK4 2DD

Lynton & Barnstaple Light Railway: Mr D. Hill, 8 Long Lakes, Williton, Taunton, Somerset TA4 4SR

Lynton & Lynmouth Lift Co: Ceri Hughes, The Cliff Railway, The Esplanade, Lynmouth, Devon EX35 6EQ

Maid Marian Locomotive Fund: Mr H. Johns, 139 Stoops Lane, Doncaster DN4 7RG

Market Drayton Railway Preservation Society:
Glyn Rowe, Shakeford Mill House, Hinstock, Market Drayton, Shropshire TF9 2SP

Maunsell Locomotive Society:
Mr J. S. Pilcher, 312 Riverside Mansions, Garnett Street, Wapping, London E1 9SZ

Merchant Navy Locomotive Preservation Society Ltd:
Howard G. Reynolds, 4 Ash Grove, Liphook, Hants GU30 7HZ

Merseyside Tramway Preservations Society:
Robert Jones, 103 Grove Road, Wallasey, Merseyside CH45 3HG

Midsomer Norton Station Project:
John Baxter, 12 Huxley Close, Shrewsbury SY2 6JR

Modern Railway Society of Ireland: Mr D. Brian King, 4 York Avenue, Whitehead, Co Antrim, N. Ireland BT38 9QT

Moseley Railway Trust: Dr John Rowlands, 10 Braxfield Court, St Annes Road West, St Annes on Sea, Lancs FY8 1LQ

National Museums Scotland: Alistair Dodds, Principal Curator of Transport, Chambers Street, Edinburgh EH1 1JF

NER 1903 Electric Autocar Trust: Stephen Middleton, Rose Lea House, 23 Brunswick Drive, Harrogate HG1 2QW

North Eastern Locomotive Preservation Group:
Mr C. Hatton, 20 Sorrell Court, Marton, Middlesbrough TS7 8RZ

North Gloucestershire Railway Co Ltd:
Mr R. H. Wales, 'Wellesbourne', Oakfield Street, Tivoli, Cheltenham, Gloucestershire GL33 8HR

Ongar Railway Preservation Society: Mr B. Ayton, 75 Highland Road, Nazeing, Essex EN9 2PU

Princess Royal Locomotive Trust Ltd:
Mr George Bailey, The Gables, Whitecross, Hallatrow, Bristol BS39 6ER

Project 62 Locomotive Group:
Richard White, 45 Cedar Crescent, North Baddesley, Southampton SO52 9FU

Railway Vehicle Preservations Ltd:
Mr Gordon Maslin, 14 Lawson Avenue, Stanground, Peterborough PE2 8PA

Red Rose Society:
Mr G. Jones, Astley Green Colliery Museum, Higher Green Lane, Astley, Tyldesley, Manchester M29 7JB

Salisbury Steam Locomotive Preservation Trust:
Mr E. J. Roper, 33 Victoria Road, Wilton, Salisbury, Wiltshire SP2 0DZ

Scottish Locomotive Preservation Trust Fund:
Mr J. Shepherd, 29 Earlspark Avenue, Glasgow G43 2HN

Shipley Glen Tramway: Councillor Dean Smith, 10 Craven Park, Menston, Ilkley, West Yorkshire LS29 6EQ

Sir Nigel Gresley Locomotive Preservation Trust Ltd:
Peter Travis, 26 Cheltenham Gardens, Halifax, West Yorks HX3 0AN

Southern Electric Group:
Mr B. Cakebread, 41 The Drive, Shoreham by Sea, West Sussex BN43 5GD

Southern Locomotives Ltd:
Mr S. Troy, 16 Arcadia Road, Istead Rise, Meopham, Kent DA13 9EH

Southwold Railway Society (The):
Mr J. Bennett, 1 Barnaby Green, Southwold, Suffolk IP15 6AP

Stainmore Railway: Mike Thompson, Manor Cottage, 1 West End, Sedgefield, Stockton on Tees TS21 2BW

Stanier 8F Locomotive Society Ltd: Mr G. Moon, 5 Orchid Fields, St Christopher's Way, Burnham on Sea, Somerset TA8 2NU

Steam Power Trust '65:
Mr A. R. Thompson, The Station House, Penshaw,
Houghton le Spring DH4 7PQ

Steeple Grange Light Railway: Martin Smith,
187 Chesterfield Road, Matlock, Derbyshire
DE4 3GA

Stephenson Locomotive Society: Mr M. A. Green,
3 Cresswell Court, Hartlepool TS26 0ES

Stratford on Avon, Broadway Railway Society:
Mr Roland Hill, 10 Garard Close, Salford Priors,
Evesham, Worcs WR11 5XG

Suburban Electric Railway Association:
Mr R. Davidson, 6 Coombfield Drive, Darenth,
Dartford, Kent DA2 7LQ

Threlkeld Quarry & Mining Museum:
Ian Hartland, Threlkeld Quarry & Mining Museum,
Keswick, Cumbria CA12 4TT

Underground Railway Rolling Stock Trust:
Mr D. C. Alexander, 13 Irvine Drive, Stoke
Mandeville, Aylesbury HP22 5UN

Urie Locomotive Society:
Mr A. Ball, 'Lavenham', Adams Lane, Selborne,
Alton, Hants GU34 3LJ

Wainwright 'C' Preservation Society:
Mr I. A. Demaid, 69 Bromley Gardens, Bromley,
Kent BR2 0ES

Waverley Route Heritage Association: Ian Macintosh,
Signal Box Cottage, Whitrope, Hawick,
Roxburghshire TD9 9TY

Weardale Railway Trust:
Mr G. Chatsfield, Stanhope Station, Bondisle,
Bishop Auckland, Co Durham DL13 2YS

Western Locomotive Association: Mr H. Coates,
5 Rake End Court, Ridware, Rugeley, Staffs
WS15 5RW

Worcester Locomotive Society Ltd: Dave Witney,
16 Willow Walk, Honiton, Devon EX14 2FX

1857 Society: Mr G. West, 21A Broad Street,
Brigtown, Cannock, West Midlands WS11 3DA

4247 Ltd: Mr N. Powles, 15 Claydon Close,
Washford, Watchet, Somerset TA23 0PQ

45163 Ltd: Jeremy Dunn, Chairman,
4 Whitlock Drive, Great Yeldham, Halstead, Essex
CO9 4EE

48624 Locomotive Soc: Keith Godley,
11 Cobnar Drive, Newbold, Chesterfield, Derbyshire
S41 8DD

6201 Princess Elizabeth Society Ltd: Mr A. Harries,
1 Ormerod Close, Sandbach, Cheshire CW11 4HA

35006 Locomotive Co Ltd: Nigel Hills, Flat 1,
55 Holland Park, London W11 3RS

*71000 Duke of Gloucester Steam Locomotive Trust
Ltd:* D. J. Brown, 11 Stirling Close, Woolston,
Warrington, Cheshirr WA1 4DW

8E Railway Association: Mr A. Ashurst,
149 St Mary Street, Latchford, Warrington, Cheshire
WA4 1EL

LM2MT 46464 Trust: Mr I. Hopley, The Carmyllie
Pilot Co Ltd, 6 Ninian Place, Portlethen AB12 4QW

Applicant Organisations

Class 15 Preservation Society

Glyn Valley Tramway Trust

Lein Amlwch — Anglesey Central Railway (2006) Ltd

North Woolwich Station Museum

34007 Wadebridge

Britain's Great Little Railways

Brookside Miniature Railway: (see main section)

Dragon Miniature Railway:
Mr B. Lomas, Wyevale Garden Centre, Otterspool,
Marple, Cheshire SK6 7HG

Eastleigh Lakeside Railway: (see main section)

Exmoor Steam Railway: (see main section)

Fairbourne Railway: (see main section)

Haigh Hall Railway: Mr T. Sharratt, Haigh Hall
Country Park, Haigh, Wigan, Lancs WN2 1PE

Little Giant Railways: Merton Hill Railway, Merton
Abbey Mills, London SW19 2RD

Moors Valley Railway (see main section)

Mull Rail (see main section)

Perrygrove Railway: (see main section)

Road, Rail & Waterway: Mr J. Shackell,
27 Witney Road, Duckington, Witney, Oxon
OX8 7TX

Rudyard Lake Railway: (see main section)

Shibden Miniature Railway: Shibden Park, Listers
Road, Halifax, W. Yorks HX3 6XG

Swanley New Barn Railway:
Mr P. Jackson, New Barn Lane, Swanley, Kent

Weston Miniature Railway:
Mr R. Bullock, Marine Parade, Weston-super-Mare,
Somerset

Preservation is not just about motive power. As the Severn Valley found out in 2007 infrastructure is just as vital. Often a visitors recollections of a day out revolve around the standard of the carriages they travel in. The North Norfolk Railway raised a lot of finance in order to restore its unique GNR Quard Art set to traffic. The funding also contributed to the construction of a carriage storage shed near Holt. Here the restored set is seen behind No 69621 approaching Weybourne. *NNR*

HERITAGE RAILWAYS
2009

NATIONAL TIMETABLE OF
SCHEDULED SERVICES

Ian Allan PUBLISHING

73082

Railways ILLUSTRATED

HORNBY magazine

HERITAGE RAILWAYS TIMETABLE AND DIRECTORY 2009

This timetable has been produced by Ian Allan Publishing in conjunctions with *Railways Illustrated* and *Hornby Magazine* and was printed by Ian Allan Printing Ltd, Hersham, Surrey.

NOTES TO THE TIMETABLE

Throughout the Timetable, the 24-hour clock is used.

Days of operation are shown. Timetable information is also provided, where available.

Many trains have on-board refreshment facilities. These are not shown herein as availability may vary according to staffing conditions and seasons of the year.

For details of Wine and Dine, Thomas the Tank Engine, Santa Specials and other out-of-the-ordinary facilities, please inquire of the appropriate railway company for details

Telephone and fax numbers, postal address and web site address of each railway is shown, where known, at the head of each entry so that specific enquiries can be made direct. Most operators have excellent web sites offering a wide range of information to help intending visitors.

The entries are mostly in alphabetical order, with the odd exception to meet space requirements.

DISCLAIMER

The timetable has been compiled from information received from operating companies and is believed to be accurate. However, neither the publisher or the HRA accept any responsibility for any loss, damage or delay which may be caused by variances between this brochure and actual operations, or any other cause. Where any railway operator has failed or declined to submit timetable information, we offer only contact details so that intending visitors can obtain this information for themselves, direct from the operator.

Previous page - BR 'Standard Five' 4-6-0 73082 *Camelot* departs Sheffield Park, Bluebell Railway, in September 2004. *Mike Wild.*

AVON VALLEY RAILWAY

0117 932 5538

Bitton Station, Bath Road, Bitton, Bristol BS30 6HD

Fax: 0117 932 5938 Web: www.avonvalleyrailway.org

2009	1	2	3	4	5	6	7	8	9	10	11	12	13	14	15	16	17	18	19	20	21	22	23	24	25	26	27	28	29	30	31
MAR																						S									
APR				S		S	S	S	S	S	S	S	S	S	S			S						S							
MAY		D	S	S			T	T								S				D	S	S	S	S	S	S		D	S		
JUN		M			D	S			M				S				M		D	S			M				S				
JUL	S			S			S				S			S				S			S			D	S			S	S	S	
AUG	D	S		S	S	S		D	S		S	S	S		D	S		S	S	S		D	S		S	S	S		D	S	S
SEP				D	S						D	S							S						S						
OCT			T	T							S					D	S						S		M	M	M				
NOV	X																											SS			
DEC				SS	SS	SS				SS	SS					SS	SS			SS	SS				P	P					

S = Steam D = Diesel M = Diesel Multiple Unit X = Gala T = Thomas and Friends SS = Santa Specials P = Mince Pie Specials

Timetable A – Steam (S) and Diesel (D)

Oldland		11.20	12.35	13.50	15.05	16.20
Bitton		11.30	12.45	14.00	15.15	16.30
Avon Riverside		11.37	12.52	14.07	15.22	16.37

Avon Riverside		11.50	13.05	14.20	15.35	16.50
Bitton	11.00	12.15	13.30	14.45	16.00	17.00
Oldland	11.07	12.22	13.37	14.52	16.07	

Timetable B – Diesel Multiple Unit (M) service

Oldland		11.15	12.15	13.15	14.15	15.15	16.15
Bitton		11.25	12.25	13.25	14.25	15.25	16.25
Avon Riverside		11.32	12.32	13.32	14.32	15.32	16.32

Avon Riverside		11.40	12.40	13.40	14.40	15.40	16.40
Bitton	11.00	12.00	13.00	14.00	15.00	16.00	16.50
Oldland	11.05	12.05	13.05	14.05	15.05	16.05	

BALA LAKE RAILWAY

01678 540666

The Station, Llanuwchllyn, Gwynedd LL23 7DD

Fax: 01678 540535 Web: www.bala-lake-railway.co.uk Email: balalake@btconnect.com

SS = Santa Specials

2009	1	2	3	4	5	6	7	8	9	10	11	12	13	14	15	16	17	18	19	20	21	22	23	24	25	26	27	28	29	30	31
MAR																															
APR			A	A		A	A	A	A	A	A	A	A	A	A	A		B	B	B		A	A		B	B	B				
MAY		A	A	A	A	A	A		A	A		A	A	A		A	A		A	A	A		A	A	A	A	A	A	A	A	
JUN		A	A	A		A	A		A	A	A		A	A		A	A	A		A	A		A	A	A		A	A		A	
JUL	A	A	A	A	A	A	A	A	A	A	A	A	A	A	A	A	A	A	A	A	A	A	A	A	A	A	A	A	A	A	A
AUG	A	A	A	A	A	A	A	A	A	A	A	A	A	A	A	A	A	A	A	A	A	A	A	A	A	A	A	A	A	A	A
SEP	A	A	A		A	A		A	A	A		A	A		A	A	A		A	A		A	A	A		A	A				
OCT	C					C					C					C					B	B	B								
NOV																															
DEC				SS	SS																										

Timetable A

Trains depart Llanuwchllyn at 11.15, 12.50, 14.25, 16.00 and return from Bala at 11.50, 13.25, 15.00, 16.35.

Timetable B

Trains depart Llanuwchllyn at 12.15, 14.25 and return from Bala at 12.50, 15.00

Timetable C

Train departs Llanuwchllyn at 14.25 and returns from Bala at 15.00

BATTLEFIELD LINE

01827 880754

Shackerstone Station, Leicestershire CV13 6NW

Fax: 01827 881050   Web: www.battlefield-line-railway.co.uk

2009	1	2	3	4	5	6	7	8	9	10	11	12	13	14	15	16	17	18	19	20	21	22	23	24	25	26	27	28	29	30	31
MAR																												A	A		
APR				A	A					A	A	S	S					A	A					S	S						▓
MAY		S	S	S				A	A						A	A						S	S	S		B				S	A
JUN						T	T						T	T					A	A				S				A	A		▓
JUL	S			A	A			B			S	S			B			A	A			B			A	A			B		
AUG	S	A						A	A						A	A						A	A						S	S	S
SEP				A	A						S	S						S	S	S						A	A				▓
OCT			A	A						S	S						S	S	S		B			A	A			B			A
NOV	A																												S	S	▓
DEC					S	S					S	S						S	S					S							S

T = Thomas and Friends S = Special event, timetable varies

Timetable A – weekends: steam/diesel/railcarservices

Shackerstone	11.45	13.20	14.40	16.00
Shenton	12.05	13.40	15.00	16.20
Shenton	12.20	13.55	15.15	16.35
Shackerstone	12.40	14.15	15.35	16.55

Timetable B – midweek: railcar service

Shackerstone	11.30	12.50	14.10	15.30
Shenton	11.48	13.08	14.28	15.48
Shenton	11.55	13.15	14.35	15.55
Shackerstone	12.13	13.33	14.53	16.13

BLUEBELL RAILWAY

01825 720800

Sheffield Park, Uckfield, East Sussex TN22 3QL

Fax: 01825 720804   Web: www.bluebell-railway.co.uk   Email: info@bluebell-railway.co.uk

2009	1	2	3	4	5	6	7	8	9	10	11	12	13	14	15	16	17	18	19	20	21	22	23	24	25	26	27	28	29	30	31
MAR	A						A	A						A	A						A	A						A	A		
APR				X	A	A	A	A	A	A	A	A	A	A	A	A	A	A	X	X	X	X	X	A	X	X	X	X			▓
MAY	X	A	A	A	B	B	B	B	X	X	B	B	B	B	B	B	A	A	B	B	B	B	B	A	A	A	A	A	A	A	A
JUN	B	B	B	B	B	A	A	B	B	B	B	B	A	A	B	B	B	B	B	X	X	B	B	B	B	B	X	X	B	B	▓
JUL	B	B	B	A	A	B	B	B	B	B	A	A	B	B	B	B	B	A	A	B	B	B	B	B	X	X	A	A	A	A	A
AUG	A	A	A	A	A	A	A	A	A	A	A	A	A	A	X	X	A	A	A	A	A	A	A	A	A	A	A	A	A	A	A
SEP	B	B	B	B	A	A	B	B	B	B	B	A	A	B	B	B	B	A	A	B	B	B	B	B	A	A	B	B	B		▓
OCT	B	B	A	A	X	X	X	X	X	X	A	A	X	X	X	X	X	X	A	A	X	X	X	X	X	X	X	X	X	X	X
NOV	X	X	X	X	X	X	A	A	X	X	X	X	X	A	X						A	A						A	A		▓
DEC					SS	SS					SS	SS							SS	SS			SS	SS		A	A	A	A	A	A

X = Special events

SS = Santa Specials

Midweek services in October are 'Autumn Tints' services with limited seating, therefore booking is advisable.

Timetable A: Trains run hourly from 11.00 from Sheffield Park to Kingscote.
Timetable B: Trains run at 11.00, 13.00 and 15.00 from Sheffield Park to Kingscote.

BODMIN & WENFORD RAILWAY   01208 73666

General Station, Bodmin, Cornwall PL31 1AQ

Fax: 01208 77963   Web: bodminandwenfordrailway.co.uk   Email: enquiries@bodminandwenfordrailway.co.uk

2009	1	2	3	4	5	6	7	8	9	10	11	12	13	14	15	16	17	18	19	20	21	22	23	24	25	26	27	28	29	30	31
MAR														X	X			A				A			A			X	X		
APR	A				A	A	A	A	A	X	X	X	X	A	A	A	X	X	X			A			A			A			▓
MAY		X	X	X		A			A		A	A					A		A	A			C	X	X	X	X	A	A	X	X
JUN	A	A	A	A	A	C	A	A	A	A	A	A	C	A	A	A	A	A	A	C	A	A	A	A	A	A	A	C	A	A	▓
JUL	A	A	A	C	A	A	A	A	A	C	A	A	A	A	A	A	A	C	A	A	A	A	A	C	A	B	B	B	B	B	X
AUG	X	X	X	B	B	B	A	A	A	B	B	B	B	A	A	A	B	B	B	B	A	A	A	B	B	B	B	A	A	A	B
SEP	B	A	A	X	X	X	X	A	A	A	A	C	A	A	A	A	A	A	C	A	A	A	A	A	A	X	X	A	A	A	▓
OCT			C	A			A			X	X			A			A			A					A	A	A	A	A	A	A
NOV	A																														▓
DEC				X	X					X	X							X	X				X	X			A	A	A		▓

X = Special events

Timetable A

Diesel

Bodmin General	10.00	11.00	12.10	13.45	14.55
Bodmin Parkway	10.12		12.27		15.12
Boscarne Jct			11.15		14.00	
Boscarne Jct			11.25		14.10	
Bodmin Parkway	10.25		12.40		15.25
Bodmin General	10.37	11.42	13.00	14.27	15.45

Diesel - operates Mon-Fri Jun 1-Sept 25

Timetable B

Bodmin General	10.15	11.25	12.35	13.05	13.45	14.55	16.05
Bodmin Parkway	10.32		12.52		14.00		16.20
Boscarne Jct		11.40		13.20		15.12	
Boscarne Jct		11.50		13.05		15.25	
Bodmin Parkway	10.45		12.25		14.10		16.30
Bodmin General	11.05	12.07	12.45	13.25	14.27	15.45	16.47

Timetable C

	D	D	D	D	D	D	D
Bodmin General	10.20	11.20	12.20	13.15	14.15	15.15	16.05
Bodmin Parkway	10.37		12.37		14.32		16.22
Boscarne Jct		11.35		13.30		15.30	
Boscarne Jct		11.50		13.45		15.40	
Bodmin Parkway	10.50		12.45		14.40		16.30
Bodmin General	11.07	12.05	13.02	14.00	14.57	15.55	16.50

All services operated by heritage diesel locomotives

BO'NESS & KINNEIL RAILWAY   01506 825855/822298

Scottish Railway Preservation Society, 17-19 North Street, Bo'ness EH51 0AQ

Fax: 01506 828766   Web: www.srps.org.uk

Trains run on April 4/5, 7-16, 18/19, 25/26; May 2-4, 9/10, 16-18, 23/24, 30/31; June 2-4, 6/7, 9-11, 13/14, 20/21, 27/28; July 1-31 (6, 13, 20 diesel days); August 1-30 (29/30 diesel days); September 5/6. 12/13, 19/20, 26/27; October 3/4, 10/11. 17/18, 24/25, 31; November 1, December 30/31. Santa Specials – November 28/29; December 5/6, 12/13, 19/20.

Standard Timetable: Trains depart Bo'ness at 11.00, 12.20, 13.50, 15.00 (and 16.15 diesel).

Midweek Timetable: Apr & June: Trains depart Bo'ness at 11.00, 12.20, 13.30.

BRECON MOUNTAIN RAILWAY

01685 722988

Pant Station, Merthyr Tydfil CF48 2UP

Fax: 01685 384854   Web: www.breconmountainrailway.co.uk   Email: enquiries@breconmountainrailway.co.uk

2009	1	2	3	4	5	6	7	8	9	10	11	12	13	14	15	16	17	18	19	20	21	22	23	24	25	26	27	28	29	30	31
MAR																					A	A		A	A			A	A		A
APR	A	A		A	A		A	A	A	A	A	B	A	A	A	A	A	A	A		A	A	A		A	A		A	A	A	
MAY		A	A	B	A	A	A		A	A		A	A	A		A	A		A	A	A		A	B	B	A	A	A	A	A	A
JUN	A	A	A	A	A	A	A	A	A	A	A	A	A	A	A	A	A	A	A	A	A	A	A	A	A	A	A	A	A	A	
JUL	A	A	A	A	A	A	A	A	A	A	A	A	A	A	A	A	A	A	A	A	A	A	A	A	A	A	A	A	A	A	A
AUG	A	A	A	A	A	A	A	A	A	A	A	A	A	A	A	A	A	A	A	A	A	A	A	A	A	A	A	A	A	B	B
SEP	A	A	A	A	A	A	A	A	A	A	A	A	A	A	A	A	A	A	A		A	A	A		A	A		A	A		
OCT	A		A	A		A	A		A	A		A	A	A		A	A		A	A	A		A	A	A	A	A	A	A	A	A
NOV	A																														
DEC																															

Timetable A: Trains leave Pant at 11.00, 12.15, 13.30, 14.45, 16.00

Timetable B: Trains leave Pant at 11.00, 12.15, 13.30, 14.45, 16.00, 17.15

Round trip takes 65mins, including a 20min stop at Pontsticill.

BURE VALLEY RAILWAY

01263 733585

Aylsham Station, Norwich Road, Aylsham, Norfolk NR11 6BW

Fax: 01263 733814   Web: www.bvrw.co.uk

No further details received – please contact for operating details.

CALEDONIAN RAILWAY (BRECHIN) LTD

01356 622992

The Station, 2 Park Road, Brechin, Angus DD9 7AF

Web: www.caledonianrailway.com

No further details received – please contact for operating details.

CHASEWATER RAILWAY

01543 452623

Chasewater Country Park, Pool Road, Nr Brownhills, Staffs WS8 7NL

Web: www.chaserail.com

2009	1	2	3	4	5	6	7	8	9	10	11	12	13	14	15	16	17	18	19	20	21	22	23	24	25	26	27	28	29	30	31
MAR	C							C							C							C							A		
APR					A		D		D	B	A	A		D					A						A						
MAY		B	A	A				A								A							B	A	A	D				B	A
JUN							B	A					X	A					X	X							X	A			
JUL				B	A			D			B	A						B	A			D			B	A			D		D
AUG	B	A		D		D		B	A		D		D		B	A		D		D		B	A		D		D		B	A	A
SEP	D				D			B	A				X	X						A							A				
OCT				A							A							A				C					D				X
NOV	C							C							C							C									
DEC						SS						SS	SS						SS	SS				SS	SS							

X = Special events

SS = Santa Specials

Timetable A - Steam Service

Brownhills West	10.30	11.45	13.00	14.15	15.30	16.45
Chasetown (Church Street)	10.50	12.05	13.20	14.35	15.50	17.05
Chasetown (Church Street)	11.00	12.15	13.30	14.45	16.00	17.15
Brownhills West	11.15	12.30	13.45	15.00	16.15	17.30

Timetables B, C, D – Diesel Service

	BCD	BCD	BCD	BCD	BCD	BC	B
Brownhills West	10.30	11.45	13.00	14.00	15.00	16.00	17.00
Chasetown (Church Street)	10.45	12.00	13.15	14.15	15.15	16.15	17.15
Chasetown (Church Street)	10.55	12.10	13.25	14.25	15.25	16.25	17.25
Brownhills West	11.10	12.25	13.40	14.40	15.40	16.40	17.40

CHINNOR & PRINCES RISBOROUGH RAILWAY

Chinnor Station, Station Road, Chinnor, Oxon OX39 4ER   **01844 353535**

Web: www.chinnorrailway.co.uk

2009	1	2	3	4	5	6	7	8	9	10	11	12	13	14	15	16	17	18	19	20	21	22	23	24	25	26	27	28	29	30	31
MAR																						A							A		
APR				A					A	A	A	A						A							X						
MAY		A	A	A				A	A							A						A	A	A							A
JUN						A								A					A							X	X				
JUL				A							A							A							A						
AUG	X	X					X	A						X	A				X	A									X	A	A
SEP					A								A							A							A				
OCT				A									A				X	X						A							
NOV	A																														
DEC					SS	SS						SS	SS						SS	SS							P	P			

A = Standard timetable X = Gala day or special timetable SS = Santa Specials P = Mince Pie Specials

Timetable A: Trains leave Chinnor at 10.30(D), 11.45, 13.00, 14.30, 16.00

CHOLSEY & WALLINGFORD RAILWAY   **01491 835067**

5 Hithercroft Road, Wallingford, Oxon OX10 9GQ.

Web: www.cholsey-wallingford-railway.com

Trains run on April 11-13, 26; May 3/4, 16/17, 24/25; June 6/7, 13/14, 20/21, 27/28; July 25/26; Aug 16, 30/31; Sept 5/6, 13, 26/27; Oct 31; Nov 1. Santa trains run Dec 5/6, 12/13, 19/20.

Trains leave Wallingford at 11.10, 12.10, 13.10, 14.10, 15.10, 16.10

Trains leave Cholsey at 11.35, 12.35, 13.35, 14.35, 15.35, 16.35

Trains may be steam or diesel hauled – please check before travelling.

CHURNET VALLEY RAILWAY   **01538 360522**

The Station, Cheddleton, Staffordshire Moorlands ST13 7EE

Fax: 01538 361848 Web: www.churnet-valley-railway.co.uk Email: enquiries@churnetvalleyrailway.co.uk

2009	1	2	3	4	5	6	7	8	9	10	11	12	13	14	15	16	17	18	19	20	21	22	23	24	25	26	27	28	29	30	31
MAR	A						A							A						A									A		
APR			A	A					A	A	B	B			A			A	A						B	B					
MAY		A	B	B				A	A							A	A						A	B	B		A			A	A
JUN						A							A	A						A	A						A	A			
JUL	A			A	A			A			A	A				A		A	A			A			A	A			A		
AUG	A	A	A		B			B	B	B		B			B	B	A		B			A	A	A		B			A	B	
SEP	A			A	A							A	A						A	A					A	A					
OCT				A								X	A						A					A			A				
NOV														X	X																
DEC					SS	SS			SS			SS	SS			SS			SS	SS			SS	SS			A	A		A	

X = Gala events
SS = Santa Specials

Timetable A

Cheddleton	10.32	11.57	13.22	14.47	16.12
Kingsley & Froghall	10.50	12.15	13.40	15.05	16.30

Kingsley & Froghall	11.10	12.35	14.00	15.25	16.50
Cheddleton	11.50	13.15	14.40	16.05	17.30

Timetable B

	D		D		D		D		D		D
Cheddleton	10.00	10.43	11.26	12.09	12.52	13.35	14.18	15.01	15.44	16.27	17.10
Kingsley & Froghall	10.17	11.00	11.43	12.26	13.09	13.52	14.35	15.18	16.01	16.44	17.27

Kingsley & Froghall	09.58	10.41	11.24	12.07	12.50	13.33	14.16	14.59	15.42	16.25	17.08
Cheddleton	10.38	11.21	12.04	12.47	13.30	14.13	14.56	15.39	16.22	17.05	17.49

CLEETHORPES COAST LIGHT RAILWAY   01472 604657

Lakeside Station, Kings Road, Cleethorpes, North East Lincs DN35 0AG

Fax: 01472 291903   Web: www.cleethorpescoastlightrailway.co.uk Email: office.cclr@btconnect.com

2009	1	2	3	4	5	6	7	8	9	10	11	12	13	14	15	16	17	18	19	20	21	22	23	24	25	26	27	28	29	30	31
MAR	A						A	A						A	A						A	A						A	A		
APR				A	B	A	A	A	A	A	B	B	C	C	B	B	B	B	B	B				A	B						
MAY	A	X	X	X	A	A	A	A	B	B	A	A	A	A	A	B	B	A	A	A	A	A	C	C	C	B	B	B	B	B	C
JUN	A	A	A	A	A	B	C	A	A	A	A	A	X	X	A	A	A	A	A	A	B	C	A	A	A	A	B	C	A	A	
JUL	A	A	A	B	C	A	A	A	A	A	B	C	A	A	A	A	A	A	B	C	A	A	A	B	B	B	C	B	B	B	B
AUG	B	C	B	B	B	B	B	B	C	B	B	B	B	B	B	C	B	B	B	B	B	B	B	C	B	B	B	B	X	X	X
SEP	A	A	A	A	X	X	A	A	A	A	A	A	A					A	A					A	A						
OCT			X	X				A	A						A	A								A	A	A	A	A	A	A	A
NOV	A					A	A						A	A							A	A						A	A		
DEC					SS	SS						SS	SS						SS	SS	SS	SS	SS	SS	SS	SS					

X = Special event SS = Santa Specials

Timetable A: Trains leave Kingsway at 11.05, 11.55, 12.45, 13.35, 14.25, 15.15, 16.05 plus 10.15 and 16.55 (May to end Sept)
Trains leave North Sea Lane at 11.30, 12.20, 13.10, 14.00, 14.50, 15.40, 16.30 plus 10.40 and 17.15 (May to end Sept)

Timetable B: Trains leave Kingsway at 10.25 and every 30mins until 17.55
Trains leave North Sea Lane at 10.47 and every 30mins until 18.17

Timetable C: Trains leave Kingsway at 10.25 and every 15mins until 17.55
Trains leave North Sea Lane at 10.32 and every 15mins until 17.55

COLNE VALLEY RAILWAY   01787 461174

Castle Hedingham, Halstead, Essex CO9 3DZ

Fax: 01787 462254   Web: www.colnevalleyrailway.co.uk   Email: info@colnevalleyrailway.co.uk

2009	1	2	3	4	5	6	7	8	9	10	11	12	13	14	15	16	17	18	19	20	21	22	23	24	25	26	27	28	29	30	31
MAR																						S						S			
APR				D		D	S			S	S	S	S			X	D		X	X						S					
MAY		D	S	S						S							X	X	X			D	S	S			X	S		D	S
JUN						S							T	T			X	X	X		T	T			X	X			X		
JUL			S							S								X				S	S		D	S			D	X	S
AUG	D	S		D	X	S		D	S		D	X	S		D	S		D	X	S		D	S		D	X	S		D	S	S
SEP		D	D				X					S							S					T	T						
OCT		T	T		X	X	X			S							S							X			X	D			X
NOV																															
DEC					SS						SS	SS						SS	SS			SS	SS								

Trains run as required on operating days

S = Steam service D = Diesel service X = Special event (further details on request) T = Thomas & Friends SS = Santa Specials

---

CORRIS RAILWAY   01527 5421580

Corris Railway Museum, Station Yard, Corris, Machynlleth, Powys SY20 9SH

Web: www.corris.co.uk

No further details received – please contact for operating details.

CRICH TRAMWAY VILLAGE   01773 854321

Crich, Matlock, Derbyshire DE4 5DP

Fax: 01773 854320   Web: www.tramway.co.uk

No further details received – please contact for operating details.

DEAN FOREST RAILWAY

01594 845840

Forest Road, Lydney, Gloucestershire GL15 4ET

Web: www.deanforestrailway.co.uk Email: info@deanforestrailway.co.uk

2009	1	2	3	4	5	6	7	8	9	10	11	12	13	14	15	16	17	18	19	20	21	22	23	24	25	26	27	28	29	30	31
MAR	A						X	A							A					A	A							A			
APR				A		A		A	A	X	A		A		T	T	T							A							
MAY		A	X	A					A							A				A	X	A		A				T	T	T	
JUN			A			A	A		A				X	X		A			A	A			A			X	X				
JUL	A			A	A		A			A	A		A			A		A	X		A	A		A	A			A	A		
AUG	A	X			A	A		A	A			A	A		A	X		A	A	T	T	T			A	A		A	X	X	
SEP		A			A	A		A			A	X		A		A	A		A			A	X	A			A				
OCT			A	A						A						A			A	A			A								
NOV	A							A																							
DEC				SS	SS						SS	SS						SS	SS				SS				X	X			

X = Special event
T = Thomas & Friends
SS = Santa Specials

Timetable A

Parkend		11.05	12.50	14.20	15.55
Norchard		11.24	13.07	14.37	16.12
Lydney Jct		11.35	13.18	14.48	16.23
Lydney Jct		11.45	13.30	15.00	16.35
Norchard	10.40	12.03	13.48	15.18	16.48
Parkend	10.55	12.18	14.03	15.33	

Trains may be operated by steam, diesel or diesel railcar.

Telephone for details before travelling.

DIDCOT RAILWAY CENTRE

01235 817200

Didcot, Oxfordshire OX11 7NJ

Fax: 01235 510621 Web: didcotrailwaycentre.org.uk Email: marketing@didcotrailwaycentre.org.uk

2009	1	2	3	4	5	6	7	8	9	10	11	12	13	14	15	16	17	18	19	20	21	22	23	24	25	26	27	28	29	30	31
MAR	O				T	T	T							O		S				O		S						O	O		
APR			O		S	O	O	O	O	S	S	S	S	S	O	O	O	O	O	S				O	O						
MAY		S	S	S					O	O						O	O						S	S	S	O	O	O	O	S	S
JUN					S	S						O	O							S	S	O	O	O	O	O	O	B	B	O	O
JUL	O	O	O	S	S	O	O	O	O	O	S	S	O	O	O	O	O	S	S	O	O	S	O	O	B	B	O	O	B	O	O
AUG	S	S	O	S	O	O	O	S	S	O	O	S	O	O	S	S	O	O	S	O	O	S	S	O	O	O	S	O	S	S	S
SEP	O	O	O	O	O	O				O	O						O	O						B	B						
OCT		T	T	T					O	O						O	O				S	S	O	O	S	O	O				
NOV	O					O	O					O	O				O	O							O	O					
DEC					X	X						X	X				X	X			X	X					O	O	O	O	O

B = Broad gauge steam day
O = Railway centre open
S = Steam day
T = Thomas & Friends
X = Day out with Thomas
& Santa Specials

EAST SOMERSET RAILWAY

01749 880417

Cranmore Station, Shepton Mallet, Somerset BA4 4QP

Fax: 01749 880764 Web: www.eastsomersetrailway.com Email: info@eastsomersetrailway.com

2009	1	2	3	4	5	6	7	8	9	10	11	12	13	14	15	16	17	18	19	20	21	22	23	24	25	26	27	28	29	30	31
MAR	A					A	A						A	A						A	A							A	A		
APR			A	B	A	A	A	A	B	B	C	C	B	B	B	B	B	B							A	B					
MAY	A	X	X	X	A	A	A	A	B	B	A	A	A	A	B	B	A	A	A	A	A	C	C	C	B	B	B	B	B	B	C
JUN	A	A	A	A	B	C	A	A	A	A	X	X	A	A	A	A	A	B	C	A	A	A	A	A	B	C	A	A			
JUL	A	A	A	B	C	A	A	A	A	B	C	A	A	A	A	B	C	A	A	A	B	B	B	C	B	B	B	B	B	B	B
AUG	B	C	B	B	B	B	B	B	C	B	B	B	B	B	B	C	B	B	B	B	B	B	C	B	B	B	B	B	X	X	X
SEP	A	A	A	A	X	X	A	A	A	A	A	A								A	A							A	A		
OCT			X	X						A	A						A	A						A	A	A	A	A	A	A	A
NOV	A					A	A						A	A						A	A							A	A		
DEC					SS	SS						SS	SS						SS	SS	SS	SS	SS	SS	SS	SS					

X = Special event
T = Thomas & Friends
SS = Santa Specials

Timetable A: Trains depart Cranmore at 11.00, 12.30, 14.00, 15.30
Timetable B: Trains depart Cranmore at 11.00, 12.30, 13.40, 15.00 (plus 16.00 Jun-Sept)
Timetable C: Trains depart Cranmore at 11.00, 12.30, 14.00, 15.00, 16.00
Timetable D: Trains depart Cranmore at 11.00, 12.00, 13.00, 14.00, 15.00, 16.00

EAST KENT RAILWAY
01304 832042
Station Road, Shepherdswell, Nr. Dover, Kent CT15 7PD.

Web: www.eastkentrailway.co.uk

2009	1	2	3	4	5	6	7	8	9	10	11	12	13	14	15	16	17	18	19	20	21	22	23	24	25	26	27	28	29	30	31
MAR																															
APR							B	B	B	B									A						B	B					
MAY		A	A	A					A							A							B	B	B						A
JUN						X							X	X							A						A				
JUL				A							A								X							A					
AUG	A	A					B	B							A	A						A	A						X	X	X
SEP						A							A						X	X											
OCT																															X
NOV	X																														
DEC					X	X						X	X						X	X		X	X								

X = Special events/timetable

Note: trains are formed mainly of heritage diesel and electric stock

Timetable A

Shepherdswell	11.30	12.45	14.00	15.15
Eythorne	11.42	12.57	14.12	15.27
Eythorne	11.55	13.10	14.25	15.40
Shepherdswell	12.07	13.22	14.37	15.52

Timetable B

Shepherdswell	11.00	12.00	13.30	14.30	15.30
Eythorne	11.12	12.12	13.42	14.42	15.42
Eythorne	11.25	12.25	13.55	14.55	15.55
Shepherdswell	11.37	12.37	14.07	15.07	16.07

EAST LANCASHIRE RAILWAY
0161 764 7790
Bolton Street Station, Bolton Street, Bury, Lancs BL9 0EY

Fax: 0161 763 4408   Web: www.east-lancs-rly.co.uk

Trains operate on March 1, 7/8, 14/15(D), 21/22. 28/29; April 4/5(S), 8-13, 15-19, 25/26; May 2-4, 6-10, 13-17, 20-25, 27-31; June 3-7, 10-14, 17-21, 24-28; July 1/2, 3-5(D), 8-12, 15-19, 22-26, 29-31; August 1/2, 5-9, 12-16, 19-23, 26-31; September 2-6, 9-13, 19/20, 26/27; October 3/4, 10/11, 17/18(D), 24/25, 31(S); November 1(S), 7/8, 14/15, 21/22; December 26/27. Santa Specials run November 28/29; December 5/6, 12/13, 19/20, 22-24. S denotes Steam Gala, D denotes Diesel Gala.

Note: dates shown include special and family events – see website for full details.

Timetable: no details supplied – please contact for actual train departure times.

EMBSAY & BOLTON ABBEY STEAM RAILWAY
01756 710614
Bolton Abbey Station, Bolton Abbey, Skipton, N Yorks BD23 6AF.

Fax: 01756 710720   Web: www.embsayboltonabbeyrailway.org.uk   Email: embsay.steam@btinternet.com

2009	1	2	3	4	5	6	7	8	9	10	11	12	13	14	15	16	17	18	19	20	21	22	23	24	25	26	27	28	29	30	31
MAR	A							A							A							A							A		
APR			A	A		A			T	T	T	T	A					A	A						A	A					
MAY		X	X	X	A			A	A		A				A	A		A				T	T	T	A					A	A
JUN		A			A	A		A				A	A		A			A	A		A				A	A		A			
JUL			A	A		A				A	A		A	A	A		B	B	A	A	A	A	A	A	X	X	A	A	A	A	A
AUG	B	B	A	A	A	A	A	B	B	A	A	A	A	A	B	B	A	A	A	A	A	B	B	A	A	A	A	A	T	T	T
SEP	A			A	A		A			X	X		A			A	A		A			X	X		A						
OCT			A	X				A	X				A	A			A	A		A				A						A
NOV	A					A								A						SS							SS				
DEC				SS	SS					SS	SS							SS	SS						X	A					

X = Special event
T = Thomas & Friends
SS = Santa Specials

Timetable A

					X
Embsay	10.30	12.00	13.30	15.00	16.30
Bolton Abbey	10.45	12.15	13.45	15.15	16.45
Bolton Abbey	11.10	12.40	14.10	15.40	17.00
Embsay	11.40	13.10	14.40	16.10	17.20

X = Runs March 1 to October 24 only

Timetable B

		ST		ST		ST		ST	
Embsay	10.30	11.10	12.00	12.40	13.30	14.10	15.00	15.40	16.30
Bolton Abbey	10.45	11.25	12.15	12.55	13.45	14.25	15.15	15.55	16.45
Bolton Abbey	11.10	12.00	12.40	13.30	14.10	15.00	15.40	16.30	17.00
Embsay	11.30	12.20	13.00	13.50	14.30	15.20	16.00	16.50	17.20

ST = Stately Steam Train (Vintage coaching stock)

EXBURY GARDENS RAILWAY

023 8089 1203

Exbury Gardens, Exbury, Nr Southampton, Hampshire S45 1AZ.

Fax: 023 8089 9940   Web: www.exbury.co.uk

Trains run daily from March 7 until November 8. Santa Specials run on December 12/13, 19-22.

Timetable: trains depart at 11.00, 11.45, 12.30, 13.30, 14.15, 15.00, 16.00 (extra trains are run at busy times with 30 or 15min frequency – subject to demand) See website for up to date information and special events.

FAIRBOURNE RAILWAY

01341 250362

Beach Road, Fairbourne, Gwynedd LL38 2EX.

Fax: 01341 250240   Web: www.fairbournerailway.com   Email: fairbourne.rail@btconnect.com

2009	1	2	3	4	5	6	7	8	9	10	11	12	13	14	15	16	17	18	19	20	21	22	23	24	25	26	27	28	29	30	31
MAR																															
APR			A	A	A	A	A	A	A	B	B	C	C	B	A	A	A	A							A	A					
MAY		B	B	B	A	A	A		A	A	A	A	A	A		A	A	A	A	A	A		B	C	C	C	C	B	A	A	A
JUN	A	A	A	A		A	A	A	A	A	A		A	A	A	A	A	A		A	A	A	A	A	A		A	A	A	A	
JUL	A	A		A	A	A	A	A		B	B	B	B	B	B	B	B	B	C	C	C	C	C	B	C	C	C	C	C	C	B
AUG	B	C	C	C	C	C	B	B	C	B	C	C	C	C	C	B	B	C	C	C	C	C	B	B	C	C	C	C	C	C	C
SEP	B	B	A		A	A	A	A	A	A		A	A	A	A	A	A		A	A						A	A				
OCT			A	A						A	A						A	A						A	A	A	A	A	A	A	A
NOV	A																														
DEC												SS	SS																		

X = Special event
T = Thomas & Friends
SS = Santa Specials

Timetable A

Fairbourne dep	11.00	12.30	14.00	15.30
Barmouth Ferry dep	11.30	13.00	14.30	16.00

Timetable B

Fairbourne dep	11.00	12.20	14.00	15.20	16.30
Barmouth Ferry dep	11.40	13.00	14.40	16.00	17.00

Timetable C

Fairbourne dep	10.40	11.30	12.10	13.00
Barmouth Ferry dep	11.30	12.10	13.00	14.20

Timetable SS (Santa Specials)

Fairbourne dep	11.30	13.30

FFESTINIOG RAILWAY

01766 516000

Harbour Station, Porthmadog, Gwynedd LL49 9NF

Fax: 01766 516005   Web: www.festrail.co.uk

No further details received – please contact for operating details.

FOXFIELD STEAM RAILWAY

01782 396210

PO Box 1967, Stoke-on-Trent, Staffordshire ST4 8YT.

Fax: 01782 396210   email: enquiries@foxfieldrailway.co.uk   Web: www.foxfieldrailway.co.uk

No further details received – please contact for operating details.

GARTELL LIGHT RAILWAY

01963 370752

Common Lane, Yenston, Templecombe, Somerset BA8 0NB.

Fax: 01963 373915   Web: glr-online.co.uk

No further details received – please contact for operating details.

GLOUCESTERSHIRE WARWICKSHIRE RAILWAY

The Railway Station, Toddington, Glos GL54 5DT.

Tel: 01242 621405   Web: www.gwsr.com

2009	1	2	3	4	5	6	7	8	9	10	11	12	13	14	15	16	17	18	19	20	21	22	23	24	25	26	27	28	29	30	31
MAR							C	C						C	C						C	C						C	C		
APR				X	X			B	B	A	A	A	A	A			B	B		A	A					X	X				
MAY		A	A	A		B		A	A			B		A	A			B			X	X	X	X	X	B	B			A	A
JUN			B	B		A	A		B	B		A	A			B	B		A	A			B	B		A	A				
JUL	B	B		A	A			B	B	X	X	X			B	B		A	A		B	B	B		A	A		B	B	B	
AUG	A	A		B	B	B		A	A		B	B	B		A	A		B	B	B		A	A		B	B	B		A	A	A
SEP		B	B		A	A			B			A	A			B		A	A				B		X	X					
OCT		C	C							X	X						C	C					B		X	X		B	B		C
NOV	C							B	B								B						B	B				B	B		
DEC					SS	SS					SS	SS						SS	SS		SS	SS	SS	SS		B	X	B	X	X	B

X = Special event/timetable

SS = Santa Specials

Timetable A

Toddington	10.30	11.30	13.00	14.15	15.15	16.35
Cheltenham (Racecourse)	11.01	12.01	13.31	14.48	15.48	17.08
Cheltenham (Racecourse)	11.15	12.15	14.00	15.00	16.00	17.20
Toddington	11.51	12.51	14.38	15.38	16.31	17.51

Timetable B

Toddington	10.30	12.15	14.30	16.15
Cheltenham (Racecourse)	11.02	12.47	15.02	16.47
Cheltenham (Racecourse)	11.20	13.05	15.20	17.00
Toddington	11.53	13.38	15.53	17.33

D = diesel hauled service

Timetable C

Toddington	10.30	11.30 (D)	13.00	14.15 (D)	15.15	16.35 (D)
Cheltenham (Racecourse)	11.01	12.01	13.31	14.48	15.48	17.08
Cheltenham (Racecourse)	11.15	12.15	14.00	15.00	16.00	17.20
Toddington	11.51	12.51	14.38	15.38	16.31	17.51

D = diesel hauled service

GOLDEN VALLEY LIGHT RAILWAY

01773 747674

Butterley Station, Ripley, Derbyshire DE5 3QZ.

Fax: 01773 570721   Web: www.gvlr.org.uk

No further details received – please contact for operating details.

GREAT CENTRAL RAILWAY

01509 230726

Great Central Road, Loughborough, Leicestershire LE11 1RW

Fax: 01509 239791   Web: www.gcrailway.co.uk

No further details received – please contact for operating details.

GREAT ORME TRAMWAY

01492 879306

Victoria Station, Church Walks, Llandudno LL30 2AZ

Fax: 01492 879781   Web: www.greatormetramway.com   Email: tramwayenquiries@conwy.gov.uk

Trams run every day from late March to late October 10.00-18.00 (17.00 during March and October).

Timetable: Trams run every 20mins (10.00, 10.20, 10.40, etc).

GROUDLE GLEN RAILWAY

01624 622138

29 Hawarden Avenue, Douglas, Isle of Man IM1 4BP

Web: www.groudleglenrailway.com Email: tbeard@manx.net

Trains run April 12/13; May 3, 10, 17, 24, 31; June 7, 14, 21, 28; July 1(E), 5, 8(E), 12, 15(E), 19, 22(E), 26, 29(E); August 2, 4(E), 5(E), 9, 11(E), 12(E), 16, 18(E), 19(E), 23, 25(E), 26(E), 30; September 6, 13, 20, 27; December 26(P). Santa Trains run on December 13, 18, 19. E denotes evening trains 19.00-21.00, P denotes Mince Pie Specials.

Timetable: Service runs continuously from 11.00-16.30 (Santa & Mince Pie Specials 15.30).

GWILI STEAM RAILWAY

01267 238213

Bronwydd Arms Station, Bronwydd, Carmarthen SA33 6HT

Web: www.gwili-railway.co.uk

2009	1	2	3	4	5	6	7	8	9	10	11	12	13	14	15	16	17	18	19	20	21	22	23	24	25	26	27	28	29	30	31
MAR																															
APR										T	T	T	T																		
MAY			B			A																		B	A	B	B	B			
JUN			B				B			B				B			B				B			B				B			
JUL	A				B			A				B			A				B			A				B	A	A	A	A	A
AUG			A	A	A	A	A		B	A	A	A	A			B	A	A	A	A	A		B	A	A	A	A	A		B	A
SEP	B	B				B							T	T					T	T							B				
OCT				B							B							B							B		B	B			X
NOV																															
DEC					SS	SS						SS	SS						SS	SS		SS	SS	SS							

T = Thomas & Friends

X = Special event

SS = Santa Specials

Timetable A: Trains depart Bronwydd Arms at 10.30, 11.50, 13.20, 14.50, 16.10

Timetable B: Trains depart Bronwydd Arms at 11.15, 12.45, 14.15, 15.45

ISLE OF MAN STEAM RAILWAY

01624 663366

Dept of Tourism & Leisure – Railways, Transport Headquarters, Banks Circus, Douglas, Isle of Man IM1 5PT

Fax: 01624 663637 Web: www.iombusandrail.info

No further details received – please contact for operating details.

ISLE OF WIGHT STEAM RAILWAY   01983 882204

The Railway Station, Havenstreet, Isle of Wight PO33 4DS

Fax: 01983 884515   Web: www.iwsteamrailway.co.uk

2009	1	2	3	4	5	6	7	8	9	10	11	12	13	14	15	16	17	18	19	20	21	22	23	24	25	26	27	28	29	30	31
MAR																			A		A				A		A				
APR		A		A		A	A	A	A	A	A	A	A	A	A				A		A	A			A				A	A	▓
MAY		B	B	B		A	A			A			A	A			A		A	A	A		A	C	C	A	A	A	A	A	A
JUN		A	A	A		A		A	A	A			A	A	A	A	A	A	B	A	A	A	A	A	A	A	A	A	A	A	
JUL	A	A	A	X	X	A	A	A	A	A	B	B	A	A	A	A	A	A	A	A	A	A	A	X	X	X	X	X	C	C	B
AUG	B	B	B	C	C	C	B	B	B	B	C	C	C	B	B	B	B	C	C	C	B	B	B	B	C	C	C	X	X	X	X
SEP	A	A	A	A	A	A	A	A	A	A	A	A		A	A	A			A		A	A	A		B	B			A		
OCT	A			A		A	A			A			A	A			A			A	A			A	A	A	A	A	A	A	
NOV	A			A			A		A			A			A		A			A		A			A			A			
DEC				SS	SS					SS	SS								SS	SS	SS	SS	SS	SS	SS		X	X	X		

X = Special event
SS = Santa Specials

Timetable A

						Ex		Ex
Smallbrook Jct		11.02	12.13	13.21		15.11		16.19
Havenstreet		11.17	12.28	13.33	14.17	15.26		16.31
Wootton		11.23	12.34		14.23	15.32		
Wootton		11.31	12.42		14.31	15.40		
Havenstreet	10.35	11.51	12.59		14.51	15.46	15.59	
Smallbrook Jct	10.48	12.03	13.11		15.03		16.11	

Ex = does not run in November

Timetable B

								O	O
Smallbrook Jct		11.02	12.13	13.21		15.11	16.19		17.20
Havenstreet		11.17	12.28	13.33	14.17	15.26	16.33		17.32
Wootton		11.23	12.34		14.23	15.32	16.39		
Wootton		11.31	12.42		14.31	15.40	16.47		
Havenstreet	10.35	11.51	12.59		14.51	15.59	16.53	17.00	
Smallbrook Jct	10.48	12.03	13.11		15.03	16.11		17.12	

O = Only runs on May 2,3; June 20; July 11.

Timetable C

						NS							
Smallbrook Jct		11.02	11.38	12.13		12.58		14.02	14.38	15.11	15.46	16.19
Havenstreet	10.40	11.17	11.53	12.28				14.17	14.53	15.26	16.03	16.33
Wootton	10.46	11.23	11.59	12.34		13.15		14.23	14.59	15.32	16.09	16.39
Wootton	10.54	11.31	12.07	12.42		13.23		14.31	15.07	15.40	16.17	16.47
Havenstreet	10.35	11.16	11.51	12.30	12.48	13.35	13.29	14.16	14.51	15.26	15.59	16.23	16.53
Smallbrook Jct	10.48	11.26	12.03	12.42		13.47		14.28	15.03	15.38	16.11	

NS = Runs non-stop from Smallbrook Jct to Wootton

Note: Fish & Chip Specials run on Tues and Thurs evenings in August

---

KEIGHLEY & WORTH VALLEY RAILWAY   01535 645214

Haworth Station, Keighley, West Yorkshire BD22 8NJ

Fax: 01535 647317   Web: www.kwvr.co.uk   Email: admin@kwvr.co.uk

2009	1	2	3	4	5	6	7	8	9	10	11	12	13	14	15	16	17	18	19	20	21	22	23	24	25	26	27	28	29	30	31
MAR	B					B	B					B	B						B	B							B	B			
APR				B	B					A	A	A	A	C		C	C	C	B	A						B	A				▓
MAY		B	X	X					B	A						A	A						B	X	X	C	C	C	C	B	A
JUN					X	X	X						B	A					B	A	X	X	X				X	X	C	C	
JUL	C	C	C	B	X	C	C	C	C	C	B	A	C	C	C	C	C	C	B	A	C	C	C	C	C	B	A	C	C	C	C
AUG	B	X	C	C	C	C	C	B	A	C	C	C	C	C	B	A	C	C	C	C	C	B	A	C	C	C	C	C	B	A	A
SEP	C	C	C	C	B	A						B	A						B	A						B	A				
OCT		B	B						B	B						B	B					X	X	X	C	C	C	C	C	B	
NOV	B					B	B						B	B						B	B							SS	SS		▓
DEC				SS	SS					SS	SS								SS	SS						B	B	B	B	B	B

X = Special event,
T = 'Thomas' event,
S = Santa trains

Timetable A

	D		D			D						
Oxenhope	09.00	10.15	11.00	11,45	12.30	13.15	14.00	14.45	15.30	16.15	17.00
Keighley	09.25	10.40	11.25	12.10	12.55	13.40	14.25	15.10	15.55	16.40	17.25
Keighley	09.40	11.00	11.45	12.30	13.15	14.00	14.45	15.30	16.15	17.00	17.45
Oxenhope	10.00	11.25	12.10	12.55	13.40	14.25	15.10	15.55	16.40	17.25	18.10

D = Heritage Diesel service
Ex = Does not run in March, Nov or Dec

Timetable B

	D	D					Ex
Oxenhope	09.00	10.15	11.00	12.30	14.00	15.30	17.00
Keighley	09.25	10.40	11.25	12.55	14.25	15.55	17.25
Keighley	09.40	11.00	11.45	13.15	14.45	16.15	17.45
Oxenhope	10.00	11.25	12.10	13.40	15.10	16.40	18.10

Timetable C

	D				
Oxenhope	10.10	11.25	13.00	14.35	16.10
Keighley	10.30	11.50	13.25	15.00	16.35
Keighley	10.40	12.10	13.45	15.20	16.55
Oxenhope	11.00	12.35	14.10	15.45	17.20

KEITH & DUFFTOWN RAILWAY

01340 821181

Dufftown Station, Dufftown, Banffshire, Scotland AB55 4BA

Web: www.keith-dufftown.org.uk

Trains run on April 10-13, 18/19, 25/26; May 1-3, 8-10, 16/17, 23/24, 30/31; June 5-7, 12-14, 19-21, 26-28; July 3-5, 10-12, 17-19, 24-26, 31; August 1/2, 7-9, 14-16, 21-23, 28-30; September 5/6, 12/13, 19/20, 26/27.

Dufftown	11.25	14.00	15.50
Keith Town	12.03	14.38	16.28
Keith Town	12.15	14.50	16.40
Dufftown	12.53	15.28	17.18

Additional trains and specials will be announced on the web site.

KENT & EAST SUSSEX RAILWAY

08700 6006074

Tenterden Town Station, Station Road, Tenterden, Kent TN30 6HE

Fax: 01580 765654   Web: www.kesr.org.uk

2009	1	2	3	4	5	6	7	8	9	10	11	12	13	14	15	16	17	18	19	20	21	22	23	24	25	26	27	28	29	30	31
MAR																					A	A						A	B		
APR			B	V	V	V	V	V	A	A	A	X	V	V	V	V	V	V							B	B					
MAY		X	X	X				B	B		B	B			B	B			A	A				A	A	X	B	B	B	B	B
JUN				B	B			B	B				B	B			B	B			B	B			B	B			B		
JUL	B	V		A	A		B	B	V		B	B		B	B	V		B	B		B	B	V		I	I		B	B	B	B
AUG	A	A	A	A	A	A	A	A	A	A	A	A	A	A	A	A	A	A	A	A	A	A	A	A	A	A	A	A	A	A	X
SEP	B	B	B		B	B		B	B	B			A	A			B	B	B		T	T		B	B	B		T	T		
OCT			A	A						A	B						B	B						B	B	C	C	C	C	C	
NOV	B																														
DEC						SS	SS					SS	SS	SS					SS	SS		SS	SS	SS	SS			C	C	C	C

V = Vintage train service (see timetable)

X = Special event/bank holiday timetable

I = Ivor the Engine event

T = Thomas & Friends

SS = Santa Specials

Timetable A

Tenterden Town	10.40	11.45	13.15	14.20	15.30
Bodiam	11.25	12.35	14.00	15.10	16.20
Bodiam	11.40	12.45	14.15	15.25	16.30
Tenterden Town	12.30	13.35	15.05	16.15	17.15

Timetable B

			D		D	
Tenterden Town	10.40	11.45	13.15	14.20	15.30	
Bodiam	11.25	12.35	14.00	15.10	16.20	
Bodiam	11.40	12.45	14.15	15.25	16.30	
Tenterden Town	12.30	13.35	15.05	16.15	17.15	

D = Heritage Diesel service
V = Vintage train service

Timetable C

			D		D
Tenterden Town	10.40	11.45	13.20	14.30	
Bodiam	11.27	12.32	14.07	15.14	
Bodiam	11.42	12.55	14.25	15.25	
Tenterden Town	12.32	13.39	15.15	16.09	

Timetable V – Vintage Trains

	V	D	V	D	V
Tenterden Town	10.40	11.45	13.15	14.20	15.30
Bodiam	11.25	12.35	14.00	15.10	16.20
Bodiam	11.40	12.45	14.15	15.25	16.30
Tenterden Town	12.30	13.35	15.05	16.15	17.15

KIRKLEES LIGHT RAILWAY

01484 865727

Park Mill Way, Clayton West, Nr Huddersfield HD8 9XJ

Fax: 01484 866333   Web: www.kirkleeslightrailway.com   Email: info@kirkleeslightrailway.com

2009	1	2	3	4	5	6	7	8	9	10	11	12	13	14	15	16	17	18	19	20	21	22	23	24	25	26	27	28	29	30	31
MAR	X					A	A					A	A							A	A							T	T		
APR			A	A	A	A	A	A	X	X	X	X	X	A	A	A	A							A	A						
MAY		A	A	A				A	A						A	A							A	A	A	A	A	A	T	T	T
JUN	A	A	A	A	A	A	A	A	A	A	A	A	A	A	A	A	A	A	A	A	A	A	A	A	A	A	X	X	A	A	
JUL	A	A	A	A	A	A	A	A	A	A	A	A	A	A	A	A	A	A	A	A	A	A	T	T	T	T	T	A	A	A	A
AUG	A	A	A	A	A	A	A	A	A	A	A	A	A	A	A	A	T	T	T	T	T	A	A	A	A	A	A	A	A	A	A
SEP	A	A	A	A	A							X	X						A	A						A	A				
OCT		A	A							A	A						A	A						A	A	A	A	A	X	X	
NOV	X					A	A							T	T						A	A						SS	SS		
DEC					SS	SS						SS	SS						SS	SS	SS	SS	SS	SS							

A = Normal Timetable

X = Special event

T = Thomas & Friends

SS = Santa Specials

Timetable:
Trains depart Clayton West at 11.00, 12.00, 13.00, 14.00, 15.00 (also 16.00 subject to demand)

LAKESIDE & HAVERTHWAITE RAILWAY   01539 531594

Haverthwaite Station, Ulverston, Cumbria LA12 8AL

Fax: 01539 530503   Web: www.lakesiderailway.co.uk   Email: l.hr@btconnect.com

2009	1	2	3	4	5	6	7	8	9	10	11	12	13	14	15	16	17	18	19	20	21	22	23	24	25	26	27	28	29	30	31
MAR																					T	T									
APR			A	A	A	A	A	A	A	A	A	A	A	A	A	A	A	A	A	A	A	A	P	A	A	A	A	A	A	A	
MAY	P	A	A	A	A	A	A	P	A	A	A	A	A	P	X	X	A	A	A	A	P	A	A	A	A	A	A	A	A	A	A
JUN	A	A	A	A	A	A	A	A	A	A	A	A	A	A	A	A	A	A	A	A	A	A	A	A	A	A	A	A	A	A	
JUL	A	A	A	A	A	A	A	A	A	A	A	A	A	A	A	A	A	A	A	A	A	A	A	A	A	A	A	A	A	A	A
AUG	A	A	A	A	A	A	A	A	A	A	A	A	A	A	A	A	A	A	A	A	A	A	A	A	A	A	A	A	A	A	A
SEP	A	A	A	A	A	A	A	A	A	A	A	A	A	A	A	A	A	A	A	A	A	A	A	A	A	A	A	A	A	A	
OCT	A	P	A	A	A	A	P	A	A	A	A	A	A	P	A	A	A	A	P	A	A	X	X	X	X	X	X	X			
NOV	X							T	T				D	D					D	D							D	D			
DEC				SS	SS							SS	SS					SS	SS												

D = Diesel weekends

X = Special event

T = Thomas & Friends

P = Pensioners Day (LA/CA postcodes)

SS = Santa Specials

Timetable

						B	C
Haverthwaite	10.40	11.50	13.00	14.05	15.10	16.15	17.20
Lakeside	10.58	12.08	13.18	14.23	15.28	16.33	17.38
Lakeside	11.15	12.30	13.35	14.40	15.45	16.50	17.48
Haverthwaite	11.33	12.48	13.53	14.58	16.03	17.08	18.06

B = does not operate after October 24
C = Operates May 24-31, July 20-August 28 and may be diedel hauled.

Note: train services connect with Lake Windermere steamer services to Bowness and Ambleside – see website for full details.

LAUNCESTON STEAM RAILWAY   01566 775665

St Thomas Road, Launceston, Cornwall PL15 8DA

Web: www.launcestonsr.co.uk

Trains run daily April 10-17; May 24-29; July 5-10, 12-17, 19-24, 26-31; August 2-7, 9-14, 16-21, 23-28, 30/31; September 1-4, 6-11, 13-18, 20-25.

Note: for 2009 only there will be no trains in June. October half-term dates to be announced.

Timetable: no further details – please see web site.

LAVENDER LINE   01825 750515

Isfield Station, Isfield, Nr Uckfield, East Sussex TN22 5XB

Web: www.lavender-line.co.uk

Trains run on March 1, 8, 15, 22, 29; April 5, 10-13, 19, 26; May 3/4, 10, 16/17(I), 24/25(I), 31; June 7, 14, 21, 28; July 5, 12, 19, 26; August 2, 5/6, 9, 12/13, 16, 19/20, 23, 26/27, 30/31; September 6, 13, 20, 27; October 4, 11, 18, 25-30; November 1, 8, 15, 22; December 27. Santa Specials run on November 29; December 5/6, 12/13, 19-22. I denotes Ivor the Engine days.

Note: service trains may be steam or diesel hauled. Check for details.

LEIGHTON BUZZARD RAILWAY

01525 373888

Page's Park Station, Billington Road, Leighton Buzzard LU7 4TN

Fax: 01525 377814 Web: www.buzzrail.co.uk Email: station@lbngrs.org.uk

2009	1	2	3	4	5	6	7	8	9	10	11	12	13	14	15	16	17	18	19	20	21	22	23	24	25	26	27	28	29	30	31
MAR														B							B							B			
APR					B					B	B	C	C		B				B							B					
MAY		B	C	C						B						B			B			B	C	C	B	B	B	B	B	B	B
JUN			D				B			D				B			D				C				D				C		
JUL	D				B			D				B				D			B				B				B			B	
AUG	B	C		B	B	B		B	C		B	B	B		B	C		B	B	B		B	C		B	B	B		B	C	C
SEP		B			X	X							B						B							B					
OCT			B													B						B				B					
NOV	C							B																							
DEC					SS	SS			SS			SS	SS			SS			SS	SS			SS	SS			SS	SS			

X = Special event
SS = Christmas Cracker special trains

Timetable A: Trains depart Page's Park at 11.00, 11.40, 12.20, 13.00, 13.40, 14.20, 15.00

Timetable B: Trains depart Page's Park ar 10.40, 12.20, 14.00, 15.40

Timetable C: Trains depart Page's Park at 10.40, 11.30, 12.20, 13.10, 14.00, 14.50, 15.40, 16.30

Timetable D: Trains depart Page's Park at 10.30, 12.00, 13.30

Timetable X: Trains depart Page's Park at 10.40, 11.15, 11.50, 12.25, 13.00, 13.35, 14.10, 14.45, 15.20, 15.55, 16.30

LLANBERIS LAKE RAILWAY

01286 870549

Rheilffordd Llyn Padarn, Llanberis, Gwynedd, Wales LL55 4TY

Fax: 01286 870549 Web: www.lake-railway.co.uk Email: info@lake-railway.co.uk

2009	1	2	3	4	5	6	7	8	9	10	11	12	13	14	15	16	17	18	19	20	21	22	23	24	25	26	27	28	29	30	31
MAR		A	A						A	A				A			B	B	B			C		B	B	B			C		B
APR	B	B		C	D	D	D	D	D	D	E	E	E	E	E	B		C	D	D	D	D	B		C	D	D	D	D		
MAY	B	C	D	D	D	D	D	B		C	D	D	D	D	B		C	D	D	D	D	B	D	E	E	E	E	E	D	C	C
JUN	D	D	D	D	B	C	C	D	D	D	D	B	C	C	D	D	D	D	B	C	C	D	D	D	D	B	C	C	D	D	
JUL	D	D	D	C	C	D	E	E	E	D	D	D	D	E	E	E	D	D	D	D	E	E	E	D	D	D	E	E	E	E	D
AUG	D	D	E	E	E	E	D	D	D	E	E	E	E	D	D	D	E	E	E	E	D	D	D	E	E	E	E	D	D	E	E
SEP	E	D	D	B		C	D	D	D	D	B		C	D	D	D	D	B		C	D	D	D	D	B		C	B	B	B	
OCT	B	B		C	B	B	B	B		C	B	B	B	B		C	B	B	B	B		B	B	B	B	B	B	B			
NOV		A	A			A	A								A	A						A	A								
DEC	A	A				SS						SS	SS						SS	SS											

S = Santa Specials

Timetable A

					x
Gilfach Ddu		11.00	12.00	13.30	14.30
Cei Llydan					
Cei Llydan		11.35	12.35	14.05	15.05
Gilfach Ddu		11.45	12.45	14.15	15.15

X = runs on Mar 15 and on other dates subject to demand

Timetable B

Gilfach Ddu		11.00	12.15	13.30	14.45
Llanberis		11.10	12.25	13.40	14.55
Cei Llydan					
Cei Llydan		11.45	13.00	14.15	15.30
Gilfach Ddu		11.55	13.10	14.25	15.40

Timetable C

Gilfach Ddu		11.45	13.00	14.15	15.30
Llanberis		11.55	13.10	14.25	15.40
Cei Llydan					
Cei Llydan		12.30	13.45	15.00	16.15
Gilfach Ddu		12.40	13.55	15.10	16.25

Timetable D

Gilfach Ddu		11.00	12.15	13.30	14.45	16.00
Llanberis		11.10	12.25	13.40	14.55	16.10
Cei Llydan						
Cei Llydan		11.45	13.00	14.15	15.30	16.45
Gilfach Ddu		11.55	13.10	14.25	15.40	16.55

Timetable E

Gilfach Ddu		10.30	11.00	11.45	12.15	13.00	13.30	14.15	14.45	15.30	16.00
Llanberis		10.40	11.10	11.55	12.25	13.10	13.40	14.25	14.55	15.40	16.10
Cei Llydan											
Cei Llydan		11.20	11.45	12.35	13.00	13.50	14.15	15.05	15.30	16.20	16.45
Gilfach Ddu		11.30	11.55	12.45	13.10	14.00	14.25	15.15	15.40	16.30	16.55

LLANGOLLEN RAILWAY

01978 860979

The Station, Abbey Road, Llangollen, Denbighshire LL20 8SN

Fax: 01978 869247   Web: www.llangollen-railway.co.uk

No further details received – please contact for operating details.

MANGAPPS RAILWAY

01621 784898

Mangapps Farm, Burnham-on-Crouch, Essex CM0 8QQ

Fax: 01621 783833   Web: www.mangapps.co.uk   Email: mangapps@tiscali.co.uk

2009	1	2	3	4	5	6	7	8	9	10	11	12	13	14	15	16	17	18	19	20	21	22	23	24	25	26	27	28	29	30	31
MAR	D						D	D						D	D						D	D						D	D		
APR				D	D					S	S	S	S					D	D						D	D					
MAY		D	S	S					D	D						D	D						D	S	S					D	D
JUN							S						D	D					D	D						D	D				
JUL				D	S						D	D						D	D						D	D					
AUG	D	S						D	D						D	D						D	D						D	S	S
SEP					D	S						D	D						D	D						D	D				
OCT			D	D						D	D						D	D						D	D						D
NOV																															
DEC					SS	SS						SS	SS						SS	SS	SS			SS							

D = Diesel service operates   S = Steam   SS = Santa Specials

Timetable: trains run at frequent intervals on operating days.

MANX ELECTRIC RAILWAY

01624 663366

Dept of Tourism & Leisure – Railways, Transport Headquarters, Banks Circus, Douglas, Isle of Man IM1 5PT

Fax: 01624 663637   Web: www.iombusandrail.info

No further details received – please contact for operating details.

MIDDLETON RAILWAY

0113 271 0320

The Station, Moor Road, Hunslet, Leeds LS10 2PQ

Web: www.middletonrailway.org.uk

No further details received – please contact for operating details.

MID HANTS RAILWAY (WATERCRESS LINE)

The Railway Station, Alresford, Hampshire SO24 9JG　　　　**01962 733810**

Fax: 01962 735448　　Web: www.watercressline.co.uk　　Email: info@watercressline.co.uk

2009	1	2	3	4	5	6	7	8	9	10	11	12	13	14	15	16	17	18	19	20	21	22	23	24	25	26	27	28	29	30	31
MAR	A					A	A						X	X	X					A	A							A	A		
APR			T	T	T	T	T	T	T	T	T	T						A	A						X	X					
MAY		B	B	B	A	A	A		B	B		A	A	A		B	X		A	A	A		B	B	B	B	B	B	X	X	X
JUN		A	A	A		B	B		A	A	A		X	X		A	A	A		B	B		A	A	A		B	B		A	
JUL	A	A		B	B		A	A	A		B	B		A	A	A		B	X		A	A	A		B	B		A	A	A	A
AUG	B	B	B	B	B	B	B	B	T	T	T	T	T	T	T	T	T	B	B	B	B	B	B	B	B	B	B	B	B	B	B
SEP	A	A	A		B	B		A	A	A	X	X	X		A	A	A		B	B		A	A		B	B		A	A		
OCT	A		B	B							B	B						B	B						X	X	X	X	X	X	X
NOV	X																														
DEC					SS	SS						SS	SS						SS	SS	SS	SS	SS	SS		X	X				

X = Special event
T = Thomas & Friends
SS = Santa Specials

Timetable A

		Diesel	Diesel		Diesel		
Alton		10.50	11.55	12.50	13.55	14.50	15.55
Alresford		11.24	12.29	13.24	14.29	15.24	16.29
Arlesford	11..00	11.43	13.00	13.43	15.00	15.43	
Alton	11.41	12.24	13.41	14.24	15.41	16.24	

Timetable B

Alton		10.50	11.55	12.50	13.55	14.50	15.55
Alresford		11.24	12.29	13.24	14.29	15.24	16.29
Arlesford	11.00	11.43	13.00	13.43	15.00	15.43	
Alton	11.41	12.24	13.41	14.24	15.41	16.24	

Diesel services are operated by heritage DMUs

MIDLAND RAILWAY – BUTTERLEY　　01773 747674

Butterley Station, Ripley, Derbyshire DE5 3QZ

Fax: 01773 570721　　Web: www.midlandrailwaycentre.co.uk

No further details received – please contact for operating details.

MID-NORFOLK RAILWAY　　01362 690633

The Railway Station, Station Road, Dereham, Norfolk NR19 1DF

Fax: 01362 698487　　Web: www.mnr.org.uk　　Email: info@mnr.org.uk

2009	1	2	3	4	5	6	7	8	9	10	11	12	13	14	15	16	17	18	19	20	21	22	23	24	25	26	27	28	29	30	31
MAR															A							B					X	X	X		
APR			B	B					B	B	B	B						B	B							C	C				
MAY		C	C	C		B			B	X			B			B	X			B			B	B			B			B	B
JUN			B			B	B		B				B	B		B				B	B						B	B			
JUL	B			C	C			B			C	C			B			C	C			B	B		C	C			B	B	
AUG	C	C			B	B		C	C				B	B		C	C			B	B		C	C			B	B	C	C	C
SEP			B			B	B			B				B	B		B			B	B			B		X	X			B	
OCT			X	X						B	B						B	B					A								X
NOV																															
DEC					SS	SS						SS	SS						SS	SS		SS	SS				X				

X = Special event
SS = Santa Specials

Note: trains are normally diesel hauled or diesel railcar services, although the railway does hire-in steam locomotives from time to time. Contact railway for further details.

Timetable A

Dereham	11.00	14.00
Wymondham Abbey	11.38	14.38
Wymondham Abbey	11.45	14.45
Dereham	12.23	15.23

Timetable B

Dereham	10.15	13.00	15.15
Wymondham Abbey	10.53	13.38	15.53
Wymondham Abbey	11.15	14.00	16.15
Dereham	11.53	14.38	16.53

Timetable C

Dereham	10.15	13.00	15.20
Wymondham Abbey	10.53	13.38	15.58
Wymondham Abbey	11.25	14.10	16.30
Dereham	12.03	14.48	17.08

MULL RAIL

01680 812494

Old Pier Station, Craignure, Isle of Mull, Argyll PA65 6AY

Fax: 01680 300595   Web: www.mullrail.co.uk

No further details received – please contact for operating details.

NENE VALLEY RAILWAY

01780 784444

Wansford Station, Stibbington, Peterborough PE8 6LR

Web: www.nvr.org.uk   Email: nvrorg@nvr.org.uk

2009	1	2	3	4	5	6	7	8	9	10	11	12	13	14	15	16	17	18	19	20	21	22	23	24	25	26	27	28	29	30	31
MAR	E						X	X						A							A							A			
APR			T	T			A			T	T	T	T	A	A	A		C	C					B	B						
MAY		T	T	D				B	B			A			C	T			A				T	T	T	A	A	A	A	B	B
JUN			A	A		B	B			A			B	B			A	A			C	C			A			T	T		
JUL	A			X	X				A			X	X			A				C	C			A			X	X			A
AUG	T	T			A	A	E	E	D	D		A	A	E	E	C	C		A	A	E	E	D	D	A	A	E	E	T	T	T
SEP		A	A		B	B					X	X			A				C	C			A			X	X				
OCT		X	X	X						E	E					E	E					T	T			T	T	T	T	T	T
NOV	T																												SS		
DEC		SS			SS	SS			SS			SS	SS			SS			SS	SS			SS	SS		A					A

X = Special event

T = Thomas & Friends

SS = Santa Specials

Timetable A

Wansford	10.30	12.30	14.30
Peterborough	11.15	13.15	15.15
Peterborough	11.30	13.30	15.30
Wansford	11.56	13.56	15.56

Timetable B

Wansford	10.30	12.30	14.30	16.15
Peterborough	11.15	13.15	15.15	17.00
Peterborough	11.30	13.30	15.30	17.15
Wansford	11.56	13.56	15.56	17.41

Timetable C

Wansford	10.15	11.50	13.25	15.00	16.35
Peterborough	11.00	12.35	14.10	15.45	17.20
Peterborough	11.15	12.50	14.25	16.00	17.30
Wansford	11.41	13.16	14.51	16.26	17.56

services may be steam or diesel hauled

Timetable D

							Y
Wansford	10.30	11.40	12.50	14.00	15.10	16.20	16.40
Peterborough	11.15	12.25	13.35	14.45	15.55	17.05	
Peterborough	11.30	12.40	13.50	15.00	16.10	17.20	
Wansford	11.56	13.06	14.16	15.26	16.36	17.46	17.00

Y = Wansford-Yarwell Jct-Wansford only

Timetable E

					Y
Wansford	10.30	11.45	13.00	14.15	15.25
Peterborough	11.05	12.20	13.35	14.50	
Peterborough	11.15	12.30	13.45	15.00	
Wansford	11.37	12.52	14.07	15.22	15.40

All services operated by heritage diesel railcar
Y = Wansford-Yarwell Jct-Wansford only

NORTHAMPTON & LAMPORT RAILWAY

Pitsford & Brampton Station, Pitsford Road, Chapel Brampton, Northampton NN6 8BA

Tel: 01604 820327   Web: www.nlr.org.uk

No further details received – please contact for operating details.

NORTH NORFOLK RAILWAY (POPPY LINE)

Sheringham Station, Sheringham, Norfolk NR26 8RA

Tel: 01263 820800   Fax: 01263 820801   Web: www.nnr.co.uk

2009	1	2	3	4	5	6	7	8	9	10	11	12	13	14	15	16	17	18	19	20	21	22	23	24	25	26	27	28	29	30	31
MAR	X						X	X						A	A						A	A						A	A		
APR				B	A		A	A	A	C	C	C	B	B	B	B	B	A			A	A	A		B	A		A	A	A	
MAY	A	C	C	C	A	A	A		B	A		A	A	A		B	A		A	A	A		X	X	X	C	C	C	B	B	B
JUN	A	A	A	A	A	B	A	A	A	A	A	A	B	A	A	A	A	A	A	A	B	A	A	A	A	A	A	B	A	A	A
JUL	A	A	A	B	X	B	B	B	B	B	B	B	B	B	B	B	X	X	X	C	C	C	C	C	C	C	C	C	C	C	C
AUG	C	C	C	C	C	C	C	C	C	C	C	C	C	C	C	C	C	C	C	C	C	C	C	C	C	C	C	C	C	C	C
SEP	B	B	B	X	X	X	B	B	B	B	B	B	B	B	B	B	B	B	B	X	X	A	A	A	A	A	A	B	A	A	A
OCT	A		B	A		A	A	A		B	A		A	A	A		B	A	A	A	A	A	A	X	X	A	A	A	A	A	A
NOV	D				D	D						D	D						D	D						D	D				
DEC					SS	SS			SC	SC		SS	SS						SS	SS			SS	SS	SS			P	P	P	P

X = Special event
SS = Santa Specials
SC = Santa Specials (schools only)
P = Mince Pie Specials

Timetable A

Sheringham	10.30	12.00	13.30	15.00
Holt	10.53	12.23	13.53	15.23

Holt	11.15	12.45	14.15	15.45
Sheringham	11.39	13.09	14.39	16.09

Timetable B

	D		D		D		D		D	DN
Sheringham	09.45	10.30	11.15	12.00	12.45	13.30	14.15	15.00	15.45	17.00
Holt	10.08	10.53	11.38	12.23	13.08	13.53	14.38	15.23	16.08	17.19

Holt	10.30	11.15	12.00	12.45	13.30	14.15	15.00	15.45	16.20	17.30
Sheringham	10.54	11.39	12.24	13.09	13.54	14.39	15.24	16.09	16.41	17.48

D = Diesel service   N = Does not operate during October

Timetable C

										D	D
Sheringham	09.45	10.30	11.15	12.00	12.45	13.30	14.15	15.00	15.45	16.30	17.40
Holt	10.08	10.53	11.38	12.23	13.08	13.53	14.38	15.23	16.08	16.53	18.00

Holt	10.30	11.15	12.00	12.45	13.30	14.15	15.00	15.45	16.30	17.10	18.10
Sheringham	10.54	11.39	12.24	13.09	13.54	14.39	15.24	16.09	16.54	17.30	18.30

D = Diesel service

Timetable D

	D	D	D	D	D	D
Sheringham	10.30	11.30	12.30	13.30	14.30	15.30
Holt	10.49	11.49	12.49	13.49	14.49	15.49

Holt	11.00	12.00	13.00	14.00	15.00	16.00
Sheringham	11.19	12.19	13.19	14.19	15.19	16.19

D = Diesel service - all services operated by heritage diesel railcar

---

NORTH YORKSHIRE MOORS RAILWAY   01751 472508

Park Street, Pickering, North Yorkshire YO18 7AJ

Fax: 01751 476970   Web: www.nymr.co.uk

Trains run daily from March 28 to November 1 and weekends in March and November. Santa Specials run on December 5/6, 12/13, 18-21.

Note: trains operate between Pickering and Grosmont with some trains continuing through to Whitby – contact or see web site for full details.

Timetable

No further details received – contact for details.

PAIGNTON & DARTMOUTH STEAM RAILWAY

Queens Park Station, Torbay Road, Paignton, Devon TQ4 6AF.　　**01803 555872**

Fax: 01803 664313　　Web: www.paignton-steamrailway.co.uk　　Email: mail@pdsr.eclipse.co.uk

2009	1	2	3	4	5	6	7	8	9	10	11	12	13	14	15	16	17	18	19	20	21	22	23	24	25	26	27	28	29	30	31
MAR																															
APR	A	A	A	A	A	A	A	A	A	A	A	A	A	A	A	A	A	A	A		A		A		A	A		A		A	
MAY		A	A	A	A	A	A	X	X		A	A	A		A	A		A	A	A			A	A	A	A	A	A	A	A	A
JUN	A	A	A	A	A	A	A	A	A	A	A	A	A	A	A	A	A	A	A	A	A	A	A	A	A	A	A	T	T	A	A
JUL	A	A	A	A	A	A	A	A	A	A	A	A	A	A	A	A	A	A	A	A	B	B	B	B	A	A	A	B	B	B	A
AUG	A	A	B	B	B	B	B	A	A	A	B	B	B	B	B	A	A	A	B	B	B	B	B	A	A	A	B	B	B	B	A
SEP	A	A	A	A	A	A	A	A	A	A	A	A	A	A	A	A	A	A	A	A	A	A	A	A	A	A	A	A	A	A	
OCT	A		A	A		A		A	A		A		A		A	A		A		A		A	A	A	A	A	A	A	A	A	
NOV	A																														
DEC					SS						SS	SS							SS	SS			SS	SS	SS						

X = Special event
T = Day out with Thomas
SS = Santa Specials

Timetable A

Paignton	10.30	12.15	14.15	16.15
Kingswear	11.00	12.45	14.45	16.45
Kingswear	11.15	13.00	15.15	17.00
Paignton	11.45	13.30	15.45	17.30

Timetable B

Paignton	9.45	10.30	11.15	12.00	12.45	14.00	14.45	15.30	16.15
Kingswear	10.15	11.05	11.50	12.35	13.20	14.35	15.20	16.05	16.50
Kingswear	10.30	11.15	12.00	12.45	14.00	14.45	15.30	16.15	17.00
Paignton	11.05	11.50	12.35	13.20	14.35	15.20	16.05	16.50	17.30

PEAK RAIL

01629 580381

Matlock Station, Matlock, Derbyshire DE4 3NA

Fax: 01629 760645　　Web: www.peakrail.co.uk　　Email: peakrail@peakrail.co.uk

2009	1	2	3	4	5	6	7	8	9	10	11	12	13	14	15	16	17	18	19	20	21	22	23	24	25	26	27	28	29	30	31
MAR	S							S							S						S	S						S	S		
APR			S	S						X	X	X	S				S	S						S	S						
MAY		S	S	S				D	S							S	S						X	X	X	S				S	S
JUN		S				S	S		S			S	S			S			S	S			S				X	X			
JUL	S			S	S			S			S	S			S			S	S			S	S		D	S			S		
AUG	X	X		S	S			S	S		S	S			S	S			S	S		D	S		S	S	S		S	S	S
SEP	S	S			S	S		S	S			S	S						S	S						X	X				
OCT			S	S						X	X						S	S						S	S		S	S			S
NOV	S							S							S							S							S		
DEC					SS	SS						SS	SS						SS	SS					SS	SS					

S = Steam hauled service
D = Diesel hauled service
X = Special Event
SS = Santa Specials

Timetable

Rowsley South	11.15	12.30	13.45	15.00	16.15
Matlock Riverside	11.35	12.50	14.05	15.20	16.35
Matlock Riverside	11.45	13.00	14.15	15.30	16.45
Rowsley South	12.05	13.20	14.35	15.50	17.05

Ian Allan Magazines

Ian Allan Magazines have a wide range of enthusiast based magazines to suit those with interests in aviation, road transport, railways and model railways. All our magazines are high quality productions and most are produced in full colour, showing off some stunning photography to best advantage.

www.ianallanmagazines.com

RAVENGLASS & ESKDALE RAILWAY

01229 717171

Ravenglass Station, Ravenglass, Cumbria CA18 1SW

Fax: 01229 717011   Web: www.ravenglass-railway.co.uk   Email: steam@ravenglass-railway.co.uk

2009	1	2	3	4	5	6	7	8	9	10	11	12	13	14	15	16	17	18	19	20	21	22	23	24	25	26	27	28	29	30	31
MAR	A					A	A							A	A						B	B	B	B	B	B	B	B	B	B	B
APR	B	B	B	B	B	B	B	B	B	C	C	C	C	C	C	C	C	B	B	B	B	B	B	B	B	B	B	B	B	B	
MAY	B	C	C	C	B	B	B	B	B	B	B	B	B	B	B	B	B	B	B	B	B	B	B	D	D	D	D	D	D	C	C
JUN	C	C	C	C	C	C	C	C	C	C	C	C	C	C	C	C	C	C	C	C	C	C	C	C	C	C	C	C	C	C	
JUL	C	C	C	C	C	C	C	C	C	C	C	C	C	C	C	C	C	D	D	D	D	D	D	D	D	D	D	D	D	D	D
AUG	D	D	D	D	D	D	D	D	D	D	D	D	D	D	D	D	D	D	D	D	D	D	D	D	D	D	D	D	D	D	D
SEP	C	C	C	C	C	C	C	C	C	C	C	C	C	C	B	B	B	B	B	B	B	B	B	B	B	B	B	B	B	B	
OCT	B	B	B	B	B	B	B	B	B	B	B	B	B	B	B	B	B	B	B	B	B	B	B	B	B	B	B	B	B	B	B
NOV	B					A	A							A	A													E	E		
DEC					E	E						E	E						E	E						A	A	A	A	A	A

Timetable A

	D		D		D
Ravenglass	10.20	11.20	12.20	13.40	14.40
Dalegarth	11.00	12.00	13.00	14.20	15.20
Dalegarth	11.20	12.20	13.40	14.40	15.40
Ravenglass	12.00	13.00	14.20	15.20	16.20

D = Diesel service.

Timetable B

				D		D
Ravenglass	10.20	11.20	12.20	13.20	14.20	15.20
Dalegarth	11.00	12.00	13.00	14.00	15.00	16.00
Dalegarth	11.40	12.40	13.20	14.40	15.40	16.10
Ravenglass	12.20	13.20	14.00	15.20	16.20	16.50

D = Diesel service.

Timetable C

	D				D				D
Ravenglass	08.50	10.20	11.20	12.00	12.40	13.40	14.40	15.40	16.40
Dalegarth	09.30	11.00	12.00	12.40	13.20	14.20	15.20	16.20	17.20
Dalegarth	09.45	11.40	12.40	13.00	13.40	14.40	15.40	16.40	17.30
Ravenglass	10.25	12.20	13.20	13.40	14.20	15.20	16.20	17.20	18.10

D = Diesel service.

Timetable E - Santa Trains

	D	D	D
Ravenglass		12.10	14.00
Dalegarth		12.50	14.40
Dalegarth	11.00	13.10	15.00
Ravenglass	11.40	13.50	15.40

D = Diesel service only.

Timetable D

	D		MT		MT	D					D		MT	
Ravenglass	08.50	10.20	10.40	11.20	11.40	12.00	12.40	13.20	13.40	14.20	14.40	15.20	15.40	16.20
Dalegarth	09.30	11.00	11.20	12.00	12.20	12.40	13.20	14.00	14.20	15.00	15.20	16.00	16.20	17.00
Dalegarth	09.45	11.20	11.40	12.20	12.40	13.00	13.40	14.20	14.40	15.20	15.40	16.20	16.40	17.20
Ravenglass	10.25	12.00	12.20	13.00	13.20	13.40	14.20	15.00	15.20	16.00	16.20	17.00	17.20	18.00

D = Diesel service MT = Monday to Thursday only

ROMNEY, HYTHE & DYMCHURCH RAILWAY

New Romney Station, New Romney, Kent TN28 8PL

01797 362353

Fax: 01797 363591   Web: www.rhdr.org.uk

No further details received – please contact for operating details.

SEATON TRAMWAY

01297 20375

Harbour Road, Seaton, Devon EX12 2NQ

Fax: 01297 625626   Web: www.tram.co.uk

Trams run daily April 2 to November 1 and weekends in March and November 7 to December 19. Santa Specials run on December 13, 20, 23, 24

Timetable: trams run from Seaton to Colyton and Colyton to Seaton at frequent intervals. First departure time from Seaton 10.00. Departure times throughout the day vary according to time of year – contact for details.

SEVERN VALLEY RAILWAY

01299 403816

The Railway Station, Bewdley, Worcs DY12 1BG

Fax: 01299 400839   Web: www.svr.co.uk

2009	1	2	3	4	5	6	7	8	9	10	11	12	13	14	15	16	17	18	19	20	21	22	23	24	25	26	27	28	29	30	31
MAR	A					X	X	X						B	B						B	B						B	B		
APR			B	B	B	B	B	B	B	C	D	D	D	B	B	B	B	B	B						B	B					
MAY		C	D	D	E	E	E	E	X	X	E	E	E	E	X	X	E	E	E	E	E	C	D	D	D	B	B	B	B	C	B
JUN	E	E	E	E	E	C	B	E	E	E	E	E	C	B	E	E	E	E	E	C	B	B	B	B	B	B	X	X	B	B	
JUL	B	B	B	X	X	B	B	B	B	B	C	B	B	B	B	B	B	B	C	B	B	B	B	B	B	C	B	B	B	B	B
AUG	C	B	B	B	B	B	B	C	B	B	B	B	B	B	C	B	B	B	B	B	B	C	B	B	B	B	B	B	C	D	D
SEP	B	B	B	B	X	X	E	E	E	E	E	C	B	E	E	E	E	E	C	B	E	E	E	E	E	X	X	X	E	E	
OCT	E	E	B	B			X	X	X	X				B	B									B	B	B	B	B	B	B	B
NOV	B					A	A					A	A					A	A									A	A		
DEC					SS	SS						SS	SS						SS	SS	SS	SS	SS	SS		X	X	X	X	X	X

X = Special event,

SS = Santa trains

Timetable A

		10.45	12.00	13.15	14.30	16.25
Kidderminster		10.45	12.00	13.15	14.30	16.25
Bridgnorth		11.52	13.10	14.22	15.37	17.32
Bridgnorth		11.15	12.35	13.45	15.05	16.15
Kidderminster		12.27	13.42	14.57	16.12	17.19

Timetable B

								SuO
Kidderminster		10.25	11.40	12.15	13.00	14.20	15.35	16.50
Bridgnorth		11.32	12.47	13.29	14.10	15.28	16.43	17.57
								SuO
Bridgnorth		10.55	12.15	13.35	14.15	14.55	16.05	17.25
Kidderminster		12.05	13.24	14.43	15.21	16.02	17.15	18.27

SuO = operates on Sundays only

Timetable C

		S or D				S or D			
Kidderminster		9.50	10.25	11.05	12.35	13.20	14.05	14.50	16.40
Bridgnorth		10.55	11.34	12.17	13.47	14.32	15.17	16.02	17.47
			S or D				S or D		
Bridgnorth		11.00	11.45	12.30	13.15	14.45	15.30	16.30	17.15
Kidderminster		12.07	12.57	13.42	14.27	15.52	16.37	17.37	18.19

S or D = May be hauled by steam or diesel locomotives

Timetable D

			X					X			
Kidderminster		9.55	10.25	11.15	12.00	12.45	13.30	14.15	15.00	15.45	16.30
Bridgnorth		11.02	11.43	12.27	13.13	13.58	14.42	15.27	16.12	16.57	17.42
			X					X			
Bridgnorth		11.10	11.55	12.40	13.25	14.10	14.55	15.40	16.25	17.10	17.55
Kidderminster		12.23	13.08	13.52	14.37	15.22	16.07	16.52	17.32	18.14	18.59

Timetable E

Bewdley		10.25	12.10	14.00	16.00
Bridgnorth		11.32	13.17	15.07	17.07
Bridgnorth		10.10	12.00	13.50	15.50
Bewdley		11.21	13.07	14.57	16.54

X = On May 24/25 and August 30/31 only this service is diesel-hauled

---

SITTINGBOURNE & KEMSLEY LIGHT RAILWAY

0871 222 1568

PO Box 300, Sittingbourne, Kent ME10 2DZ

Web: www.sklr.net

2009	1	2	3	4	5	6	7	8	9	10	11	12	13	14	15	16	17	18	19	20	21	22	23	24	25	26	27	28	29	30	31
MAR																															
APR				A						B	C	B	C						A							A					
MAY			C	C						A							A						B	B		A					A
JUN						A								A							C							A			
JUL			X	X						A							A		A					C			A				
AUG		B		A				C		A					B			A				B		A				C	C	C	
SEP		A			A					A							A				C	C									
OCT																															
NOV																															
DEC					SS	SS						SS	SS						SS	SS			SS			X					

X = Steam & Beer Festival

SS = Santa Specials

Note: this railway is under threat of closure – please check that it is operating before travelling

Timetable A: Trains run hourly from 13.00 to 16.00

Timetable B: Trains run hourly from 11.00 to 16.00

Timetable C: Trains run from 11.00 – special themed days (contact for details)

SNAEFELL MOUNTAIN RAILWAY   01624 663366

Dept of Tourism & Leisure – Railways, Transport Headquarters, Banks Circus, Douglas, Isle of Man IM1 5PT

Fax: 01624 663637   Web: www.iombusandrail.info

No further details received – please contact for operating details.

SNOWDON MOUNTAIN RAILWAY   01286 873470

Llanberis, Caernarfon, Gwynedd LL55 4TY

Fax: 01286 872518   Web: www.snowdonrailway.co.uk

No further details received – please contact for operating details.

SOUTH DEVON RAILWAY   0845 345 1420

The Station, Buckfastleigh, Devon TQ11 0DZ

Fax: 01364 642170   Web: www.southdevonrailway.org

Trains run March 1, 8, 15 and then daily from March 21 to November 1, then November 7; December 30/31. Santa specials run December 5/6, 12/13, 19-23.

No further details received

SOUTH TYNEDALE RAILWAY   01434 381696

The Railway Station, Alston, Cumbria CA9 3JB

Talking Timetable: 01434 382828   Web: www.strps.org.uk   Email: strps@hotmail.com

Trains run on April 10-14, 16, 18/19, 25/26; May 2-24, 9/10, 16/17, 23-26, 28, 30/31; June 2, 4, 6/7, 9, 11, 13/14, 16, 18, 20/21, 23, 25, 27/28; July 2, 4/5, 7, 9, 11/12, 14, 16, 18-31; August daily, September 1, 3, 5/6, 8. 10, 12/13, 15, 17, 19/20, 22, 24, 26/27; October 3/4, 10/11, 17/18, 24/25, 27-29, 31. Santa Specials run on December 5/6, 12/13, 19-21.

Timetable:
Trains leave Alston at 11.00, 12.15, 14.15, 15.30.
Trains leave Kirkhaugh at 11.30, 12.45, 14.45, 16.00

Trains are steam hauled most weekends in the high season, bank holidays and daily in August, and on Sundays in the low season. Other trains may also be steam hauled, otherwise trains are diesel hauled. Please check with the railway for details.

SPA VALLEY RAILWAY

West Station, Royal Tunbridge Wells, Kent TN2 5QY

01892 537715

Web: www.spavalleyrailway.co.uk   Email: enquiries@spavalleyrailway.co.uk

2009	1	2	3	4	5	6	7	8	9	10	11	12	13	14	15	16	17	18	19	20	21	22	23	24	25	26	27	28	29	30	31
MAR																	T	T										T	T		
APR			A	B						X	X	X	X			C	C	A	B						X	X					
MAY			A	B	B				A	B						X	X					X	X	X				C	C	A	B
JUN				C		A	B				C		A	B				C		X	X				C		X	X			
JUL		C		A	B				C		A	B				C	A	X					C		A	B					C
AUG	A	B				C	X	X	X				C	C	A	B				C	C	A	B				C	C	X	X	X
SEP				A	B					C	C	A	B						X	X						A	B				
OCT			T	T						T	T							A	B					X	X				C	C	A
NOV	B																														
DEC					SS	SS						SS	SS						SS	SS	SS	SS	SS			C	C				

X = Specail event/timetable
T = Day out with Thomas
SS = Santa Specials

Timetable A

Tunbridge Wells West	10.50	12.05	13.50	15.05	16.35
Groombridge	11.04	12.19	14.04	15.19	16.49

Groombridge	11.34	12.49	14.34	15.49	17.22
Tunbridge Wells West	11.48	13.03	14.48	16.03	17.36

Timetable B

Tunbridge Wells West	10.35	11.50	13.35	14.50	16.15
Groombridge	10.49	12.04	13.49	15.04	16.29

Groombridge	11.19	12.34	14.19	15.34	17.02
Tunbridge Wells West	11.33	12.48	14.33	15.48	17.16

Timetable C

Tunbridge Wells West	10.50	12.15	14.15	15.30
Groombridge	11.06	12.31	14.31	15.46

Groombridge	11.37	12.50	14.50	16.05
Tunbridge Wells West	11.55	13.08	15.08	16.23

Timetable A & B

Note: Services are expected to be extended to Eridge during 2009, whereupon the last departure from Tunbridge Wells West will leave 15 minutes earlier.

Timetable C

Note: Train services are not extended to Eridge during 2009 on these operating days.

STRATHSPEY RAILWAY

Aviemore Station, Dalfaber Road, Aviemore PH22 1PY

01479 810725

Web: www.strathspeyrailway.co.uk

2009	1	2	3	4	5	6	7	8	9	10	11	12	13	14	15	16	17	18	19	20	21	22	23	24	25	26	27	28	29	30	31
MAR																												A	A		
APR	A	A	A	A			A	A	A	A	A		A	A		A	A		A	A		A	A		A	A		A	A		
MAY		A	A	A		A	A		A	A			A	A		A	A			A	A		B	B	A		A	A		A	A
JUN			A	A	A	A				A	A	A	B	B			A	A	A	A				A	A	A	A	A	A	A	
JUL	A	A	A	A	A	A	A	A	A	A	A	A	A	A	A	A	A	A	B	B	A	A	A	A	A	A	A	A	A	A	A
AUG	A		A	A	A	A	A	A	A	A	A	A	A	A	A		A	A	A	A	A	A	A		A	A	A	A	A	A	A
SEP		A	A	A	A			A	A	A	A			A	A	A	A				A	A	A	A						A	
OCT	A		A	A			A	A		A	A			A	A			A	A			A	A		B	B			A	A	
NOV																															
DEC												SS	SS						SS	SS				SS		W					W

W = Winter Timetable (see below)
SS = Santa Specials

Timetable A

Broomhill		11.30	13.30	15.40
Boat of Garten	10.00	11.50	13.50	16.00
Aviemore	10.15	12.05	14.05	16.15

Aviemore	10.30	12.30	14.45	16.25
Boat of Garten	10.50	12.50	15.05	16.40
Broomhill	11.15	13.15	15.30	

Timetable B

Broomhill		10.30	11.30	12.30	13.30	14.45	15.40	16.30
Boat of Garten	10.00	10.50	11.50	12.50	13.50	15.05	16.00	16.50
Aviemore	10.15	11.05	12.10	13.05	14.05	15.30	16.15	17.05

Aviemore	10.30	11.30	12.30	13.30	14.45	15.40	16.25	17.15
Boat of Garten	10.50	11.50	12.50	14.05	15.05	16.00	16.40	17.30
Broomhill	11.15	12.15	13.15	14.30	15.30	16.25		

Winter and Santa Specials Timetable

Trains depart Aviemore at 11.00, 14.00 (16.00 to Boat of Garten only)
Trains depart Boat of Garten (for Aviemore) at 12.30, 15.25
Trains depart Boat of Garten (for Broomhill) 11.15, 14.20
Trains depart Broomhill at 12.00, 15.10

SWANAGE RAILWAY

01929 425800

Station House, Swanage, Dorset BH19 1HB

Fax: 01929 426680   Email: info@swanagerailway.co.uk   Web: www.swanagerailway.co.uk

2009	1	2	3	4	5	6	7	8	9	10	11	12	13	14	15	16	17	18	19	20	21	22	23	24	25	26	27	28	29	30	31
MAR	B						B	B						B	B						X	X						B	B		
APR				B	B		B	B	B	C	C	C	C		C	B	B	B	B	B	B	A	A	A	A	A	B	B	A	A	A
MAY	A	C	C	C	A	A	A	X	X	X	A	A	A	A	A	B	B	A	A	A	A	C	C	C	B	B	B	B	B	B	B
JUN	A	A	A	A	A	B	B	A	A	A	A	A	B	B	A	A	A	A	A	B	B	A	A	A	A	A	B	B	A	A	
JUL	A	A	A	B	B	A	A	A	A	A	B	B	B	B	B	B	B	C	C	C	C	C	C	C	C	C	C	C	C	C	C
AUG	C	C	C	C	C	C	C	C	C	C	C	C	C	C	C	C	C	C	C	C	C	C	C	C	C	C	C	C	C	C	C
SEP	B	B	B	B	B	B	B	B	B	B	B	X	X	X	A	A	A	A	A	A	A	B	B	A	A	A	A	B	B	A	
OCT	A	A	B	B	A	A	A	A	A	B	B	A	A	A	A	A	B	B	A	A	A	A	A	B	B	B	B	B	B	B	B
NOV	B						B	B						B	B						B	B						B	B		
DEC					SS	SS						SS	SS					SS	SS		SS	SS	SS			A	A	A	A	A	A

X = Special event

SS = Santa Specials

Timetable A

	DT								D	D	D	D
Swanage	09.00	09.50	11.10	12.30	13.50	15.10	16.30	18.15	19.15	20.25	21.55	
Norden Park & Ride/*Corfe Castle	09.20	10.13	11.33	12.53	14.13	15.33	16.53	18.35	19*31	20*41	22*11	
Norden Park & Ride/*Corfe Castle	09.25	10.30	11.50	13.10	14.30	15.50	17.10	18.43	19*56	21*30	22*30	
Swanage	09.45	10.53	12.13	13.33	14.53	16.13	17.33	19.03	20.13	21.47	22.47	

D = Diesel service operates

* Terminates at Corfe Castle (operates Friday evenings only May 1 to Sept 4)

T = Runs on Tuesdays (market day) only

Timetable B

	DT	D		D		D		D		D		DA	D		D	D	
Swanage	09.00	09.50	10.30	11.10	11.50	12.30	13.10	13.50	14.30	15.10	15.50	16.30	17.10	18.15	19.15	20.25	21.55
Norden Park & Ride/*Corfe Castle	09.20	10.13	10.53	11.33	12.13	12.53	13.33	14.13	14.53	15.33	16.13	16.53	17.33	18.35	19*31	20*41	22*11
Norden Park & Ride/*Corfe Castle	09.25	10.30	11.10	11.50	12.30	13.10	13.50	14.30	15.10	15.50	16.30	17.10	17.45	18.43	19*56	21*30	22*30
Swanage	09.45	10.53	11.33	12.13	12.53	13.33	14.13	14.53	15.33	16.13	16.53	17.33	18.08	19.03	20.13	21.47	22.47

D = Diesel service operates.
* Terminates at Corfe Castle (operates Fri & Sat evenings May 16 to Sept 5)
T = Runs on Tuesday (market day) only
A = Runs April to October only

Timetable C

	DT															D	D	D	D	D
Swanage	09.00		09.50	10.30	11.10	11.50	12.30	13.10	13.50	14.30	15.10	15.50	16.30	17.10	17.40	18.15	19.15	20.25	21.55	23.00
Norden Park & Ride/*Corfe Castle	09.20		10.13	10.53	11.33	12.13	12.53	13.33	14.13	14.53	15.33	16.13	16.53	17.33	18.03	18.35	19.35	20.45	22*11	23*17
Norden Park & Ride/*Corfe Castle	09.25	09.50	10.30	11.10	11.50	12.30	13.10	13.50	14.30	15.10	15.50	16.30	17.10	17.45		18.43	19.45	20.55	22*30	23*30
Swanage	09.45	10.13	10.53	11.33	12.13	12.53	13.33	14.13	14.53	15.33	16.13	16.53	17.33	18.08		19.03	20.13	21.47	22.47	23.47

D = Diesel service operates.   * Terminates at Corfe Castle   T = Runs on Tuesday (market day) only

TALYLLYN RAILWAY
01654 710472

Wharf Station, Tywyn, Gwynedd LL36 9EY

Fax: 01654 711755   Web: www.talyllyn.co.uk   Email: enquiries@talyllyn.co.uk

2009	1	2	3	4	5	6	7	8	9	10	11	12	13	14	15	16	17	18	19	20	21	22	23	24	25	26	27	28	29	30	31
MAR	X						A								A							A							A		
APR			C	C	B	B	B	B	B	B	B	D	D	D	D	B	B	B	B	B	C	C	C	C	C	C	C	C	C	C	
MAY	C	D	D	D	B	B	B	B	B	B	B	B	B	B	B	B	B	B	B	B	B	B	B	E	E	E	E	E	X	E	B	B
JUN	B	B	B	X	B	B	B	B	B	B	X	B	B	B	B	B	B	B	X	B	B	B	B	B	B	X	B	B	B	B	
JUL	B	X	B	B	B	B	B	B	X	B	B	B	B	B	B	X	B	B	B	D	D	D	D	D	D	D	E	E	E	E	E
AUG	D	D	E	E	E	E	E	D	D	E	E	E	E	E	X	D	E	E	E	E	E	D	D	E	E	E	X	E	E	E	E
SEP	E	D	D	D	D	D	B	B	B	X	B	B	B	B	B	B	X	B	B	B	B	B	B	X	B	B	B	C	C	C	
OCT	C	C	C	C	C	C	C	C	C	C	C	C	C	C	C	C	C	C	C	C	C	C	C	B	B	B	B	B	B	B	B
NOV	B																														
DEC																			SS	SS			SS			A	A	A	A	A	A

X = Special event

SS = Santa Specials

Timetable A

Tywyn Wharf	10.30	13.50
Nant Gwernol	11.26	14.43
Nant Gwernol	11.35	14.55
Tywyn Wharf	12.55	16.15

Timetable B

Tywyn Wharf	10.30	11.40	13.50	15.00
Nant Gwernol	11.26	12.33	14.43	16.08
Nant Gwernol	11.35	12.45	14.55	16.17
Tywyn Wharf	12.55	14.00	16.15	17.10

Timetable C

Tywyn Wharf	11.40	14.50
Nant Gwernol	12.36	15.43
Nant Gwernol	12.45	15.55
Tywyn Wharf	14.00	17.10

Timetable D

Tywyn Wharf	10.30	11.40	13.20	14.30	16.10
Nant Gwernol	11.26	12.33	14.13	15.23	17.18
Nant Gwernol	11.35	12.45	14.25	15.35	17.27
Tywyn Wharf	12.55	14.00	15.45	16.50	18.20

TANFIELD RAILWAY
0191 3887545

(postal address) 22 Coverley, Gt. Lumley, Chester-le-Street, Co. Durham. DH3 4LS

Fax: 0191 3874784   Web: www.tanfield-railway.co.uk   Email: info@tanfield-railway.co.uk

Trains run every Sunday throughout the year and Wednesdays and Thursdays during the school summer holiday. Santa trains run November 28/29; December 5/6, 12/13, 19/20, 23/24.

Timetable: no further details received. See web site for details.

TEIFI VALLEY RAILWAY
01559 371077

Henllan Station, Henllan, Newcastle Emlyn, Ceredigion SA44 5TD

Fax: 01559 371077   Web: teifivalleyrailway.com

2009	1	2	3	4	5	6	7	8	9	10	11	12	13	14	15	16	17	18	19	20	21	22	23	24	25	26	27	28	29	30	31
MAR																															
APR										A	A	A	A	A	A	A	A	A	A	A											
MAY			A	X						A							A							A	A	A	A	A	A	A	A
JUN	A	A	A	A			A	A	A	A	A			A	A	A	A	A			A	A	A	A	A			A	A	A	
JUL	A	A				A	A	A	A			A	A	A	A	A	A	X	A	A	A	A	A	A	A	A	A	B	B	B	B
AUG	B	B	B	B	B	B	B	B	B	B	B	B	B	B	B	B	B	B	B	B	B	B	B	B	B	B	B	B	B	B	A
SEP	A	A	A			A	A	A	A	A			A	A	A	A	A			A	A	A	A	A			A				
OCT																										A	A	A	A	A	X
NOV																															
DEC												SS	SS						SS	SS			SS	SS	SS						

X = Special event

SS = Santa Specials

Note: Haloween (Oct 31) trains leave Henllan at 17.30, 18.30, 19.30

Santa Specials run at 12.00, 13.00, 14.00, 15.00, 16.00, 17.00

Timetable A: Trains leave Henllan at 12.00, 13.30, 14.30, 15.30

Timetable B: Trains leave Henllan at 11.00, 12.00, 13.30, 14.30, 15.30, 16.30

VALE OF GLAMORGAN RAILWAY

01446 748816

Barry Island Station, Romanswell Road, Barry, Vale of Glamorgan

Fax: 01446 749018   Web: valeglamrail.co.uk

No further details received – please contact for operating details.

VALE OF RHEIDOL RAILWAY

01970 625819

Park Avenue, Aberystwyth, Ceredigion SY23 1PG

Fax: 01970 623769   Web: www.rheidolrailway.co.uk   Email: info@rheidolrailway.co.uk

2009	1	2	3	4	5	6	7	8	9	10	11	12	13	14	15	16	17	18	19	20	21	22	23	24	25	26	27	28	29	30	31
MAR																															
APR							A	A	A	A	A	A	A	A	A	A		A		A	A	A		A			A	A	A		▓
MAY		A	A	A	A	A	A		A		A	A	A	A		A		A	A	A	A		A	A	B	B	B	B	B	A	A
JUN	A	A	A	A	A	A		A	A	A	A	A		A	A	A	A	A		A	A	A	A	A	A		A	A			▓
JUL	A	A	A	A	A	A	A	A	A	A	A	A	A	A	A	A	A	A	A	A	A	A	A	A	A	A	B	B	B	B	A
AUG	A	A	B	B	B	B	B	A	A	A	B	B	B	B	B	A	A	A	B	B	B	B	A	A	A	B	B	B	B	A	A	B
SEP	B	B	B	A	A		A	A	A	A		A		A	A	A	A		A		A	A	A	A		A		A	A	A	▓
OCT	A		A			A	A	A		A			A	A	A		A			A	A	A		A			A	A	A		
NOV																															▓
DEC																															

Timetable A

Aberystwyth	10.30	14.00
Devil's Bridge	11.30	15.00
Devil's Bridge	12.30	16.00
Aberystwyth	13.30	17.00

Timetable B

Aberystwyth	10.30	12.15	14.00	15.45
Devil's Bridge	11.30	13.15	15.00	16.45
Devil's Bridge	12.30	14.15	16.00	17.45
Aberystwyth	13.30	15.15	17.00	18.45

WELLS & WALSINGHAM LIGHT RAILWAY

Wells-next-the-Sea, Norfolk NR23 1QB

01328 711630

Web: www.wellswalsinghamrailway.co.uk

Trains run daily from April 4 to November 1 -   Journey time is 30mins in each direction

Timetable

April 4-Jul 31 and September 1-30
Trains leave Wells at 10.30, 12.00, 14.00, 15.30
Trains leave Walsingham at 11.15, 12/45, 14.45, 16.15

August 1-31
Trains leave Wells at 10.15, 11.45, 13.30, 15.00, 16.30
Trains leave Walsingham at 11.00, 12.30, 14.15, 15.45, 17.15

October 1-November 1
Trains leave Wells at 11.00, 12.45, 14.30
Trains leave Walsingham at 11.45, 13.30, 15.15
Note: some trains may be hauled by tram engine. Additional train may be run at peak times

---

WELSH HIGHLAND RAILWAY (PORTHMADOG)

Tremadog Road, Porthmadog, Gwynedd LL49 9DY

01766 513402

Fax: 01766 513402   Web: www.whr.co.uk

No further details received – please contact for operating details.

WELSH HIGHLAND RAILWAY (CAERNARFON)

Harbour Station, Porthmadog, Gwynedd LL49 9NF　　　**01766 516000**

Fax: 01766 516005　　Web: www.festrail.co.uk

Trains operate between Caernarfon and Rhyd Ddu

Note: services are due to be extended to Beddgelert and Porthmadog in spring 2009. Contact railway or visit web site for full details

---

WELSHPOOL & LLANFAIR LIGHT RAILWAY

The Station, Llanfair Caereinion, Powys SY21 0SF　　　**01938 810441**

Fax: 01938 810861　　Web: www.wllr.org.uk　　Email: info@wllr.org.uk

2009	1	2	3	4	5	6	7	8	9	10	11	12	13	14	15	16	17	18	19	20	21	22	23	24	25	26	27	28	29	30	31
MAR																															
APR			D	D	D	D	A	A	A	B	B	B	A	A	A	A	A	A						A	A						
MAY		B	B	B				A	A							A	A						B	B	B	A	A	A	A	A	A
JUN		D	D	D		A	A		A	A	A		A	A		A	A	A		A	A		A	A	A		C	C		A	
JUL	A	A		A	A		A	A	A		A	A		A	A	A		C	C	A	A	A	A	A	A	A	A	A	A	A	A
AUG	A	A	A	A	A	A	A	C	C	A	A	A	A	A	A	A	A	A	A	A	A	A	A	A	A	A	A	A	B	B	B
SEP	A	A	A	X	X	X		A	A	A		A	A		A	A	A		A	A				A	A						
OCT		D	D						D	D							D	D						D	D	D	D	D	D	D	D
NOV	D																														
DEC											SS	SS						SS	SS												

X = Special event

SS = Santa Specials

Timetable A

Welshpool			11.15	14.15	17.05
Llanfair			12.06	15.05	17.55
Llanfair	09.45	13.00	15.45		
Welshpool	10.35	13.50	16.35		

Timetable B

Welshpool			11.15	12.40	14.15	15.40	17.05
Llanfair			12.05	13.30	15.05	16.30	17.55
Llanfair	09.45	11.30	13.00	14.30	15.45		
Welshpool	10.35	12.20	13.50	15.20	16.35		

Timetable C

Welshpool			11.15	12.40	14.15	17.05
Llanfair			12.05	13.30	15.05	17.55
			vintage			
Llanfair	09.45	11.30	13.00		15.45	
Welshpool	10.35	12.20	13.50		16.35	

WENSLEYDALE RAILWAY　　　**01677 425805**

Leeming Bar Station, Leases Road, Leeming Bar, Northallerton, North Yorkshire DL7 9AR

Fax: 01677 427029　　Web: www.wensleydalerailway.com

No further details received – please contact for operating details.

WEST LANCASHIRE LIGHT RAILWAY　　　**01772 815881**

Station Road, Hesketh Bank, Nr Preston, Lancs PR4 6SP

Fax: 0845 130 3777　　Web: www.westlancs.org.uk

No further details received – please contact for operating details.

WEARDALE RAILWAY

01388 526203

Stanhope Station, Station Road, Stanhope, Bishop Auckland, Co. Durham DL13 2YS

Web: www.weardale-railway.org.uk   Email: enquiries@weardale-railway.org.uk

2009	1	2	3	4	5	6	7	8	9	10	11	12	13	14	15	16	17	18	19	20	21	22	23	24	25	26	27	28	29	30	31
MAR	A					A	A							A	A					A	X						A	A			
APR	B		B	B	B	B	B	B	B	X	X	X	X	B	B	B	B	B	B	B		B			B	B			B		
MAY			B	B	B	B	B	B		B	B		B	B	B		B	B		B	B	B		B	X	B	B	B	B	B	B
JUN			B	B	B		B	B		B	B	B		B	B		B	B	B		B	X		B	B	B		B	B		B
JUL	B	B		B	B		B	B	B		B	X		B	B	B		B	B	B	B	B	B	B	B	B	B	B	B	B	B
AUG	B	B	B	B	B	B	B	B	B	B	B	B	B	B	B	B	B	B	B	B	B	B	B	X	B	B	B	B	B	B	B
SEP	B	B	B	B	B	B	B	B	B	B	B	B	B	B	B	B	B	B	X	X	X	B	B	B	B	B	B	B	B	B	
OCT		B	B				B			B	B			B			B	B		B			A	A		A	A	A			A
NOV	A					A	A							A	A													SS	SS		
DEC				SS	SS						SS	SS							SS	SS	SS	SS	SS	SS	SS	P	P	P	P	P	P

X = Special event

SS = Santa Specials

P = Mince Pie Specials

(as Timetable A)

Timetable A

Wolsingham	10.30	12.30	14.30
Stanhope	10.55	12.55	14.55
Stanhope	11.30	13.30	15.30
Wolsingham	11.55	13.55	15.55

Timetable B

Wolsingham	10.30	13.00	15.30
Stanhope	10.55	13.25	15.55
Stanhope	11.45	14.15	16.30
Wolsingham	12.10	14.40	16.55

Note: Trains may be steam or diesel hauled – check for details

---

WEST SOMERSET RAILWAY

01643 704996

The Railway Station, Minehead, Somerset TA24 5BG

Fax: 01643 706349   Web: www.west-somerset-railway.co.uk   Email: info@west-somerset-railway.co.uk

2009	1	2	3	4	5	6	7	8	9	10	11	12	13	14	15	16	17	18	19	20	21	22	23	24	25	26	27	28	29	30	31
MAR							B	B						B	B						X	X				X	X	X	X		
APR	B	B		B	B		B	B	B	C	D	D	D	D	D	B	B	B		B	B	B		B	B		B	B	B		
MAY	C	D	D	D	B	B	B		B	B	B	B	B		C	C	C	C	C	C	C	D	D	D	D	D	D	D	D	D	D
JUN	C	C	C	C	C	C	C	C	C	C	C	C	X	X	X	C	C	C	C	C	C	C	C	C	C	C	C	C	C	C	
JUL	C	C	C	X	X	C	C	C	C	C	C	C	C	C	C	C	C	C	C	D	D	D	D	D	D	D	D	D	D	D	D
AUG	D	D	D	D	D	D	D	D	D	D	D	D	D	D	D	D	D	D	D	D	D	D	D	D	D	D	D	D	D	D	D
SEP	C	C	C	C	C	C	C	C	C	C	C	D	C	C	C	C	C	C	C	C	C	C	C	C	C	C	C	C	C	C	
OCT	X	X	X	X		B	B	B		B	B			B	B	B		B	B		B	B	D		X	X	C	C	C	C	B
NOV	B	A				A	A																								
DEC				X	SS	SS						SS	SS	X	X	X			SS	SS			SS	SS			B	B	X	X	B

X = Special event/timetable

SS = Santa Specials

Timetable A

		D		D
Minehead	10.15	12.20	14.15	16.05
Bishop's Lydeard	11.31	13.36	15.31	17.21
		D		D
Bishop's Lydeard	10.25	12.30	14.25	16.15
Minehead	11.40	13.45	15.36	17.30

D = Diesel multiple unit service

Timetable B

Minehead	10.15	12.20	14.15	16.05
Bishop's Lydeard	11.31	13.36	15.31	17.21
Bishop's Lydeard	10.25	12.30	14.25	16.15
Minehead	11.40	13.45	15.36	17.30

Timetable C

			D			D
Minehead	10.15	12.20	13.15	14.15	16.05	16.55
Bishop's Lydeard	11.31	13.36	14.51	15.31	17.21	18.11
			D			D
Bishop's Lydeard	10.25	11.40	12.30	14.25	15.05	16.15
Minehead	11.40	12.53	13.45	15.36	16.34	17.30

D = Diesel multiple unit service

Timetable D

		D	S or D			D	S or D	
Minehead	10.15	11.10	12.20	14.05	15.00	16.05	16.55	17.55
Bishop's Lydeard	11.50	12.56	13.43	15.30	16.25	17.21	18.11	19.07
		D	S or D			D	S or D	
Bishop's Lydeard	09.35	10.25	11.25	12.30	14.10	15.05	16.00	16.55
Minehead	10.44	11.42	12.51	13.47	15.29	16.34	17.30	18.23

D = Diesel multiple unit service.
S or D = Steam or diesel haulage. During July, August and September these trains are diesel hauled on Saturdays

Above: Dating from 1934 this Southern Railway 'Schools' class 4-4-0 No 30926 *Repton* once saw service in the Garden of England. It can now be found climbing the Yorkshire Hills on the North Yorkshire Moors Railway, seen here as it rolls into Goathland in August 2008. *Phil Barnes*

Below: This privately preserved Great Western Railway 0-4-2T No 1450 and auto-trailer No 178 can be seen in action at a number of lines around the country. The train is seen here descending Freshfield bank on the Bluebell Railway. *Phil Barnes*

Preserved on the Mid-Hants Railway BR Standard Class 5 No 73096 presents a wonderful sight at it powers a six coach train up 'the Alps'. *MHR*

INDEX

Numbers in italics refer to the Timetable pages

HERITAGE STEAM ARCHIVE

Heritage Steam Archive   Volume 34

SOUTH WEST ENGLAND

23 locomotives from Hampshire to Cornwall

You can hear 120 of the locomotives featured in this edition hard at work on:

HERITAGE STEAM ARCHIVE
an expanding series of Audio CDs, average playing time 57 minutes, covering over 25 years of steam on main and preserved lines.

Over twenty-five years of sound recording!

1 The Stanier Sound
2 46229 on the S & C
3 Sounds of the Southern
4 48773 on the Main line
5 75014 on the Kyle Line
6 Swindon Safari
7 The LMS before Stanier
8 Stanier Staccato
9 Eastern Excellence
10 48773 on The Buxton Peaks
11 Main Line Standards
12 Princess Margaret Rose

13 Return to Swindon
14 LMS Jubilees
15 London Midland Lineside
16 Southern Comfort
17 Mogul Miscellany
18 Hamilton Highlights
19 High Standards
20 A Bunch of Fives
21 The Jacobite
22 West Highland Fling
23 Steam Around Britain
24 Cumbrian Climax

25 The Heart of the NYMR
26 73096 on the Main Line
27 North of the Border
28 North Wales & Cambrian
29 Steam in the South East
30 South & Central Wales
31 48151 on the Main Line
32 Steam in the Midlands
33 The Welsh Marches Route
34 South West England

Plus our 'Real Days' series of digitally-remastered recordings featuring over 50 locos in the 1960s:

- RD 1   Freight & Shunting in the Real Days
- RD 2   Passenger Trains in the Real Days
- RD 3   The Belfast Boat Express
- RD 4   Mixed Traffic in the Real Days

£5 each from selected retail outlets or £6.00 by post from 22 Woolacombe Close, Latchford, Warrington, WA4 2RU

For detailed catalogue please send an SAE or visit our website:

www.heritagesteam.co.uk

Heritage Steam Archive   Volume 3

THE WELSH MARCHES ROUTE

Recordings of 4930 5051 6960 7802 30777 43106 45000 45596 46201 46229 & 80079 on the Shrewsbury - Newport line